APPLICATION AND
OPERATION OF AUDIOVISUAL
EQUIPMENT IN EDUCATION

APPLICATION AND OPERATION OF AUDIOVISUAL EQUIPMENT IN EDUCATION

FRED JOHN PULA
BOSTON UNIVERSITY
BOSTON, MASSACHUSETTS

JOHN WILEY & SONS, INC. NEW YORK · LONDON · SYDNEY

Copyright © 1968 by John Wiley & Sons, Inc.

Library of Congress Catalog Card Number: 68–16507
GB 471 70228X
Printed in the United States of America

PREFACE

We are living in a world of change. The change is reflected in our mode of transportation, the house we live in, the food we eat, the nature of our work. Changes are taking place even in our schools, slowly at first, but gradually accelerating as the new methodologies prove themselves. The gap from idea to practice is shrinking fast.

One change that is becoming increasingly evident is the growth in instructional technology—the increased use of instructional materials and equipment to aid the teacher in the classroom. This equipment allows the teacher to reach large numbers of students by the visual presentation of the pertinent material. This equipment also promotes self-instructional capabilities in individuals or small groups. The teacher is freed, as a result, to extend her range of operations and to reach more students.

The efficient utilization of audiovisual equipment and materials by the classroom teacher requires the acquisition of a new set of skills and understandings. The capabilities of the equipment and the systematizing of instruction by the use of this equipment are two areas that are dealt with in this book, the purpose of which is to give primary emphasis to the operation of audiovisual equipment. The intent is to make the unfamiliar easy to understand and the complex simple to operate.

It is the hope that a study of this book will enable the reader to use the equipment with a great deal more confidence than he now enjoys; for it is confidence, confidence built on knowledge, that is needed to increase the effectiveness of audiovisual instruction. The creative teacher, with a world of audio and visual materials at her fingertips, can transport the student from the confines of the classroom to "where the action is." Today's sophisticated student, exposed as he is to the electronic communications devices in the home, looks to the school to communicate information in an equally effective and interesting manner.

Today's teacher may still have the option in many communities of using or not using communications technology in the classroom. Children still learn and get by, even though they may find the competition from others increasingly to their disadvantage. The day is not too distant, however, when the option will no longer be available. Teachers will have to make

v

use of television, the motion-picture projector, the overhead projector, tape recorder, and other types of equipment in order to provide the volume of information and quality of understanding that is needed. Readers of this book should be well-prepared for that eventuality.

Fred John Pula

Boston, Massachusetts
February 1968

CONTENTS

APPLICATION AND OPERATION
OF AUDIOVISUAL EQUIPMENT
IN EDUCATION

1

THE NEED FOR TECHNOLOGY IN
EDUCATION

A favorite criticism of education and educators used to be that it took 20 years for a new idea to be adopted. This is no longer necessarily true, for The "Space Age" in which we are living is the result of the applications of science and technology not only to our efforts to reach the moon but also to every aspect of our lives. The telephone, which now allows us to speak to our friends no matter where in the world they may be, will soon permit us to see them as well. High fidelity stereophonic recording makes listening to fine music an accepted norm. Airplanes and automobiles, as well as superhighways, are revolutionizing transportation. Refrigeration and climate control in the house keep us comfortable as we eat seasonal foods the year round. Housewives' gadgetry reduces drudgery in the home. The machine assumes the role of both the man on the farm and the man on the assembly line. Automation is sweeping through business and industry. As medical science continues to reduce the death rate among children, it is also extending the life expectancy of adults.

These tremendous steps are being effected through the application of science and technology. Our educational system is also showing signs of "moving forward." The "egg crate" design of schools is gradually giving way to the influence of multipurpose classrooms, and new experiments in methodology are encouraging students to remain in school longer. But the most significant changes are being made in the communication of information within the schools. Innovational instructional media are being widely adopted and have become an integral part of teaching in many school systems. Despite the decentralized character of our educational system, the impetus for this revolution in instructional technology can be attributed in great part to the many assistance programs of the federal government.

The cultural lag decried in our schools is slowly disappearing as new programs prove the effectiveness of the new educational media. The situation is similar to one in agriculture, a field in which it took more than 20 years for hybrid corn to be accepted by the farmers; however, later, hybrid oats were fully accepted within a span of only three years.[1]

Our school systems are acquiring large amounts of equipment such as overhead projectors, tape recorders, television sets, language laboratories, and motion-picuture and slide projectors. But acquisition of equipment means little if there is inadequate understanding on the part of teachers as to how this equipment is to be operated and integrated into regular class presentations. Stories of projectors gathering dust in closets, television sets not being connected, or language laboratories improperly used are all too familiar to many administrators and teachers. Superintendents and principals are gradually recognizing this problem and are providing the needed leadership to encourage teachers in the use of such instructional media. Use of this equipment, however, requires more than just a favorable attitude on the part of the teacher and administrator, it also requires the acquisition of special knowledge relating to the operation of the equipment. Such specialized knowledge is now being provided in our teacher-training institutions as well as in special inservice training programs.

Tables 1.1 and 1.2 show the impact of technology in our schools. A recent survey indicates a tremendous increase in the number of schools purchasing equipment in the period from 1960 to 1965. The overhead projector is proving to be the most popular item; several million dollars have been spent nationally on it alone.

Although books will continue to play an important role in education Figure 1.1, the equipment associated with instructional technology—utilization of newer instructional media—has developed to the point at which its effective use in instruction requires considerable understanding and skill (Figure 1.2). Deliberate, organized study—together with appropriate practice—should allow us to gain the following information:

1. A rapidly growing body of knowledge related to communication devices and their operation.
2. Suitable materials and the methods for finding, producing, and utilizing them.
3. The learning theories that support the use of such equipment, and the administration of programs aimed at making modern media available to all learners.

A corollary assumption is that such skills and understandings are

[1]Neal E. Miller, *Graphic Communication and the Crisis in Education, Audiovisual Communication Review,* **5**, No. 3, 1957, p.2.

Table 1.1   Elementary Innovation 1955–1965
(percent use)

	1955–56	1960–61	1965–66
Team teaching	5	15	30
Ungraded school	7	14	31
Film and film strip projectors	74	94	95
Language laboratory	7	20	52
Tape recorders	40	66	81
Programmed learning	5	15	51
Overhead projectors	3	15	60
Television	13	45	72

Schools for the Sixties, NEA (1400 principals), 1963, McGraw-Hill.

The impact of instructional technology is reflected in the figures of increased use of audiovisual equipment and the new structuring of our school programs. Later studies by Eleanor Godfrey have borne out the earlier predictions.

Eleanor P. Godfrey, "Audiovisual Media In the Public Schools, 1961–1964," Bureau of Social Science Research, Washington, D.C., 1965.

too vital to modern pedagogy to be left to happenstance or incidental treatment. That the instruction is sorely needed is evident from the remarks of Donald White, executive vice-president of the National Audiovisual Association, when he appeared before the House Sub-Committee on Education in 1963:

"The need for continued support of the acquisition of educational tools is outlined by a recent survey completed under a contract with the United States Office of Education. In this it was revealed that out of a million and a half teachers, only about 5% make regular use of audiovisual equipment and materials. Another 15% are occasional users—a total of 80% are not yet making any use at all of modern teaching tools."

Table 1.2   Secondary Innovation 1955–1965
(percent use)

	1955–56	1960–61	1965–66
Films and film strip projectors	96	99	99
Language laboratory	6	35	83
Tape recorders	76	96	99
Programmed learning	5	13	65
Overhead projectors	4	8	35
Television	18	51	86

Schools for the Sixties, NEA (1400 principals), McGraw-Hill, N.Y., 1963.

Figure 1.1   Books will continue to play an important role in our schools; but the new instructional technology provides for other sources of information.

John H. Fischer, president of Teachers College, Columbia University, recently wrote:

"Teacher education will have to respond to the fast-breaking technological developments in communication media and in machines for storing and retrieving information. Modern technology has been producing potential teaching tools faster than teachers have learned to use them. As a consequence, schools are far less efficient than they could be if teachers were properly prepared to use even the simpler devices already available."[2]

Significantly, an issue of *The NEA Journal* reported on a survey conducted by the NEA Research Division to learn how new teachers judge their undergraduate programs:

"Of those polled (a scientifically selected cross-section of the nations's 1.5 million public school teachers), 60% felt that they had had insufficient training in the use of audiovisual methods and materials."[3]

[2] R. C. Wheeler, *Wisconsin Survey, Audiovisual Instruction*, **10**, No. 7, Sept. 1965, p.568.
[3] "Teacher Opinion Poll", *The NEA Journal*, December 1963.

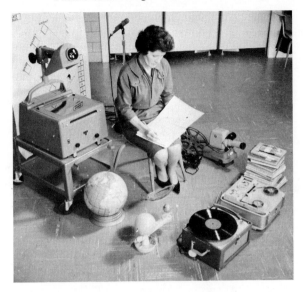

Figure 1.2 The equipment and materials available to the classroom teacher require careful selection and preparation for most effective use.

FACTORS CONTRIBUTING TO THE NEED FOR TECHNOLOGY IN THE CLASSROOM

Even from these few selected references it is quite clear that much attention is being directed to the new instructional technology. The impetus for this interest has arisen from several different directions, one of which is the shortage of classrooms and classroom buildings. In 1964 $2.7 billion was spent for new school-building construction; in 1965 expenditures of $2.8 billion were made; and in 1966 $2.9 billion; yet we are still short of classrooms. To compensate for the shortage and inadequacy of current facilities, school administrators are turning more frequently to instructional devices that will allow available teachers to reach more students.

The shortage of good classroom teachers is another factor resulting in the increasing interest in educational technology. Video-tape allows a good teacher to reach an unlimited number of students, as previously that teacher was restricted to a single class of perhaps 30 students. Motion-picture film has proved to be adaptable for individual viewing as well as for large-group viewing. Film strips, audiotapes, records, and other materials simplify the matter of preserving good teaching and making it available to those who most need it.

The tremendous growth in our school population is a major factor contributing to our shortage of classrooms and teachers and, in turn, sparking interest in instructional technology. This increase is considered a natural growth by some; but it also reflects a growing tendency for youngsters to remain in school longer. In 1966 55.8 million children, teenagers, and young adults returned to classrooms—From kindergarten to the college graduate-school level. A breakdown of this figure shows 49.9 million pupils enrolled in elementary and secondary schools and some 5.9 million students in colleges and universities.

The population trend alone assures the continued need for classrooms and good instruction; fo the period 1956–1966, school and college enrollment increased from 42.6 million to 55.8 million (or 39%). Elementary school attendance during this same period rose from 27.7 million to 35.2 million; that in high schools from 7.6 million to 12.6 million; and that in colleges from 3.1 million to 5.9 million. The rising trend in enrollments is shown in Figure 1.3.

The United States Office of Education foresees total enrollments of 62 million by 1973. The greatest increase will be at the college level, which is already beginning to feel the impact of the postwar baby boom.

GROWTH OF NEW INFORMATION THROUGH RESEARCH AND EXPERIMENTATION

The pressures resulting from inadequate classrooms, lack of good teachers, and increasing school population all contribute to the increased interest in instructional technology. Yet, interest, in itself, will not overcome the lack of communicating the tremendous amount of new information resulting from research in private business and industry. Research and development produce that factual information from which all technological progress starts. A convenient yardstick for determining the amount of new factual information made available each year is the number of dollars invested by government and industry in research and development. Currently the annual expenditure is approximately $22.5 billion, a sum that has grown enormously in the last few years. The statement has been made that more money was spent on research and scientific inquiry in the last ten years than in the previous 180 years—and more has been discovered, as well.

With this tremendous mountain of information being made available, it is to the credit of school administrators that they have striven to make more efficient the use of pupil and teacher time through the use of new instructional devices.

OUR RAPIDLY EXPANDING EDUCATIONAL SYSTEM

Enrollment in elementary, secondary and higher education has increased by 31% in ten years.

1956-57

Total: 42.6 mil.

Elementary and secondary 39.5 mil.

Higher education 3.1 mil.

1966-67

Total: 55.8 mil.

Elementary and secondary 49.9 mil.

Higher education 5.9 mil.

The number of degrees conferred by higher institutions has risen by 77%.

1956-57

409,000 degrees

1966-67

722,000 degrees

And total spending for all fields of learning in the U.S. has grown by 124%.

1956-57

$21.8 bil.

1966-67

$48.8 bil.

Figure 1.3   Our rapidly expanding educational system is one of the factors contributing to an increased interest in instructional technology.

7

Industry is already moving beyond what it calls "conventional" audiovisual devices (Figures 1.4–1.8). A subsidiary of General Telephone and Electronics has installed a communications system at Texas A & M University that transmits written data through conventional telephone circuits for visual display before an audience. This "blackboard by wire" is already being used to transmit a chemistry course twice a week to a group located 250 miles away.

International Telephone and Telegraph Corporation is sending television pictures over ordinary telephone lines in an experiment being conducted at the University of California. This procedure could eventually result in a great reduction in the costs of local television systems.

IBM is developing the use of the computer as an aid in instruction. The company points out, however, that computer-assisted instruction is not intended as a substitute or replacement for a human teacher. The educator, not the computer expert or the computer, must ultimately decide what values computer-assisted instruction holds for better education. The system maintains continuous control over a wide variety of learning materials so that each individual student can progress at his own rate.

Figure 1.4 Increased interest is being shown in study areas completely equipped with audio playback equipment and closed-circuit television. *Courtesy of Dage-Bell Corp.*

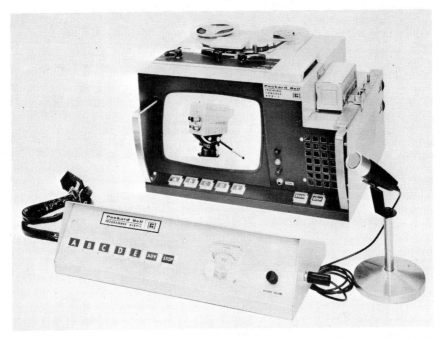

Figure 1.5   Teaching machine produced by the Packard Bell Corp. combines the features of a slide projector and tape recorder for individualized instruction.

At the same time, the system evaluates students' responses and guides each student individually toward mastery of the subject being presented.

The Xerox Corporation is busily engaged in experimenting with programmed instructional materials which envision an approach toward teacherless classrooms.

Raytheon's Division of Educational Electronics has pioneered in another direction with its Learning Center System, a complex that makes both audio and video programing available to educators in one package. Students, while seated in study alcoves, can select through push-button controls one of any number of programs available according to a printed study schedule. The instructor or attendant at his console can monitor, add to, or delete instruction.

These devices are not the dreams of impractical inventors. Rather they are among the many systems developed to meet the educational needs of today and tomorrow. Teachers interested in improving the effectiveness of instruction need to understand these systems and should help in their evaluation under various classroom conditions. But first, complete familiarity with the operation and use of the basic audiovisual materials and equipment is highly recommended.

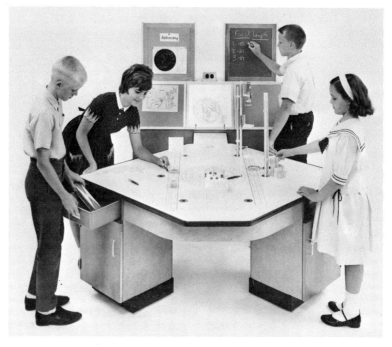

Figure 1.6   A science/math discovery work center for elementay school level is introduced by E. H. Sheldon Equipment Co. of Muskegon, Michigan.

INADEQUACIES OF VERBAL INSTRUCTIONAL METHODS

Some of the more basic reasons for the increase in instructional technology have been described: increased pupil enrollment, teacher-classroom shortage, and the increased amount of technical information to be communicated. The main consideration is the growing realization that verbal communication, both printed and spoken, is no longer adequate to effect the tasks of education now facing the teacher.

The principal problem in the classroom is that of using words. The problem with words is that there are not nearly enough of them, even though the Third International Edition of the Merriam-Webster Dictionary has a listing of 450,000. Of this number, most college graduates recognize 20,000. We converse, however, with the mere 8000 words which comprise the working vocabulary of the average person.[4] The world we live in is a complex world, and it is becoming increasingly complex day by day. Yet

[4]Laurence K. Hamilton, *Visual Communication*, an unpublished paper presented at the Seminar on Visual Communication, Holyoke, Massachusetts, October 1957.

Figure 1.7 Use of microfilm helps to meet the problems of storage space for all the printed materials needed by students today. *Courtesy of University Microfilms. Inc.*

most people try to describe this infinite world with a mere handful of words. They try to describe all the things they see and all the things they feel in this limitless, dynamic world with a limited and relatively static language. It is no wonder, therefore, that misunderstandings are frequent, and that children may fail to grasp the meaning of even a well-prepared presentation.

With so few words in our practical vocabulary, each word must do several jobs. The common basic words acquire many diverse meanings; for instance, "*a fast* race horse is one which runs rapidly unless he is tied *fast*, and then he is not *fast* because he is *fast*! If we observe a religious *fast*, we abstain from food and drink; on the other hand, one who gorges himself on food and drink is said to be living a *fast* life."[5]

The following excerpt, although from a piece of fiction, focuses on this matter of meanings—meanings that individuals attach to various

[5] Laurence K. Hamilton, *op. cit.*, p. 1.

Figure 1.8 Using American Seating Company's experimental carrels, students aim light seekers to select audio material.

words:

"Humpty Dumpty said: 'There's glory for you.' 'I don't know what you mean by glory,' Alice said. Humpty Dumpty smiled contemptuously. 'Of course you don't—'til I tell you. I meant, there's a nice knockdown argument for you.' 'But glory doesn't mean a nice knockdown argument,' Alice objected. 'When I use a word,' Humpty Dumpty said in a rather scornful tone, 'it means just what I choose it to mean, neither more nor less.'"[6]

Here is an example of what can happen when words have more than one meaning: A school boy wrote on an examination paper that the American Revolution wrote "nasty letters" to the French Revolution. When his teacher saw his paper, she called him to her desk and said, "Johnny, this is ridiculous. I am ashamed of you. Why on earth did you put such a thing on your paper?" He replied, "Teacher, it was in the book." He then brought the book back to the desk and opened it up. It was there; he was right. This is what it said: "The American Revolution corresponded roughly with the French Revolution." Because there is but a limited

[6]Lewis Carroll, *Through the Looking Glass*, London, Macmillan & Co., 1956, pp. 129–130.

number of words, each word has more than one meaning; and when a teacher assumes that a word means the same thing to all students in the class, the teacher is often wrong.

Dr. Raymond Wyman, a leading spokesman for audiovisual education, has often commented on his belief that teachers place far too much emphasis on one means of communication—that of words. "We *tell* students, and we provide them with written materials so much of the time. Words are wonderful! They are easily produced, reproduced, stored, and transported. But the overuse or exclusive use of words can result in serious problems; chiefly, the problems of verbalism and forgetting."[7]

Webster defines verbalism as "an empty form of words." The term is used to describe a situation in which someone has used or adopted words or phrases without considering what they mean. Words that are filled with meaning for one person may be devoid of meaning for another. A person must carry meaning *to* a word before he can carry meaning *from* that word.

Forgetting is a natural consequence of the overuse of words. We often forget what we are told or what we have read primarily because we fail to develop an insight into the importance of words.

Some degree of communication can be achieved through the use of verbal symbols if the instructor is able to direct the attention and hold the interest of the class through the material being presented. But even if the students engross themselves in every word of the teacher, the problems noted above will invariably intrude on the understanding of the information presented. The accompanying diagram (Figure 1.9) graphically illustrates this point. The teacher originates a verbal signal, and on its utterance it becomes an auditory signal. Upon reaching the ear of the student, this signal must go first to the frontal lobe of the brain—that part of the brain which controls our social behavior and our inhibitions (the brain's switching center). From here the message is transferred to the back of the brain where relevant (?) data is stored. (The question mark is in order because much of these data are composed of prejudices, fixations, and superstitions, as well as the first-hand experiences of the student.)

The student takes the teacher's tender new idea and twists and distorts it. He finally makes the idea fit into his experience and says, "Yes, I understand." But this "understanding" is only an interpretation of the original idea being communicated.

Sometimes the teacher gets no response at all, in which case he must start all over again and say, "Now what I am trying to tell you is this. . . ." Hopefully, the teacher eventually succeeds in receiving the desired response.

This is the pattern of communication. Never underestimate the power

[7] Raymond Wyman, *The Option Is Ours*, Technifax Corporation, Holyoke, Mass, 1957, p. 2.

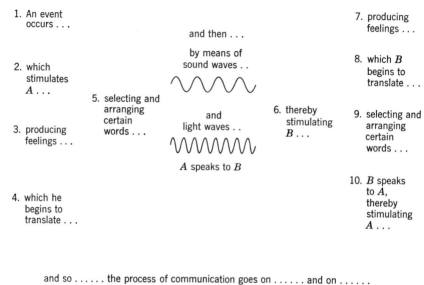

and so ...... the process of communication goes on ...... and on ......

Figure 1.9   Reactions to a stimulus situation do **not** guarantee that communication has been achieved. From J. W. Coffman, *The Role of Visual Communication*, pamphlet published by Tecnifax Corp., Holyoke, Massachusetts, 1957, p. 5.

of students to misunderstand the teacher. In fact, be absolutely astounded if the students do comprehend new information on its initial presentation.

The classroom teacher must be aware of the barriers to effective communication that result from verbal presentations: verbalism, daydreaming, lack of attention and interest, and misdirected meanings of words. Recognizing these shortcomings of verbal presentations, the teacher should search out a more direct approach for the transmission of information in the classroom.

SELECTED REFERENCES

Barnouw, Erik W., *Mass Communications*. New York: Holt, Rinehart, & Winston 1956.

Brooker, Floyd E., "Communication in the Modern World," in *Audio-Visual Materials of Instruction*. 48th Yearbook of the National Society for the study of Education, Part I. Chicago. University of Chicago Press, 1949, 4–19.

Brown, James W., Richard Lewis, and Fred F. Harcleroad. *Audio-Visual Instruction Materials and Methods*. Part I, Chapter 1. New York: McGraw-Hill, 1964.

Brown, James W. and James W. Thornton, Jr. (eds.). *New Media in Higher Education*. NEA, 1963.

Chandler, B. J. *Education and the Teacher*. New York: Dodd, Mead, 1961, Chapter 4.

Cross, A. J. Foy, and Irene F. Cypher. *Audio-visual Education*. New York: Crowell, 1961.

Cypher, Irene F. "A Touch of Realism in the Classroom," *Audiovisual Instruction,* **1**, No. 3, 70–71 (1966).

Dale, Edgar, *Audio-visual Methods in Teaching* (rev. ed.) Part I, New York: Holt, Rinehart & Winston, 1961, Chapters 1–4.

Dececco, John P. *Human Learning in the School.* New York: Holt, Rinehart & Winston, 1963. Chapters 5–6.

Deutschmann, Paul J., Lionel C. Barrow, Jr., and Anita McMillan: "The Efficiency of Different Modes of Communication." *AV Communication Review,* **9**, 263–270. (November-December 1961).

Ely, Donald P. (ed.). "The Changing Role of the Audiovisual Process in Education: A Definition and a Glossary of Related Terms," Technological Development Project Monograph No. 1. (Prepared by the Commission of Definition and Terminology of the NEA.) *Audiovisual Communication Review,* **2**, (No. 1, Suppl. 6. January-February, 1963).

Finn, James D. "Automation and Education: I. General Aspects," *Audio-visual Communication Review,* **5**, 343–360 (1957).

Haas, Kenneth B., and Harry Q. Packer. *Use of Audio-visual Aids* (3rd ed.), Englewood Cliffs, N. J.: Prentice-Hall, 1955, Chapter 17.

Kinder, James S., *Audio-visual Materials and Techniques* (rev. ed.), New York: American Book, 1959, Chapters 1 and 2.

Mass Media and Education, 53rd Yearbook of the National Society for the Study of Education, Part I. Chicago: University of Chicago Press, 1954.

NEA Project on Instruction: *Education in a Changing Society,* NEA, 1963.

Sands, Lester B., *Audio Visual Procedures in Teaching.* New York: Ronald Press, 1956, Chapters 1 and 3.

Schramm, Wilbur. *Communications in a Modern Society.* Urbana: University of Illinois Press, 1948.

Schramm, Wilbur. *The Process and Effects of Mass Communication.* Urbana: University of Illinois Press, 1954.

Seipman, Charles A., "Mass Communications and Its Relations to the Crises in Education," in *Schools on the Threshold of a New Era,* Official Report, Washington, D. C.: American Association of School Administrators, 1957, pp. 80–89.

Stone, C. Walter. "Some New Frontiers for Newer Media." *AV Communication Review,* **9**, 163–172 (July to August, 1961).

Wittich, Walter Arno, and Charles Francis Schuller. *Audiovisual Materials: Their Nature and Use* (3rd ed.), New York: Harper, 1962, Chapter 1.

INSTRUCTIONAL MATERIALS

And No Bells Ring, 16-mm film, 30 min., sound, b & w or color, National Association of Secondary-School Principals, NEA, 1960.

Audio-Visual Materials in Teaching, 16-mm film, 12 min., sound b & w, Coronet, 1956.

Child of the Future, 16-mm 60 min. sound, b & w, McGraw-Hill, 1965.

Communications in Modern Life, 35-mm film strip, 35 frames, silent, b & w, McGraw-Hill, 1956.

Communications Primer, 16-mm film, 22 min., sound, color, Museum of Modern Art, New York, 1956.

Making Yourself Understood, 16-mm film, 14 min., sound, b & w, Encyclopaedia Britannica, 1954.

Not by Chance, 16-mm film, 28 min., sound, b & w, NEA, 1957.

What Greater Gift?, 16-mm film, 28 min., sound, b & w or color, NEA, 1957.

2

THE CASE FOR
INSTRUCTIONAL MEDIA

"Experience is the best teacher." We have heard this so often and from so many learned individuals that we take the statement at face value without investigating its deeper significance. "Some people never learn from their mistakes" and "History always repeats itself" seem contrary to the first statement, yet the latter two also have their share of proponents.

Behavioral psychologists who have devoted their life's work to the study of how we learn have set forth many theories and proposed many hypotheses concerning the learning process, but there is as yet little agreement among them. A suggestion has been made that there may be as many methods of learning as there are individuals engaged in a learning activity. If this is true, it certainly complicates the task of the classroom teacher who attempts to stimulate learning in a group of 40 individuals.

DIRECT AND PURPOSEFUL EXPERIENCES AND LEARNING

There are some general areas of agreement however, whether the psychologists profess Gestaltism, behaviorism, connectionism, structuralism, or any other system of learning. We learn a great deal of what we know by *performing* some activity. A lasting impression is one that results from the use of several sense organs rather than just one. For example, learning to tie one's shoe-strings involves use of verbal instructions, demonstrations, and manipulative practice in order to master the task. A person can learn about golf by reading a book, but he will score well only through practice and playing the game. As the principal character in the novel *The Counterfeit Traitor* pointed out on witnessing the abrupt execution of a "stubborn" slave-laborer, reading one thousand stories of atrocities did not have the impact on him as did watching one such act of inhumanity.

In each of the above illustrations learning was accomplished through experience; but it necessarily had to be direct and purposeful experience. The learner was caught up in the drama of the situation or in the activity of the situation. His interest was aroused and his attention was held by the activity. Interest and attention are dependent upon the degree of understanding that an individual can bring to a given situation. This understanding in turn is dependent on the previous learning, attitudes, and environmental influences on the student. To illustrate, the most graphic description of the Battle of Tours will have little effect on a student who has been "transported" out of the classroom by the sound of an airplane engine.

Information can be acquired through rote memorization, but whether this method also represents acquired knowledge is a debatable point. Information that is memorized usually is retained only long enough to fulfill the requirements of a course and is then conveniently forgotten. Retention and recollection are short-lived when material is studied with a short-range goal in mind.

The relationship between learning through direct, purposeful experience and retention can be illustrated by the following example: "Reflect for a few seconds on anything of significance from your past. . . . What was the nature of your remembrance? Did you see a picture? Did you hear a sound? Did you recall printed words or spoken words? . . . " The usual reponse is that a *visual image* was recollected. The expression "I remember it as clearly as if it had happened yesterday," is a common one. The significant point is that most people "see a picture" when asked to recollect something from the past. The implication of this simple experiment for learning and retention is quite obvious. If students tend to recall visual impressions of things that arouse their interest and hold their attention, we as teachers should be as graphic and pictorial in our presentations as our resources will allow. It is the graphic portrayal of information that stimulates learning and makes that learning more lasting.

Today's students, more than ever before, are being exposed to visual experiences through television, the movies, and various live presentations. The improved modes of transportation allow us easy access to places of interest and enable us to watch events as they occur instead of reading about them later. Educators should not ignore this predisposition toward concepts that are visual; they should make use of those audiovisual devices that are available for classroom teaching.

PERCEPTION AND LEARNING

Edgar Dale, professor of Education at Ohio State University, has written that the student's ability to understand happenings inside the classroom as well as outside the classroom is an outgrowth of his ability to perceive. Our perceptions depend on our ability to use all senses in acquiring both an understanding of our surroundings and an understanding of the interplay between our sense organs. "The root of understanding, thinking and attitude formation is real experience. . . . The responsibility for producing firsthand experiences which may lead to understanding affects many areas of the curriculum. . . . In our schools, we are investigating a complex physical and social environment often characterized by phenomena that are too big, too small, too fast, or too slow to be captured for classroom study."[1] It is within this context—this need—that we must provide the experiences in as realistic and meaningful a manner as we can contrive.

CLASSIFICATION OF AUDIOVISUAL EQUIPMENT AND MATERIALS

This text is concerned with instructional materials and equipment for the classroom, generally classified either as listening (audio) or as viewing (visual) approaches to instruction. Much attention has been given to finding the proper term to describe the new methodology. A term that continues to be popular, despite the introduction of more explicit terms, is *audiovisual*. Thus we speak of audiovisual materials and audiovisual equipment and technology synonymously with instructional materials or instructional resources and technology.

Whatever the label, the technology is not new. It has a history that will be referred to as we consider the various types of equipment. Recent events, however, have heightened the interest in the audiovisual field. To insure a mutual understanding of terms, it might be well to spell out certain examples of audiovisual material and equipment. Some of the materials are primarily for viewing: silent motion-pictures and film strips, transparencies, microprojections, and projections with the opaque and overhead projector. Other nonprojected materials that appeal to the sense of sight are the chalkboard, feltboard, and bulletin board, as well as textbook illustrations, photographs, prints, etchings, charts, graphs, posters, maps, and globes.

In the audio area the sense of hearing is utilized to gain information from phonograph records, electrical transcriptions, radio broadcasts, and magnetic tape recordings. Television and sound motion pictures appealing to both the sense of sight and hearing have become the most effective of the audiovisual materials.

[1]Edgar Dale, *Audiovisual Methods In Teaching*, Holt, Rinehart & Winston, New York, 1961, p. 46.

Models, mockups, dioramas, specimens, collections, and various other representations and displays are widely used. Dramatizations and role-playing offer many possibilities for increased learning through sight and sound as well as through doing.

The above hardly presents a complete list but it does serve to indicate the range and possibilities of what are referred to as instructional or audiovisual materials and techniques.

EFFECTIVE UTILIZATION OF AUDIOVISUAL EQUIPMENT AND MATERIALS

In the past several years much attention has been given to the specific needs of schools for projection and audio equipment as well as to the changing content of the curriculum. Much of this book is given over to an analysis of audiovisual materials and equipment and to a description of their operation and use. It is worth noting here, however, that the teacher with only this limited knowledge would accomplish little to improve learning in the classroom without consideration of certain other factors.

Effective utilization of audiovisual materials and equipment in the classroom requires attention to these four factors (Figure 2.1):

1. Adequate preparation of the teacher.
2. Preparation of the students.
3. Presentation of the material.
4. Follow-up activities to insure the understanding of the materials presented.

Preparation of the Teacher

When correctly used, audiovisual materials can play an integral part in the presentation of information. There should be no separation of ideas between the presentation by the teacher and that set forth in the materials. One should complement the other. The joint effort of the teacher and the "visiting expert" should provide for a concise, clear treatment of the material being studied. Co-ordinating this activity, of course, is the teacher. In preparing a lesson the teacher should carefully plan what subject matter is to be treated. The objectives should be set forth and the audiovisual materials selected to accomplish those objectives. The teacher is in the most favorable position of deciding whether the objectives can be accomplished by use of more traditional materials and methods or whether a motion-picture film, a film strip, a slide series, or an audiotape, etc., should be used.

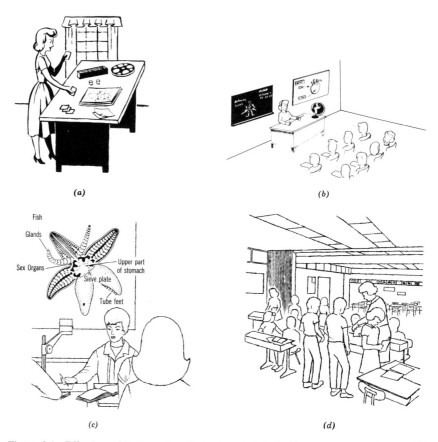

Figure 2.1   Effective utilization of audiovisual materials in the classroom requires careful attention to (a) teacher preparation, (b) student preparation, (c) presentation of material, and (d) follow-up.

The significant point to be made is that after the selection is made, the teacher must necessarily be fully aware of the nature of the aid and must integrate it into his presentation so that a smooth exposition of information is achieved. Overheard in one classroom after the students had viewed a television program was the remark of the teacher, "Now I'll tell you how it really should be done."

The teacher should thoroughly preview the material that is to be used. Teacher guides for television and radio programs should be consulted. It may be found that only a portion of a film or film strip has specific meaning for the lesson. In that event, only that portion should be used. The teacher should never be taken by surprise by what appears on the screen or what comes out of the loudspeaker. The objectives of the lesson should always be kept in mind. Teachers have found that by adhering to the objectives, their lessons are clearer, more easily understood, and are accomplished with a minimum waste of class time.

Preparation of the Students

It follows that since it is important for the teacher to prepare himself for the use of audiovisual materials, it is also important that he prepare the students. The student's understanding of the material will be heightened if his perception is directed toward the significant areas. In viewing a film, for example, students should be looking for answers to questions that were raised earlier; new vocabulary words with queries as to their meanings could be listed; the search for comparisons and contrasts and relationships between new material and already-learned material should be encouraged. The reason for participating in the learning experience should be made clear; otherwise the attention of the student may be misdirected and the objectives not achieved.

The previous learning, attitudes, and interests of individual students will affect their perception of new information and their understanding of it. The guidance of the teacher in helping students to perceive the desired factual information is of great importance; without such directions, results could be as varied in number as there are students in the room.

Presentation of the Information

The effectiveness of an audiovisual presentation, despite the elaborate preparation of the subject matter and the students, can fail if the equipment is operated incorrectly or if the materials are mishandled. It is hoped that study of the chapters following will tend to minimize such occurrences. The concentration of the students on the subject matter can be disrupted easily by showing slides upside-down, running film backwards, improper framing and focus, and numerous other errors that lead to ineffectual presentations.

There are also other considerations that should be reckoned with in presentations. Proper light control should be provided so as to allow for clarity of projected images while maintaining adequate desk-level illumination; screens should be large enough to allow everyone in the room to read the projected information; screens should be placed high enough so that material can be comfortably viewed; volume should be adjusted to suit everyone (not just the hard-of-hearing or those in the front row); and ventilation and temperature should be maintained at a level that will ensure alertness during audiovisual presentations. Distractions of all kinds should be eliminated so that full attention can be directed to the material at hand.

Few people have considered the classroom as a theater. Yet many teachers have used the techniques of the showman to insure the success of a particular lesson. Careful planning and attention to the details of presentation are prerequisites to the successful use of audiovisual materials and equipment.

Follow-up

The lesson should not be considered complete when the lights come on or the record player is turned off. That moment is the critical time—the time to determine how well the objectives of the lesson have been achieved. Such assessment can be determined through informal discussions, through planning of class projects, through consideration of questions noted before the start of the lesson, by reviewing vocabulary words, and, of course, through the written quiz or examination. This latter method is a good evaluative device but should not necessarily be used as a motivational device for attracting attention to the presentation. Too often a negative reaction is the result and information retained just long enough to be used on a test is then forgotten.

Developing a teacher's proficiency in the operation of audiovisual equipment and use of audiovisual materials is the primary objective of this text; but it should be re-emphasized that, regardless of the subject matter, the grade level, or the nature of the student, the four-step plan noted earlier in this chapter should be rigidly observed.

SELECTED REFERENCES

"Audio-visual Instruction," *The National Elementary Principal*, **40**, (entire issue; January, 1961).

"Audiovisual Specialist: Agent of Change," *Audiovisual Instruction*, **10**, 454–458 (June-July 1965).

"The Audio-visual Tools for Learning," *The Nation's Schools*, **67** (entire issue; February 1961).

Batchelder, H. T., *Audio-visual Methods in Teaching*, 28th Yearbook of the Association for Student Teachers, Lock Haven, Pennsylvania, 1950.

Brickell, Henry, *Organizing New York State for Educational Change*, New York State Department of Education, Albany, New York, 1961.

Brown, James W., Richard B. Lewis, and Fred F. Harcleroad, *Audio-visual Instruction Materials and Methods*, New York: McGraw-Hill, 1964, Chapter 2.

Cross, A. J. Foy. "The Unit in Modern Teaching," *Audiovisual Instruction*, **3**, 168–169 (September 1958).

Dale, Edgar, *Audio-visual Methods in Teaching* (rev. ed.), New York: Holt Rinehart & Winston, 1962. Chapters 5 and 9.

Erickson, Carlton W. H. *Fundamentals of Teaching with Audiovisual Technology*, New York: Macmillan, 1965, Chapter 1.

Finn, James, "Automation and Education: Technology and the Instructional Process," *AV Communications Review*, **8**, 5–26, 1960.

Haas, Kenneth B., and Harry Q. Packer, *Preparation and Use of Audio-visual Aids* (2nd. ed.), Englewood Cliffs, N. J.: Prentice-Hall, 1955, Chapters 15 and 16.

Instructional Materials in the Elementary Schools, 35th Yearbook of the Department of Elementary School Principals, Washington, D. C., NEA, 1956.

"The Media Specialist: Agent of Change," *Audiovisual Instruction*, **10**, 454–458 (June-July 1965).

NEA Project on Instruction. *Deciding What To Teach*. NEA, 1963.

"The Systems Approach," *Audiovisual Instruction*, **10** (entire issue; May 1965).

Witt, Paul W. F. "Some If's about AV," *Audiovisual Instruction*, vol. 3, 178–179 (September 1958).

INSTRUCTIONAL MATERIALS

"Audiovisual Materials in Teaching," $13\frac{1}{4}$ min., sound b & w, or color, Coronet, 1956.

"Bringing the Community to the Classroom." 45 frames, silent, color, b & w, Wayne University, 1953.

"Discovering Individual Differences," 16-mm. film, 17 min., sound, b & w, McGraw-Hill, 1955.

"Effective Learning in the Elementary School," 16-mm. film, 20 min., sound, b & w, McGraw-Hill, 1956.

"Effective Use of Audiovisual Materials," 45 frames, silent, color, Basic Skills Films, 1957.

"The Improvement of Teaching Through Audiovisual Materials," $33\frac{1}{3}$ rmp (LP), Educational Recording Services.

"Improving Teaching Through Audiovisual Materials," 20 min., $33\frac{1}{3}$ rmp (LP), 12", Educational Recording Service, 1952.

"Making Teaching Effective," 38 frames, sound, b & w, Ohio State University, 1952.

"New Tools for Learning," 19 min., sound, b & w, Encyclopaedia Britannica Films, 1952.

3

BASIC INFORMATION FOR THE OPERATION OF AUDIOVISUAL EQUIPMENT

With the increased emphasis now being placed by school administrators on technology in the classroom, it is significant to note those factors that have limited or restricted teacher utilization of audiovisual materials and equipment. Research by Dr. Gaylen Kelley at Boston University has brought out that one of the major deterrents to the use of equipment is the lack of information that teachers have concerning the operation of the equipment. [1] Corollary to this are the myths and unfounded fears that arise to haunt the uninformed user. The teacher is apt to react negatively to the slightest incident by thinking, "I knew this would happen if I tried to use that machine. I certainly won't try *that* again."

The fears can be allayed, the myths exploded, and operation of audiovisual equipment made pleasant and enjoyable by understanding certain basic technical information. Some of the characteristics of the equipment are general enough so that it would be well to consider them now and so provide a foundation for the later study of the individual units. The major areas to be considered here deal with electricity, sound, and optics.

ELECTRICITY

Electrical current is a commodity we use constantly and about which we know very little. It is because of this lack of knowledge that some students and teachers are fearful of using audiovisual equipment in the classroom. Stated simply, any classroom equipment that requires electrical

---

[1] Gaylen B. Kelley, "An Analysis of Teacher's Attitudes Toward The Use of Audiovisual Materials," Unpublished dissertation, Boston University, 1959.

current can be plugged into a standard wall outlet. Such an outlet provides electricity that is usually rated at 117 volts (V), alternating current. Alternating current (ac) is a pulsating current. It is graphically depicted as a series of waves:

There are 60 cycles or pulsations per second in our electrical current—so rapid that we are not conscious of these fluctuations. During thunderstorms or during power failures these pulsations may slow down; and it is then that we can detect the "flickering" in the light bulbs. The use of alternating current at 117 V is almost universal in the United States. There are still, however, a few isolated localities that may be using a type of electricity called direct current (dc), which is more expensive to generate, difficult to transport, and requires expensive modifications for standard equipment to utilize it. It is a good idea to check with the custodian before utilizing the power outlets, however, for the accidental use of direct current in ac-rated equipment could result in costly damage, especially to motors.

The standard electrical voltage used in audiovisual equipment is 117–120 V. This may vary plus or minus several volts and can be checked by using a voltmeter. Variations in excess of 5% should be corrected by the local power company or by an electrician. Under-voltage will cause slow-down of motors and loss of light from lamps. Over-voltage could cause a strain on operating motors and could shorten considerably the life of projection lamps.

Every piece of equipment has fastened to it a manufacturer's name plate. In addition to listing the name of the corporation and the model number, it was standard practice to indicate the voltage, amperage (amp.), and wattage (Figure 3.1) utilized by the particular piece of equipment. However, now that the rating of 117–120 V ac is so common for audiovisual equipment, this information is often omitted.

Amperes (amp.) has reference to the quantitative flow of electrons from a given power source. Most homes have circuits rated at 15 amp., although newer homes have an increased rating of 20 and 30 amp. The usual power supply from the wall outlets in new classroom-buildings is 30 amp.

It is important for the classroom teacher to know what the amperes rating for outlets in the room actually is. Operation of equipment that draws more amperage than is provided for will result in the abrupt termination of electrical service when a fuse is "blown" or a circuit breaker is activated. If there is a power failure, it is recommended that equipment be disconnected before the fuse is replaced or the circuit breaker is reset.

The capacity of a wall outlet to provide effective power for audiovisual

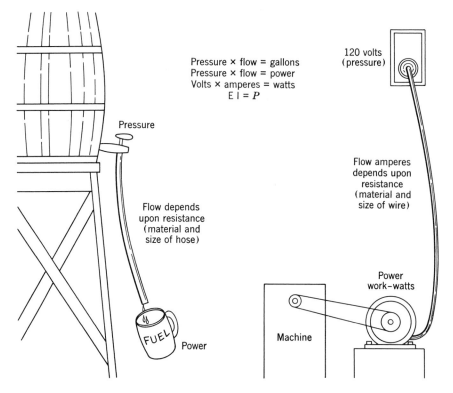

Pressure × flow = gallons
Pressure × flow = power
Volts × amperes = watts
$$E\,I = P$$

120 volts
(pressure)

Pressure

Flow amperes
depends upon
resistance
(material and
size of wire)

Flow depends
upon resistance
(material and
size of hose)

Power
work–watts

FUEL

Power

Machine

Figure 3.1   The basic electrical terms of volts, amperes, and watts are more understandable when considered as equivalents of pressure, flow, and power. *Courtesy of the University of Mass.*

equipment can be easily determined by noting the amperes that each piece of equipment requires. This information is on the manufacturer's name plate. A quick comparison of the amperage required with the rated output of the outlet will indicate whether there is sufficient power in the room; for example, a film-strip projector utilizing 5 amp. and an overhead projector drawing 10 amp. can be used safely at the same time from the same outlet rated at 15 amp. However, an overhead projector and a motion-picture projector each drawing 10 amp. could not be operated together from the same outlet; the result would be a power failure.

The ampere rating sometimes is omitted from the name plate and instead *wattage* is given. *Watts* are a product of volts times amperes and an expression of the work done, or power generated, by the equipment. Amperage can be calculated by dividing volts into watts (A = W/V). A tape recorder, for example, that has noted on its name plate an operating voltage of 120 V and a power rating of 525 W could draw 4.4 amp:

$$\frac{525 \text{ watts}}{120 \text{ volts}} = 4.4 \text{ amp.}$$

The electrical cord or wire that connects audiovisual equipment to wall outlets has been carefully selected by the manufacturer as to size (wire diameter), and has been completely insulated with plastic, fiber, and rubber sheathing so as to eliminate any possibility of electrical shock. If the power cord is not long enough to reach an outlet, an extension cord is used. The size of the wire in the extension cord should be sufficient to conduct the required current. Size is determined by the diameter of the wire. No. 18 wire is used in desk lamps, radios, clocks, and other light appliances. It should not be used in an extension cord for audiovisual equipment. A heavier wire (No. 14 or No. 12), properly insulated, is recommended. The smaller, finer wire offers too much resistance to the required heavy flow of electricity. If used, it may become extremely hot and may even dry out or burn through the insulation. A lengthy light-wire cord will also cause a voltage drop that will affect the operation of the equipment.

Many teachers have puzzled over "defective" equipment in the classroom only to discover later, to their chagrin, that the extension cord was not connected to the power cord or that the plug was not in the outlet. Cords are easily stepped on, pushed, and tripped over. To prevent separation, the power cord should be loosely knotted with the extension cord. A loose knot around a chair leg or table leg will help to absorb any strain on the wall plug.

Most cords terminate with a two-prong plug that fits most wall outlets. More recently, manufacturers have adopted a new three-wire cord terminating in a three-prong plug. The third wire is a ground wire, which offers further protection against accidental shocks. It also tends to reduce hum in audio systems. These plugs require a matching three-hole wall receptacle. When this receptacle is lacking, a special adapter plug (Figure 3.2) can be used. A short wire runs from this adapter plug and can be fixed to the screw holding the plate of the wall outlet.

The third wire is designed to improve safety and operation of audiovisual equipment. This effort should not be thwarted by twisting away the third prong or failing to fasten securely the ground wire.

SOUND

The "audio" portion of audiovisual equipment is often overlooked because of the impact of visual projections. Sound in any form—whether

Figure 3.2   Adapter plugs can be used to fit a three-prong plug to a two-prong outlet.

naturally produced, on record, on magnetic tape, or on a sound track—is important and merits consideration at this point.

A sound is the result of vibrations of the originating body, whether it is the vocal chords responding to passage of air, wood responding to a rap, or the strings of a banjo vibrating to a pluck. Vibrations must pass through some medium for transmission to be effected. This medium could be any of the following: air, water, metal, plastic, or wood; but the more solid the material, the better the sound is transmitted. Sound travels through the medium of air at a speed of 1087 feet per second (fps) at sea level and at a temperature of 0°C. Compared with light, sound moves rather slowly, as can be deduced if we listen to the sounds from an observed distant action.

Sound waves differ in three ways: frequency, amplitude, and quality. These characteristics are graphically depicted in Figure 3.3 as they might appear on an instrument called the oscilloscope. These waves can be compared with the wave motion in water. Frequency has reference to

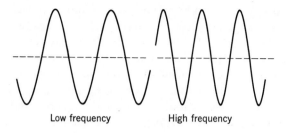

Low frequency   High frequency

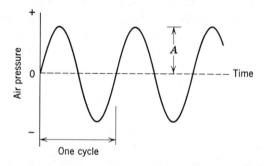

Figure 3.3 Sound waves are invisible but they can be depicted graphically. The chief characteristics of sound waves are their frequency, their amplitude, and their quality.

the number of waves that pass a given point in a set time. This is usually expressed as cycles per second (cps). We can hear sound in the frequency range of about 30 cps to 18,000 cps. This ability, however, is dependent upon our age and general physical condition. The older the person, the more limited is the frequency range.

Most sound play-back equipment operates in the range of 40 to 8000 cps. "Hi-fi" equipment will increase the range up to 20 to 25,000 cps; but these extremes add little to the appreciation of recorded sound inasmuch as few people can hear them. In music, *pitch* has reference to sound frequency. Middle C on the piano has a frequency of 256 cps, with the range from the lowest to the highest note being 27 to 4096 cps.

The volume or loudness of sound is characterized by the amplitude, or the *height* of the sound wave. The greater the distance between the height and the depth of a wave, the greater is the intensity. Loudness or intensity of sound-reproducers is measured in power units (watts) or power ratios (decibels). These measurements can be confusing because the intensity of sound is not proportional to the amplitude or power in watts; for example, a sound that is doubled in measured intensity is heard as being only slightly louder. The term *decibel* is often used as a measurement of sound for this reason—because it is a ratio between two amounts of power and indicates the proportional differences between the intensities of sound.

The quality of sound is depicted graphically as differences in the shape of the sound wave. Harmonics and overtones, the beating of several frequencies in the same sound at the same time, result in tones that are identifiable with different vibrating bodies. For example, a buzz saw and a violin may both produce sounds of the same frequency and intensity, but because of this added characteristic called *quality*, we can distinguish between the sounds.

The value or worth of sound-reproducing equipment lies in its ability to duplicate the original sound. Cheap, inexpensive equipment may fail to do the job well; the frequency, intensity, and quality of sound may not be equal to that of the original sound. Such distortions can be detected by measuring instruments. High-fidelity equipment is now able to reproduce sound with distortion of less than 1%. It is capable of reproducing all the original frequencies and of amplifying them by the same amount over the entire audible range.

The analogy of waves in water, might at this point be helpful in explaining how sound is transmitted by means of the sound wave. A large ocean wave may be 50 ft. between crests; a motor boat traveling between the crests may create waves of only 5 ft. between crests; and wind blowing over the water may create ripples on the surface of these waves. All of these waves may be carried by the water at the same time. Sounds are carried in the air in this manner. The capability of sound-reproducing equipment to duplicate waves with true fidelity is a measure of its quality.

As explained above, sound emanates from any vibrating body—whether from skin stretched taut over a framework or from vocal chords acted upon by air forced from the lungs and through the mouth. For centuries man has tried to extend his range of communication by amplifying these vibrations. His greatest advance had to wait for the discovery and control of electricity, however. It was Edison, building on the work of earlier scientists, who was first able to demonstrate how mechanical sound or energy could be changed into electrical energy, built up (amplified), and then converted back into mechanical energy or air vibrations. This discovery made possible the development and use of such modern devices as public address systems, radios, sound motion pictures, recordings, and television. All audio equipment uses the three elements basic to Edison's experiments: the pickup, the amplifier, and the reproducer. The following paragraphs will treat each of these briefly. Greater detail will be offered in other sections of this book.

Pickups

Any device that changes mechanical vibrations or sound waves into electrical energy is called a pickup. They are available in great number, but we can simplify our classification by referring to the more common types: microphones, cartridges in record-player arms, and photoelectric cells. In physical appearances they are different, but their function is the same.

Microphones. Microphones come in all shapes and sizes and in a wide price range. They are usually referred to according to their construction as either crystal, dynamic, or velocity microphones.

The *crystal* microphone uses a small crystal of rochelle salt which is connected to a diaphragm. Air vibrations striking the diaphragm bend the crystal and induce a corresponding electrical vibration which is then carried by the microphone cord, a specially shielded cable, to the amplifier. Depending upon its size and shape, this microphone can pick up sound from all directions (nondirectional) or from one direction. It is the least expensive of the microphones available and is also the least sensitive to sound vibrations. However, it *is* serviceable and is usually found with most portable recording equipment. Special care should be taken not to drop a crystal microphone or subject it to temperatures over 120°.

The *ceramic* microphone is similar to the crystal microphone in every respect except that the ceramic element will withstand higher temperatures.

The *dynamic* microphone receives sound vibrations on an extremely thin diaphragm which is attached to a coil of wire. The coil is in a magnetic field and induces electrical vibrations by the generator principle. The microphone accepts sound from all directions and is especially rugged. It is used when rough handling is expected. Because of its wide range, it is used for productions involving a large orchestra, cast, or chorus.

The *velocity* microphone is also known as the *ribbon* microphone. Air vibrations are changed into electrical vibrations by means of a suspended ribbon that vibrates between the poles of a permanent magnet. It will pick up sound only from front or back and thus is bidirectional. It is sensitive, expensive, and easily damaged; therefore, it is used primarily for small groups or individual pick-up when high fidelity is needed.

The less-expensive microphones generate electrical vibrations that can be transported over short distances only—up to 25 ft. There is also the danger of picking up noise in the cable, no matter how well shielded it is. The more expensive microphones yield a lower output, but this output can be transported over longer distances with less ambient noise and with greater fidelity. The microphone cables are specially sheathed and insulated to minimize the pick-up of other sources of sound vibrations.

Record-Player Cartridge. Sound recorded on phonograph records can be played back by using inexpensive devices; for example, a low volume of limited frequencies of sound can be reproduced by using a very fine needle fixed rigidly into the point of a paper cone. Reproducing recorded sound with high fidelity requires the use of electronic devices. Instead of being attached to a paper cone, the needle, with a fine long-wearing point, is fixed into an electromagnetic unit called a *cartridge.* Such devices are made of plastic or metal and are of two types—*crystal* and *magnetic.* The function of both is the same: to change the mechanical vibrations received by the needle traveling in the groove of the record into corresponding electrical vibrations. The crystal cartridge or pickup is inexpensive and serviceable; thus it is most widely used. The magnetic pickup is more expensive, but it produces greater fidelity and frequency response and is thus much superior in performance. The signal is weaker, however, and does require additional equipment to strengthen it.

Photoelectric Cells. Another important method of sound pickup is the *photoelectric cell;* its principle application is with the optical sound track of motion picture film. In recording sound on film mechanical vibrations are converted into electrical vibrations that activate a diaphragm. The diaphragm, in response to sound vibrations, opens and closes a light trap which allows a fluctuating pattern of light to strike the film. The film is then developed through regular photographic processes. The result is called an *optical sound track.* In playback a concentrated beam of light is focused on the optical sound track. The vibrations printed on the film cause an intermitent or blinking light which is directed at a photoelectric cell. The effect of this blinking light on the cell serves to convert these vibrations once again into electronic vibrations.

Amplifiers

The electrical signal or vibration generated by the microphone, phono-cartridge, or optical sound track, is weak and can be measured in milliamperes (thousandths of an ampere). It is the function of the amplifier to make strong electrical signals out of weak ones. This is necessary because loudspeakers require a strong signal for actuation.

The signal strength is built up (Figure 3.4) through various stages by using vacuum tubes, more commonly known as radio tubes. Today these tubes are giving way to transistors, which serve the same function but are more compact, more sensitive, and longer-lived. Amplifiers can be simple and inexpensive or multistage for high-fidelity reproduction. School equipment usually falls into the middle range.

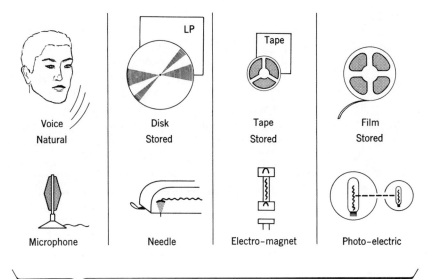

Voice — Natural | Disk — Stored (LP) | Tape — Stored | Film — Stored

Microphone | Needle | Electro-magnet | Photo-electric

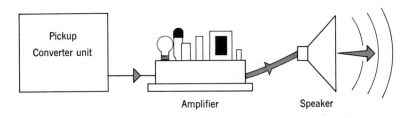

Pickup Converter unit

Amplifier | Speaker

Figure 3.4 Sound waves, whether natural or stored, require a buildup in their intensity to improve their audibility. Sidney C. Eboch, *Operating Audiovisual Equipment,* **Chandler Publishing Co.**

Most amplifiers, besides increasing signal strength, have these features:

1. Connections for receiving signals from various types of pickup—microphones, record players, tape recorders, etc.
2. Output terminals for sending the strengthened signal to loudspeakers or recorders.
3. Tone controls for adjusting bass or treble characteristics of sound.
4. Low hum or noise-level controls.
5. Fidelity sufficient to reproduce programs with an illusion of realism.
6. Frequency response range adequate to reproduce clearly and without distortion the full range of audible sound (30 to 15,000 cps).

Loudspeakers

Reproducers or loudspeakers change the electrical impulses that have been built up by the amplifier into sound or pressure waves. Most speakers in use today are of the permanent-magnet, dynamic variety. They operate in a manner similar to that of the dynamic microphone, but in reverse. The electrical vibrations from the amplifier are sent through a magnetic field which causes a corresponding displacement of the diaphragm. The vibration of the diaphragm sets up the mechanical vibration in the air that our ears perceive as sound.

Loudspeakers of serviceable quality (good reproducers of sound) are available in most audio equipment for classroom use. The loudspeaker is compact and is adequate for the needs of the classroom. For larger rooms and auditoriums, separate speakers in special enclosures are needed. These can range in size up to 15 in. in diameter. The speaker components are constructed to be sensitive to various levels of power (watts). It is important for maximum effectiveness to match the power rating of a loudspeaker with the power output of an amplifier.

One of the determinants of quality in a speaker is the speaker's capability of responding to all frequencies for high-fidelity reproduction. A large paper cone, or diaphragm, is needed to reproduce the low frequencies (bass tones). Higher tones are produced with a separate small cone, or a portion of the larger cone is made to operate at higher frequencies. The speakers reproducing high frequencies are commonly called "tweeters," and those reproducing low tones are called "woofers."

Extensive research and experimentation in loudspeakers has resulted in the development of small compact speakers capable of responding to the audible frequency range. This development, with the use of transistors, should produce some startling changes in the design and size of audio equipment.

Permanently mounted speakers for auditoriums or large rooms require special installation. The box or enclosure containing the speaker is important to the effective operation of the speaker. It must be of the correct size and constructed of solid material. It should have a closed back and two openings in the front, one circular and the other rectangular: *a bass reflex cabinet.* It is recommended for use with better-quality speakers.

The rate at which electrical vibrations will pass through the voice coil varies. Resistance to the flow of current in the voice coil is measured in ohms and is called the "impedance" of the speaker. It is important when setting up sound systems to group speakers with like power ratings and connect them to the correct impedance outputs of the amplifier. (This information is clearly marked on both speakers and amplifiers.)

Careful selection and matching of pick-ups, amplifiers, and speakers will pay great dividends in the pleasure and utility obtained from the reproduced sound.

OPTICS

Much of the material in the text is concerned with projected images. The visual material takes many forms: slides, transparencies, motion-picture film, and even flat pictures. These images are brilliantly illuminated by projection lamps and recreated in enlarged form on the screen. The mechanics of this operation involve the careful matching of lamps, reflectors, and lenses with the projection material being used. This inter-relationship will be considered briefly in this section.

Lenses

An element that is most important to a projection system—but which often seems mysterious to users of equipment—is the lens. As operators of projection equipment, teachers should have some knowledge of the characteristics of lenses and should understand the part they play in the projection of images on the screen.

Lenses serve two functions; thus there are generally two sets of lenses in a projector. The first is to gather the light from the lamp and direct it through a specifically designated area (*condensing lenses*). The other function is to recreate the image on the screen (*the objective lens*). Other terms used interchangeably in reference to this latter lens are *projection* or *magnifying lens.*

Condensing lenses spread the light evenly over or through the material to be projected. Usually combinations of condenser lenses (Figure 3.5)

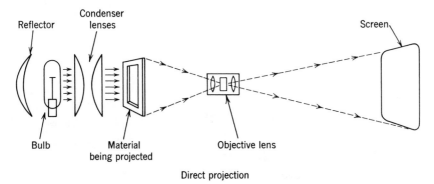

Direct projection

Figure 3.5   Condenser lenses are light-gathering lenses that direct illumination through the image that is being projected. Objective or projection lenses direct the image onto the screen.

are needed to produce the desired results. They are located nearest the lamp and are designed to withstand high temperatures. Even so, they may crack or break. Replacements can be obtained from the manufacturer, but care should be exercised in replacing them in the correct order. The condensing lens should be cleaned regularly with a soft cloth or tissue and lens-cleaning fluid.

In some projectors it is possible to position an additional glass disk between the lens elements. This device is called a *heat filter* and it cuts down the intensity of heat passing through the system without appreciably affecting the illumination from the lamp.

The objective lens is the most important part of any projector, for on it depends the sharpness and clarity, the illumination, and the size of the projected image. The projection lens inverts the image and, for that reason, slides and other transparent materials must be inverted when placed in the projector. Projectors such as the opaque or the overhead use mirrors to correct the inversion, so that material is placed right-side-up in the projector.

Lenses differ in many respects, but there are three characteristics that are of special concern to us: focal length, aperture, and f number.

Focal Length.　The focal length of the lens (Figure 3.6) is the distance between the image and the lens when the sun or another light source is focused on a screen. The effective focal length for a lens is ordinarily indicated on that lens by the manufacturer, but the actual measurement will vary somewhat. As the projector is moved away from the screen, the lens

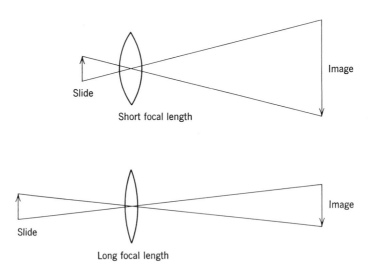

Figure 3.6　Focal length of a lens in a projector can be measured roughly as the distance between the lens and the image to be projected.

is brought nearer to the slide in order to bring the recreated image into focus. The classroom teacher should recognize the importance of focal length because it determines the size of the screen image at a given distance. Merely by changing the lens it is possible to change the position of the projector and still hold the same size screen image.

There is a logical relationship that exists between the various factors in projection. It can be expressed as an equation:

$$\frac{\text{width of slide}}{\text{width of screen}} = \frac{\text{focal length}}{\text{projection distance}}$$

By knowing any three factors, it is possible to solve for the fourth. Note that areas are not compared but that horizontal widths are. Of course, the same unit of measurement should be employed for all factors.

The widths of the image areas of projected materials vary. The following are the widths of materials most widely used:

	Image width (in.)
16-mm. motion-picture film	0.38
Single-frame filmstrip	0.9
Double-frame filmstrip	1.34
2 × 2 slide	1.3
Lantern slide, $3\frac{1}{4}$ × 4	3.0
Opaque and overhead	10.0

Lenses can be interchanged to suit the conditions desired. However, standard lenses provided by equipment manufacturers are as follows:

	Focal length (in.)
16-mm. motion-picture projector	2
35-mm. filmstrip and slide projector	5
2 × 2 slide projector	5
$3\frac{1}{4}$ × 4 lantern slide	12
Overhead projector	14
Opaque projector	18

With the above information known it is easy to calculate the required projection between a given projector and a screen of given size. For example, a 16-mm motion-picture projector would have to be placed 30.7 ft. from a screen to fill a 52 × 70 in. area:

$$\frac{0.38 \text{ in.}}{70} = \frac{2 \text{ in.}}{x}$$

$$0.38x = 140$$

$$x = 368.4 \text{ in. or } 30.7 \text{ ft.}$$

From a study of the above equation, several observations can be made:

1. The projected image becomes larger as the projection distance is increased.
2. The wider the slide size, the wider the screen width.
3. A longer focal length lens makes a smaller projected picture.

Such relationships can be demonstrated through the manipulation of the various factors involved. This is usually avoided by the classroom teacher because of the movement of tables, chairs, screens, and projection equipment that is required.

For those who would prefer to solve their projection problems without the need for extensive calculations or movement of furniture and equipment, comprehensive, easy-to-read tables are available. These tables are supplied by the major equipment manufacturers and they facilitate the task of selecting the correct equipment for a particular projection situation.

A few basic ratios (if remembered when no other assistance is available) may help to simplify the solution of projection problems:

Projector	Lens focal focal length (in.)	Ratio— projection distance to screen width
16-mm. motion-picture projector	2	5.3
8-mm. motion-picture projector	$\frac{3}{4}$	4.7
Single-frame filmstrip projector	5	5.5
Overhead projector	14	1.5
Opaque projector	18	1.8

From a rapid scrutiny of this table, one can see, for example, that for the overhead projector to be used with a six-foot screen, it would have to be placed approximately nine feet from the screen. (6 ft × 1.5 = 9 ft).

Aperture. The diameter of a lens determines the amount of light that it is able to project onto the screen. The greater the diameter, or aperture, the more the light rays that will be transmitted if the focal length remains the same. Shortening the focal length while maintaining the same aperture, however, could accomplish the same thing.

f Number. The light-gathering ability of a lens is determined by the relationship between focal length and aperture. The ratio of the two is used to compare lenses and is called the *f number.* The smaller the *f* number, the greater is the light gathering ability of the lens. For lenses used to magnify the image greatly, the *f* number will be low—approaching 1. As the rate of magnification decreases, the *f* number increases. Stated another way, as the focal increases, the *f* number increases. The diameter of the lense does not vary greatly because of the projection costs involved and the design changes that would be required in the projection equipment.

Lenses play a most important part in the structure of a projector. Their function and the relationships that determine the screen size, projector distance, and brilliance of image are readily evident. Focal length, aperture, and f number are the characteristics that identify lenses and set forth the capability of a projector.

Projection Lamps

Lenses gather light and direct it onto a screen. However, before this can be done, there must be a source of light. The projection lamp (Figure 3.7) is designed for just this purpose. It is sometimes incorrectly referred

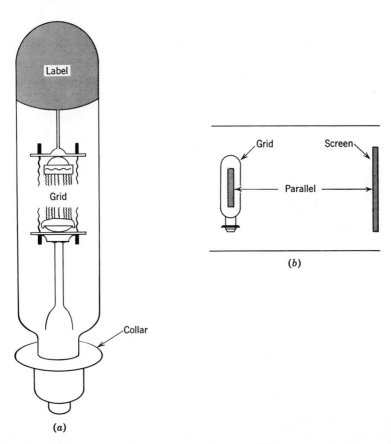

Figure 3.7   (a) Construction of a typical projection lamp. (b) The orientation of lamp grid to projection screen. Sidney C. Eboch, *Operating Audiovisual Equipment*, Chandler Publishing Co.

to as a "bulb." There are striking differences between household bulbs and projection lamps.

The lamp is the one expendable item in a projector. Its life is rated at between 10 and 25 hours. The wattage is ordinarily high (as much as 1,000 W for the overhead projector), but it can be as low as 150 W for a compact filmstrip projector. High wattage means that much heat is being given off; thus a cooling system (usually involving a fan), is necessary. When the fan is on a separate switch, it is a good practice to keep the fan on for a full minute after the lamp is turned off.

Projection lamps have a clear glass envelope and are tubular in shape. This shape allows the filament or grid in the lamp to be closer to the condensing lens and also facilitates cooling of the lamp.

The filament of the lamp must be positioned parallel to the screen to ensure that maximum light emission will be directed toward the screen. Several lamp bases are designed to lock the lamp in the socket—at the same time guaranteeing that the filament is in proper position. Such bases are called *prefocus bases*. One such type is the bayonet base, which is smooth and cylindrical and has two pins on its sides. It is fitted into a socket, depressed, turned 90°, and is locked into place.

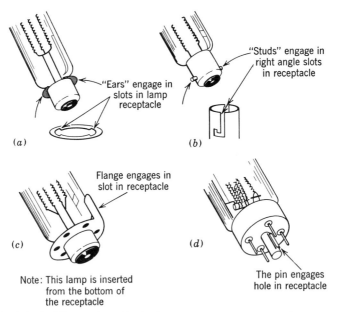

Figure 3.8 A basic difference in projection lamps is in the construction of the bases. (*a*) The medium prefocus base; (*b*) the bayonet-type base, largely used for low-wattage projection lamps; (*c*) the special flanged projection lamp, such as that used with the Bell and Howell projector; and (*d*) the newer pin-type base used in many current projectors.

The medium prefocus base (Figure 3.8*a*) is the most popular one used today. This base, which is also smooth and cylindrical, has two narrow lips of metal of unequal size on the sides of the collar. The lamp with this base is fitted into a socket, pressed down, turned clockwise one quarter turn, and is locked into position.

Some machines use a base with two posts (bipost); others have a four-pin base with a special key that guarantees correct placement. The latest overhead projectors use a new high-intensity lamp that actually has no base, but both ends of the lamp rest on electrical contacts.

Lamps are expensive and should be treated with care. Projectors should not be jarred or jolted when the lamp is on and projectors should not be tilted excessively. Projecting on the ceiling, for example, is not conducive to long lamp life. Contrary to popular belief, turning the lamp on and off does not necessarily shorten its life. If anything, short periods of cooling between longer periods of use may help extend the life of the lamp.

Replacement of lamps is a task that all teachers must face when using projection equipment. To facilitate this task, it is always wise to have a replacement lamp readily at hand. It should be the correct one for the projector. The code designation, although having no meaning in itself, does identify the lamps. Some typical lamp codes are as follows:

CTS   1000-w lamp for Bell & Howell Motion Picture Projector, Model 552.
DFY   1000-w lamp for Bell & Howell Motion Picture Projector, Model 385.
CZX   500-w lamp for Bell & Howell Filmstrip Projector Model 724G.
DDB   750-w lamp for RCA Motion Picture Projector, Model 400.
DRS   1000-w lamp for Beseler Opaque Projector, Model 6200.
DNE   150-w lamp for 8-mm projection.

Lamps of different codes are interchangeable. However, the wattage should be the same, the filaments must have an identical structure, and the base and contact points must be compatible with the socket.

SCREENS

For successful viewing of projected pictures a proper screen is essential. The screen should be large enough, be placed high enough, and reflect sufficient light so that everyone in the viewing area is able to view the material comfortably. The screens available to the classroom teacher are numerous, but they can be classified according to the type of screen surface, shape and size, and mounting.

Surface Materials

Screen surfaces are of a variety of materials. The *matte* screen (Figure 3.9a) has a smooth, flat-white surface. The image appears uniform regardless of the viewing angle, but the reflective power of this screen is not very great. The matte screen surface is best used in square rooms or in broad viewing areas. Visibility is best within the 35° angle formed on either side of the axis of light from the projector. The material used for matte

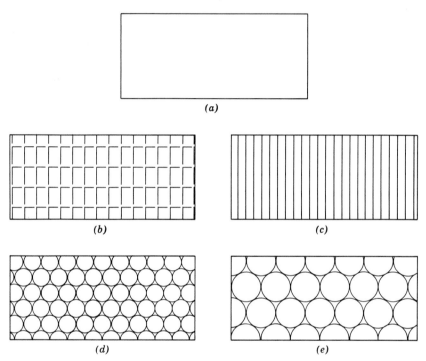

Figure 3.9   Types of projector screen surface. (*a*) Matte white: a white vinyl surface with supported fabric backing for superior hanging. Lightly textured surface achieves a grainless image over a wide viewing angle. Fungus and flame resistant, washable. (*b*) Silver lenticular: optically engineered multilenticular embossing on a silver coated vinyl base. Recommended for color, black and white, or stereo in partly lighted as well as darkened rooms. Assures complete light control for maximum brightness on the axis with minimum fall-off at side angles. Fungus and flame resistant, washable. (*c*) Silver lenticular: fine-line vertical embosing on a silver coated base. Recommened for use with color or black and white in either darkened or partly lighted rooms. Lenticulation spreads light over a wide viewing angle. Surface is fungus resistant. (*d*) Glass-beaded: microscopic silica grains of highly reflective quality for improved sharpness, depth, color, and brightness at every viewing angle. Ideal for color or black and white projection in normally darkened rooms. Fungus and flame resistant, easily cleaned. (*e*) Glass-beaded: fine glass beads chemically coated to produce very bright images under ordinary projection conditions. Use for color or black and white in normally darkened rooms.

screens is varied: wallboard, plywood, vinyl plastic, or cloth. The matte screen is widely used, its important characteristic being the flat white surface.

The *beaded-screen* surface (Figure 3.9d and e) is covered with millions of silica particles glued to a white fiber base. It has high reflectance at a narrow angle (15°) from the axis of light and reflects colors extremely well. It is best used in a long, narrow room where the seating is confined to a narrow angle directly in front of the screen.

The *lenticular* screen (Figures 3.9b and c) is made of heavy plastic or fabric with a corrugated surface. Horizontal and vertical markings are embossed into the silver surface. This allows for a high reflection of the projected image at a wide angle; in this way it combines the favorable features of both the matte and the beaded surfaces. Because of the nature of the material and its bulk, the size of the lenticular screen is restricted to a maximum area of 70 × 70 in.

A *translucent* screen surface is used in those situations when it is desired to remove the projector from the viewing area. In such instances the projector is placed behind the screen and the image is directed on the rear of the screen surface (Figure 3.10). The viewers in front "look through" the translucent screen at the projected image. The translucent screen is especially effective in brightly lit classrooms. The angle of viewing is narrow, being about equal to that for the beaded screen.

Methods of Mounting

The methods of mounting the screen are varied (Figure 3.11). Home construction of screens can be no more involved than tacking up a white cloth or painting a white rectangle on a smooth wall surface. But greater

Figure 3.10 Rear-view projection with translucent screen.

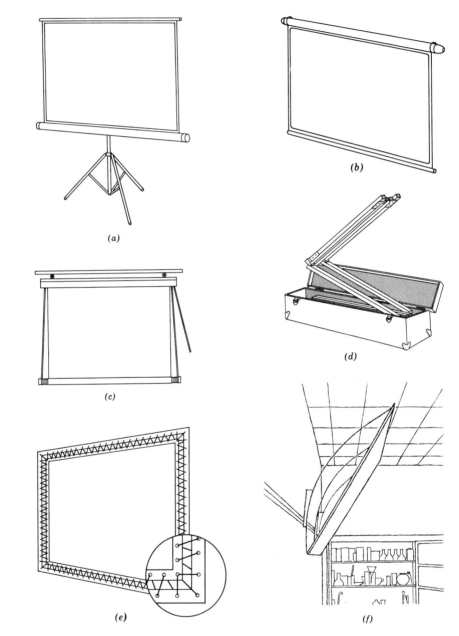

(a)

(b)

(c)

(d)

(e)

(f)

Figure 3.11 Methods of mounting screens are varied: (a) portable tripod; (b) portable wall type; (c) wall and ceiling rope-and-pulley type; (d) portable fast-fold; (e) grommet type; (f) tilt type.

flexibility in setup, transport, and storage is provided by other techniques. The wall screen is wound on a spring-loaded roller; its operation is similar to that of a window shade. For classroom use the case can be hung on the map rail and the screen drawn down. When not in use the screen surface is drawn back into the case by the spring-activated roller. The weight and bulk of this screen limits its size to a maximum of 70 × 70 in.

Larger units are available for auditorium use, but these screens are raised and lowered by electrical motors and are designed for permanent installation. The tripod screen is quite similar to the wall screen. The screen surface is rolled out of a metal case; however, in this instance the case is joined to a metal shaft and a collapsible tripod. This highly portable unit can be set up on any flat floor or table surface. The base of the screen can be set at various levels from 12 to 48 in. to accommodate various viewing conditions.

A recent innovation is the tilting screen, which is joined by metal rods to brackets fixed to the wall. The screen can be adjusted to various angles of tilt in order to eliminate projection distortions such as the "Keystone effect" (Figure 3.13). Although the brackets are fixed, the screen can be removed for cleaning or for use in another area.

Screens larger than 70 in. in width require more rigid and specialized mounting. For semipermanent installations, large screen surfaces are lashed to a wooden frame or metal pipe frame. Portable fast-fold screens made of vinyl plastic are also available. These screens can be stretched out and clipped to a light-weight metal frame. The frame is so constructed that it can be quickly expanded from a compact bundle. A screen measuring 10½ ft. × 14 ft. can be assembled from material easily transported in a packing case.

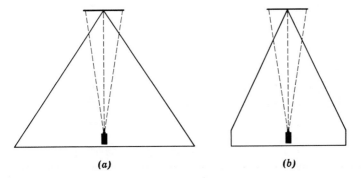

(a)   (b)

Figure 3.12 Audience seating arrangement according to types of screen. (a) Matte-type screen: use in a short room where class can spread out. (b) Beaded-type screen: use in a narrow room where angle of view is small.

Sizes of Screens

The sizes of screens vary considerably, and teachers may be confused about the proper size for a classroom. One rule that has a great deal of merit states that no one should be seated farther from the screen than *six times the width of the screen.* According to this rule, the recommended screen width for a 30-ft classroom would be 5 ft (60 in.).

There seems to be little justification for use of a square screen. Most of the projected materials are rectangular, the ratio of height to width

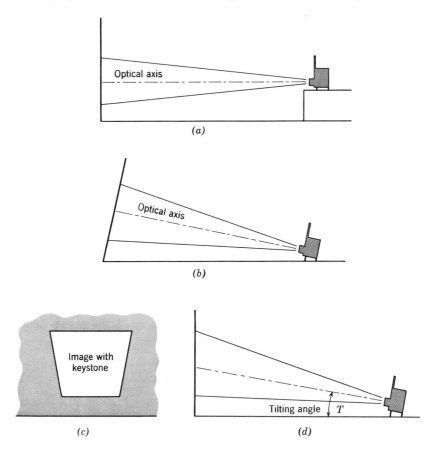

Figure 3.13 Avoid the "keystone" effect in projected images. (*a*) Vertical screen. (*b*) Tilted screen. If the optical axis is not square with the screen there will be a keystone effect of the image, which will look like a trapezoid instead of a rectangle (*c*) The keystone is not noticeable by viewers if the tilting angle (*d*) is less than 6°. It is slightly noticeable when the angle is between 6° and 9°. Above 9° viewers will notice a distortion of the image.

being 3:4. This relationship is known as the *aspect ratio*. Motion pictures, 35-mm. slides, bantam slides, and overhead transparencies all use the horizontal format. This rectangular format is especially important when ceiling heights limit the level to which screens can be raised. With a square screen there is always the danger that the bottom will be too low to be visible to everyone in the classroom.

The choice of screen surface and its mounting is influenced by the size and shape of the room as well as by the number of the students that need to be accommodated (Figure 3.12). Both the location of the screen and its size are factors that are important to the development of a good viewing area (Figure 3.14). It cannot be overemphasized that the finest projection equipment, the most illustrative visual aids, and the most fastidious preparation of students will all be for nothing if the students are not able to view the material clearly and comfortably. Good room design and proper choice of screen will ensure the successful showing of visuals.

Width of screen (in.)	Size of seating area	Maximum number of viewers (6 sq ft per person)
40	135	23
50	238	40
60	340	56
70	482	80
84	654	110
96	848	141
108	1078	180
120	1338	220
132	1650	276
144	2000	334

Figure 3.14   Screen capacity and size of audience. A picture does not have to fill the screen, but if it does, determine whether the screen is large enough to accommodate the audience. A quick glance at the audience capacity table will show the size screen required; for example, for a class of 40 (assuming the room is large enough—6 sq ft per person), a screen that will hold at least a 50-in. picture will be satisfactory.

SELECTED REFERENCES

Brown, James W., Richard B. Lewis, and Fred F. Hatcleroad, *Audiovisual Instruction Materials and Methods*, New York: McGraw-Hill, 1964, pp. 525–527 and 535–538.

Dale, Edgar, Audiovisual Methods in Teaching (rev. ed.), New York: Holt, Rinehart & Winston, 1961, pp. 218–225 and 259–268.

Davidson, Raymond L. *Audiovisual Machines*, Lubbock, Texas: Texas Tech Press, 1964, Chapters 1 and 2.

Eboch, Sidney C. *Operating Audiovisual Equipment.* San Francisco: Chandler, 1960. Chapters 1 and 4.

Finn, James D., *The Audiovisual Equipment Manual.* New York: Holt, Rinehart & Winston, 1957.

Haas, Kenneth B., and Harry Q. Packer, *Preparation and Use of Audiovisual Aids,* (3rd ed.), Englewood Cliffs, N. J.: Prentice-Hall, 1955, Chapters 1–4.

Kinder, James S., *Audio-Visual Materials and Techniques* (2nd ed.), New York: American Book Co., 1959, pp. 113–124 and Chapter 9.

Planning Schools for use of Audio-Visual Materials: No. 1, Classroom (rev. ed.), Washington, Department of Audiovisual Instruction, NEA, 1958.

Sands, Lester B., *Audio-visual Procedures in Teaching,* New York: Ronald Press, 1956, pp. 284–286, 304–305, 318–321, 341, 343, 370–371, 545, and 634.

Wittich, Walter Arno, and Charles Francis Schuller, *Audio-visual Materials, Their Nature and Use* (3rd ed.), 347–357, 411–413. New York: Harper, 1962, pp. 332–336.

Wyman, Raymond, *Audiovisual Devices and Techniques,* Amherst: University of Massachusetts, 1960, Chapter 4.

INSTRUCTIONAL MATERIALS

"Facts About Film," 15 min., sound, color, International Film Bureau, 1959.

"Facts About Projection" 16 min., sound, color, International Film Bureau, 1959.

"Projecting Motion Pictures," 10 min., sound, b & w, University of California Extension, Educational Film Sales Department.

"Routine Checking of Audio-visual Equipment," 46 frames, silent, b & w, State College of Washington.

4

STILL PROJECTION EQUIPMENT

LANTERN SLIDE PROJECTOR

In an earlier section dealing with the technical considerations for the use and operation of audiovisual equipment the importance of the lamp and lens to projection was stressed. This importance was recognized early by Athanasius Kirscher who originated the predecessor to the slide projector in 1643 and called it the "magic lantern." The images that were projected on the wall were primarily etched or drawn on glass. This method was used until the introduction of photography in 1843. The original size of the slide was $3\frac{1}{4} \times 4$ in., and some of these slides are still in existence. The "Keystone 500" series was especially popular during the early 1900's. Since 1920 and the popularization of miniature photography, however, the $2\frac{1}{4} \times 2\frac{1}{4}$, the 2×2, and the 35-mm slides have attracted more attention; this interest also led to the development of other projectors.

Basic Design

The lantern slide projector was the first unit developed, and a study of this projector reveals that its basic elements are still generally used in current models (Figure 4.1). It employs the principle of horizontal straight-line projection with a lamp, reflector, condensing lens, slide carrier, and objective lens. All elements are contained in a lightweight metal case. Few models have any moving parts except for the slide carrier and possibly a bellows arrangement to separate the 12-in. focal-length projection lens from the slide carrier. Units designed for auditorium use or large lecture halls are equipped with 1000-W lamps and the requisite cooling fan.

The lantern slide projector is designed to be used on any solid surface. Its base supports the lamp house and the optical system. The projected image can be raised or lowered by operating and elevating a tilting device. The bellows allow for a rough focus to be obtained; fine focus is then obtained by adjusting a rack-and-pinion focusing knob.

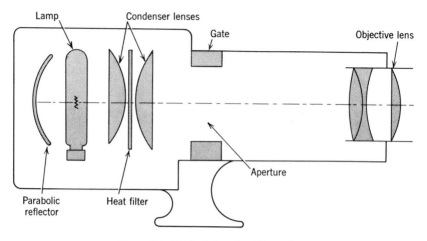

Figure 4.1   Basic design of a slide projector.

As is evident in Figure 4.2, the elements operate to produce an image on the screen in the following manner: the lamp emits its light rays in all directions. Its strongest rays are to the front and rear, however, because the filaments in the lamp are aligned parallel to the screen. The mirror reflector behind the lamp helps direct these light rays forward through the condensing lens. The lens gathers and refracts (bends) those rays into a strong beam of light which passes through the slide and comes to a point at the center of the objective lens. The objective lens is a diverging lens in that it spreads the light rays and directs them onto the screen surface. The optical system inverts the image that is projected; therefore, in order that the image be read correctly, the slide is inverted when placed in the slide changer. Normally, a symbol called a "thumb-mark" is placed on the slide mount. A right-handed person would hold that corner when inserting the slide into the projector. The "thumb-mark" would be in the lower left-hand corner if the slide were read while being held.

The early slide changers were made of wood. Although inexpensive and serviceable, they were subject to wear and were easily broken. The same type of changer today is made of metal. It consists of an outer frame with a rectangular opening equal to the slide size and an inner part consisting of two apertures. One aperture is in the stationary or outer frame; the second aperture can be loaded with a slide. Keeping both apertures loaded permits the projectionist to move from one slide to the next without any flicker of light interrupting the viewing continuity.[1]

[1]Raymond L. Davidson. *Audiovisual Machines*, Lubbock: Texas Technological College, 1964, p. 13.

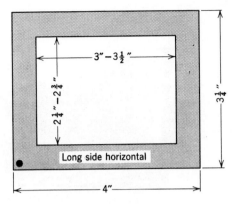

Figure 4.2 Standard slide dimensions.

The typical projection lens in the $3\frac{1}{4} \times 4$ lantern slide projector has a 12-in. focal length and is capable of projecting an image 54 in. wide at a distance of 20 ft. It is possible to interchange lenses of various focal lengths in order to move the projector forward or backward without changing the size of the projected image. The accompanying table (Figure 4.3) indicates the relationship that exists between focal length, projection distance, and screen size. The teacher should have some understanding of this relationship. It is important to note, however, that unless the condensing lens is changed with any change in the projection lens, there may be inefficient use of the light rays emitted by the lamp and the projected image may subsequently not be so bright as it could be.

Maintenance of Projectors

The instructions for the care and operation of the lantern slide projector can be applied to other projectors as well. The condensing lens and the

Lens Focal Length	Screen width						
	50"	60"	70"	84"	8'	9'	10'
5"	8'	12'	14'	16'	18'	20'	20'
9"	13'	15'	18'	21'	24'	27'	30'
12"	17'	20'	23'	28'	32'	36'	40'
16"	22'	27'	31'	37'	43'	48'	53'
20"	28'	33'	39'	47'	53'	60'	67'
24"	33'	40'	47'	56'	64'	72'	80'

Figure 4.3 The recommended projection distances are shown for various screen widths and focal lengths of lenses.

(a)

(b)

Figure 4.4 Typical lantern slide projectors. *Courtesy of Charles Beseler Co. and American Optical Co.*

projection lens should be kept free from dirt and finger marks. The lens surfaces can be wiped clean with a lint-free cloth after washing with a lens-cleaning fluid. A small soft brush should be used to remove dust and lint from the lens and from the apertures.

Lamps do burn out, sometimes at inopportune moments; therefore a basic rule is always to have a replacement lamp available with the equipment. Lamp bases vary; thus the methods of removing lamps will also vary. In the lantern slide projector the lamp should be pressed down and turned one-quarter turn to the left (counterclockwise); the lamp can then be lifted out.

Operating Procedures

The general instructions for the operation of the lantern slide projector (Figure 4.4) are applicable to the several models currently available:

Set up
1. Place projector on a flat, sturdy surface.
2. Connect power cord to electrical outlet and to machine (if the cord is not permanently attached to the projector).
3. Place slide changer in projector and fasten securely.

Adjust
1. Turn on lamp.
2. Move objective lens so that a bright rectangle of light is focused on the screen.

(c)

Figure 4.4 *(continued)*

3. Center the light on the screen by elevating or tilting the projector.
Operate
1. Insert slide in changer and project image on screen.
2. Turn off light and remove last slide from the projector at the conclusion of the showing.
3. If a cooling fan is present, allow the fan to operate for a short time after the lamp is turned off.
Pack up
1. Remove changer, disconnect the power cord, and place the projector and accessory parts in the carrying case.

Types of Slides

One of the attractions of the lantern slide projector is the ease with which slides can be produced. Hand-made slides can be the result of student projects and activities as well as the teacher's effort to visualize a lesson. Materials involved are readily available and the varieties of available effects provide for meaningful projections.

There are several types of hand-made lantern slides. The description of the techniques involved in their production will be left to a later chapter dealing with the construction of transparencies for overhead projection, but a general listing of the types of slides would include the following:

1. Matte-surface acetate or glass with drawings and lettering in pen, pencil, or colored markers and tapes.
2. Typing or drawing on cellophane, with cellophane sandwiched between two pieces of glass for projection.
3. Cutouts of shapes and silhouttes mounted between two pieces of glass for projection of shadow images.
4. Clear or gelatin-coated slides for drawing with acetate inks and with transparent colored pencils.

In producing these slides it must be kept in mind that the images will be enlarged 20 to 50 times. Since this magnification includes errors as well, the work should be done as accurately as possible. Careful planning before the start of work on a slide will tend to minimize the errors and eliminate any false starts. A premiliminary sketch or layout is especially recommended in instances in which children are involved in the project.

Photographic Slides. The camera is a versatile tool in the production of all kinds of materials. The black and white $3\frac{1}{4} \times 4$ slide is usually photographed with a $2\frac{1}{4} \times 3\frac{1}{4}$ (or smaller) camera, using standard exposure techniques. The negative is developed in the darkroom and then printed onto a $3\frac{1}{4} \times 4$ glass plate. After its development, the positive print is covered with glass, which protects the image surface of the plate. The two pieces of glass are taped together along the glossy edges and the slide is then ready for projection.[2]

Color slides can also be exposed in the camera, but they must be developed and printed by professional processors. A new development in photography by the Polaroid Corporation has reawakened interest in the $3\frac{1}{4} \times 4$ slide. With this process it is possible to expose, develop, fix, and mount a slide ready for projection within three minutes. This produces an immediacy that is difficult to achieve in any of the other areas of projection.

Advantages of the Lantern Slide Projector

The lantern slide projector is the oldest projection technique currently in use. Its use in the classroom and auditorium is reflective of the appeal that it has for teachers. It is easily set up and operated; necessary transparencies can either be purchased or produced locally in the classroom (production of transparencies by students provide effective learning experiences). The slides, being manually inserted into the machine, can be edited to fit a particular learning situation; they can be kept on the screen or omitted, depending upon the progress of the lesson. Adaptibility and flexibility of presentations are the strong features of this method of presentation.

There are limiting factors, however, that have prompted teachers to search out other methods of projection. These factors include the lack of variety in commercial slides; a tendency of glass slides to be broken; the bulky nature of the equipment; the wide separation of the projector from the screen; and the slide's limited area for creative design.

All these objections combine to restrict the widespread use of the lantern slide projector. It has, however, played a significant part in the development of projection techniques in the classroom and has provided the basis for more advanced developments in this area.

2 × 2 SLIDE AND FILMSTRIP PROJECTORS

The 2×2 slide-filmstrip projector is currently the most widely used projector in the classroom. It is used by the teacher for general class presentations; it is used by small groups of students for review purposes or for specialized projects; and it is used by individuals for remedial and enrichment purposes.

[2]R.E. de Kieffer and Lee Cochran, *Manual of Audiovisual Techniques*, Edgewood Cliffs, N.J. Prentice-Hall, 1962, p. 121.

Basic Design

The arrangement of the optical elements follow the same basic horizontal arrangement of the lantern slide projector. Accessory attachments allow it to be used as a 2 × 2 slide projector or as a filmstrip projector. In the treatment of this projector we will describe its physical characteristics, (Figure 4.5), then the 2 × 2 slides, and, finally, the filmstrips. The projectors that are adapted only for 2 × 2 slides or only for filmstrips, will be described as well.

The projection lamp is usually one rated at 500 W; it is fan-cooled. The units designed for small group or individual viewing are convection-cooled and utilize 300-W lamps. Fan-cooled projectors are always preferred because of the added protection from heat given to the optical system and to the slides. The condensing lens is suited to directing the light through an aperture that measures 2 × 2 in., although the area of effective use in the slide measures 1.3 × 1.3 and that for the single-frame filmstrip, 0.675 × 0.9. The projection lens is much closer to the aperture than in the lantern slide projector, the focal length being normally 5 in.

Basic Operating Procedures

The projector is compact, light in weight, easily operated, and readily adapted to any viewing situation. To use the projector, the following general instructions are applicable:

Set up
1. Connect power cord to electrical outlet.
2. Insert slide changer. Fasten in position with thumb screw or spring lock.

Adjust
1. Turn on power switch.
2. Focus beam of light to desired width and establish proper projection distance for that screen size.
3. Place slide in changer and focus.
4. Elevate or tilt projector to desired height.

Operate
1. Project slides. Keep adjusting focus since film that is not glass-mounted will show a tendency to "pop" or expand slightly when heated.
2. Remove changer after last slide and remove slide from changer.
3. Turn off lamp but allow cooling fan to operate for at least a minute before turning it off.

Pack up
1. Level the projector.
2. Unplug power cord.
3. Pack the projector, cord, and changer into the case.

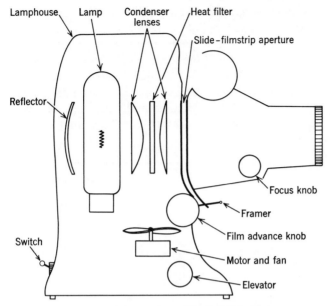

Figure 4.5   **Principal parts of the slide-filmstrip projector.**

The slide changer can be one of two types. The first is a frame with two apertures that operates inside a larger holder with a single aperture. Slides are loaded on both sides; frame and slide are moved in for projection.

In the second there is a single aperture in the inner frame as well as the outer frame. The slide is pushed into position and the carrier is then drawn back, leaving the slide in the aperture area. The next side in turn pushes the first one out of the way as it is set in position. One type of changer pushes the slide and then pulls it out in the same position. Another pushes the slide in for projection and then out the other side of the carrier.

Slides

The 35-mm camera is the principle means of producing slides for the 2 × 2 projector. The black-and-white slides can be processed in any darkroom, but color slides must be developed and printed by commercial processors to achieve uniform quality. After processing, the exposed film is either trimmed and laminated in a cardboard frame or sealed between two pieces of glass. Although the glass frame is more fragile and expensive, such slides can be kept cleaner; they also minimize projection difficulties. Glass holds the film rigidly in position during projection, thus allowing an even focus over the entire image area. Cardboard-mounted slides will eventually expand and will necessitate adjustment of focus.

The image area of the slide is rectangular, either vertically or horizont-ally (Figure 4.6). The super slide, square 2 × 2, is rarely used. When both vertical and horizontal slides are to be used, it is necessary to adjust the projector to the screen so that the screen is able to contain both type images. The effectiveness of a slide will be significantly decreased if part of the projection falls on the wall instead of completely on the screen. Most slides being produced today are horizontally oriented, and with the trend towards horizontal screens, it does not seem likely that this pattern will be

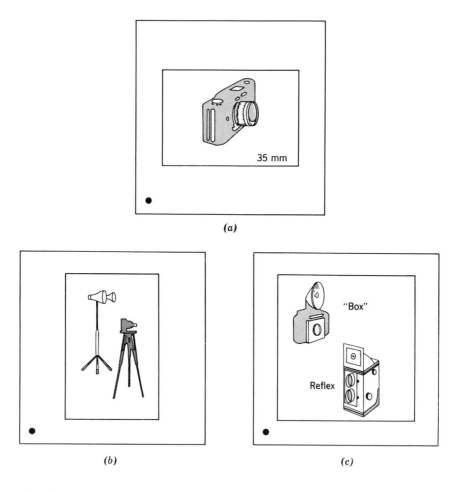

Figure 4.6 Classifying 2 × 2 slides by dimensions of picture area. (Note the mark in lower left-hand corner. When inserted in the projector, the slide is rotated so that the mark is located in the upper right-hand corner.) (a) Horizontal; (b) vertical; (c) super.

altered. It is, of course, necessary to invert slides before placing them into the projector (Figure 4.7).

2 × 2 slide has appeal for children as well as teachers because the slide can be produced by anyone owning a 35-mm. camera. Visual reports of field trips, vacations, laboratory experiments, and special projects can be accomplished with great interest and appeal for the participants involved. Commercially, slides are available on a variety of topics including art reproductions, scenic spots throughout the world, and plant and animal life.

Programming Slides. A question often raised is: "How many slides should be used in a presentation?" The answer, of course, is dependent upon the subject matter and the extent to which the subject matter is to be explored. Sometimes a single slide will be sufficient to stimulate thinking and discussion on a particular topic. In other cases a whole series of slides may be needed to achieve the objectives of the lesson. Teachers find it convenient to assemble slides into sets or categories. Complete sets can be used in presentations, or individual slides drawn from several sets can be assembled for a new presentation. The sets range from 10 to 40 units and can be boxed in those units. Most slides can be marked and titled on the slide frame; when identified in this manner, they can be easily returned to the original sets.

The medium of slide projection is primarily a visual one with the words necessarily having to be supplied by the instructor. The visuals should be carefully selected in order that their presentation of information be clear and readily understandable. The verbal commentary accompanying the visual should emphasize and draw attention to the pertinent parts of

"OK, wise guys—So I did put a slide in upside down!"

Figure 4.7 **Slides must be inverted before putting them in the projector.** *Courtesy of Graflex Inc.*

the illustration. A sketch or a paper plan of the slides to be used during a presentation is recommended; previewing the slides helps to establish relationships and tie together the basic ideas in the presentation. It also enables the instructor to make any judgements necessary as to the technical quality of the slides or their suitability for the presentation.

As with the $3\frac{1}{4} \times 4$ slides, the significant feature of the 2×2 slide presentation is the flexibility that the teacher has in assembling the visuals. Slide sets can be edited, omissions easily corrected, and deletions made in instances where time becomes a factor or where there is a change in focus of interest.

To sum up, slides are particularly valuable to the teacher because they are so easy to create, assemble, and present to audiences. However, because of their size, they are easily lost and are somewhat difficult to keep track of. There is also the tendency to use too many of them. These difficulties fade into insignificance, however, when the many benefits to the instructional program of such slides are assessed.

Selected Slide Projectors.   This section has so far been concerned with the nature of 2×2 slides and the basic projector in which they are used. The projector requires that slides be placed manually into the slide changer and then pushed into proper position. This projector serves a double function in that, with the addition of an accessory attachment, it will handle filmstrips as well. A full description of filmstrips and their use will be given in the next section.

Some projectors have been designed to handle 2×2 slides exclusively. By concentrating their design efforts in projecting this one size, manufacturers have developed accessories that greatly facilitate the slide presentation: greater light output, magazine-loading for slides, tray-loading for slides, remote control operation, zoom control on lenses, and automatic edit and reject mechanisms for random slide selection. All of these developments have simplified considerably the process of projecting 2×2 slides.

Descriptions of several of the leading (2×2 miniature) slide projectors are presented below, and the special features of each are detailed.

MINIATURE SLIDE PROJECTORS

Bausch & Lomb Balomatic

Bausch & Lomb manufactured two projectors with the following distinctive features: preheating of slides and maintaining them at a constant temperature so that they do not "pop" or lose their focus, and brightness control of the image on the screen achieved by rotating the rim of the objective lens. This second feature, which controls the opening and closing of an iris diaphragm, is especially useful for avoiding the washed-out appearance of an overexposed slide.

The Balomatic is designed for 2 × 2 slides. The slides are loaded into trays or magazines which are inserted into the projector from the rear. A click-stop positions the tray for the projection of the first slide as soon as the master control knob is turned to "operate." Slides are advanced by pressing the change lever on the machine or pressing the advance button on the remote control cord. The change mechanism works in reverse by holding the change lever down for $\frac{1}{2}$ second. A control is available for automatic timing of slide changes at various time intervals. Slides can be removed or replaced with the tray in the machine by turning the master control knob to EDIT and pressing down the edit lever, while removing the slide.

The lamp is a tube type, 500 W, Code CZA. It is simply replaced by removing a panel at the rear of the projector and swinging out the entire lamp house for easy access.

Graflex Slide Projector

Graflex, Inc. produces a 2 × 2 slide projector equipped with a 4-in. lens (Figure 4.8). Other focal lengths of 3, 5, 7, and 10 in. are also available.

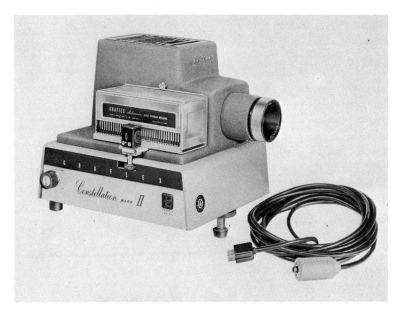

Figure 4.8 Graflex 2 × 2 slide projector. *Courtesy of Graflex, Inc.*

Slides to be used in this projector are mounted in metal frames and inserted into the tray. The slides are maneuvered out of the tray and into the projector by means of a mechanism called the Airequipt Automatic Slide-Changer. Index numbers in the tray, which is inserted at the rear of the unit, facilitate control over the slide program. Defective frames are easily removed. The lamp used is 500 W, Code DAK.

As is the case with all projectors, Graflex's Constellation Mark II has special controls for leveling the projector as well as for elevating the projected image.

Kodak Projectors

Eastman Kodak Company has designed several projectors to handle 2×2 slides. Its most distinctive unit is the Kodak Carousel projector (Figure 4.9). The slides are placed in individual compartments of a round tray that sits on top of the projector. Gravity-feed puts the slides into projection position. The controls for automatic operation, slide-changing, and focusing are conveniently located at the rear. The unit can also be operated by remote control.

The magazine of the Carousel Projector may be rotated to any desired slide by pressing the tray-release button. Individual slides can be examined

Figure 4.9   The Kodak Carousel projector. *Courtesy of Eastman Kodak.*

or changed by pressing the EDIT button and lifting the slide from the magazine. Push-button controls, even for lamp brightness, are attractive features of this projector.

Factors Affecting Projection of 2 × 2 Slides

The primary concern of anyone using a projector should be the student's ability to read clearly the projected image. The projection should be large enough so that everyone in the viewing area can identify and understand the elements being depicted. The relationship between focal length. screen size, and projection distance was treated in some detail in Chapter 3. Lengthy calculations are not necessary for standard situations. Quick reference to tables such as that shown in Figure 4.10 can provide instant

Lens Focal Length	Screen Width												
	30″	40″	50″	60″	70″	84″	8′	9′	10′	12′	14′	16′	18′
3″	6′	7′	9′	11′	13′	16′	18′	20′	22′	27′	31′	36′	40′
4″	7′	10′	12′	15′	17′	21′	24′	27′	30′	36′	42′	48′	54′
5″	9′	12′	16′	19′	22′	26′	30′	34′	37′	45′	52′	60′	67′
6″	11′	15′	19′	22′	26′	31′	36′	40′	45′	54′	63′	72′	80′
7″	13′	17′	22′	26′	30′	37′	42′	47′	52′	63′	73′	84′	84′
8″	15′	20′	25′	30′	35′	42′	48′	54′	60′	72′	84′	95′	107′

Figure 4.10 Projection table for 2 × 2 slides. *Courtesy of Florez. Inc.*

information such as: the correct focal length lens to use in a restricted area, the size of image that might be obtained with a given lens at a fixed projection distance, or the projection distance that is necessary to produce a desired image size with a given focal-length lens.

Certain relationships can be memorized, but the tables can help to solve any number of special situations that may arise. For example, to determine what lens to use when a projector must be placed 19 ft from a 60-in. screen, the student can refer to the column headed 60 and read down the column until the projection-distance figure, 19 ft, is reached. Reading across the line to the left, one finds that the recommended focal length of the lens in this case is 5 in.

Producing Slides with Sound

One of the special advantages in the use of the slide projector is the need for a verbal commentary to draw attention to the areas of particular interest. This is the function of the teacher or the student. Its effect lies in the spontaneity and the pertinence of the remarks to the situation at a given moment, and is in marked contrast to a "canned" presentation.

Carefully prepared verbal presentations to accompany slides are needed at times to guarantee completeness in the coverage of the material. This may be true in a series depicting the evolution of a new volcano, or a tour through a museum or through the White House. This need is met, in part, by recording the commentary on magnetic tape and using audible as well as electronic signalling devices to change the slides automatically.

One method makes use of a stereophonic tape recorder. The commentary is recorded on one track and the activating signal on another track. In playing the tape the commentary is played back through one sound system and the signal is fed into a synchronizer that amplifies the signal. This strengthened impulse is then able to activate a slide changer. One synchronizer of this type is produced by the Voice of Music Corporation.

A second method employs an audible signal recorded on the same track as is the commentary. This signal is fed into a synchronizer which activates the slide changer. Such a synchronizer is available from Eastman Kodak.

A third method makes use of a *striping* technique. A highly reflective mark is placed on the tape where a slide change is desired. When this mark reflects light into a photoelectric cell, it closes a circuit in the remote control outlet of the slide projector and so activates the slide changer. The Mark-Q-Matic Synchronizer produced by Allied Radio works on this principle.

FILMSTRIP PROJECTORS

Joining individual slides into a continuous strip seemed to be a logical outgrowth of the effort to produce visuals in series. Filmstrips are literally just that—strips of film, measuring appoximately $1\frac{1}{2} \times 36$ in., on which are imprinted a series of pictures in a fixed sequence. The idea of the filmstrip is believed to have originated in Los Angeles during World War I by the Stillfilm Company. The first film was not perforated, however, and was drawn by hand between two pieces of glass.

The perforated filmstrip, as we now know it, was introduced in 1922 by J. H. Bray as the Brayco film and projector. The projector was battery-operated and had a film advance knob and an aperture to accomodate the $\frac{3}{4} \times 1$ in. frames of the filmstrip.

Other improvements and other trade names followed. But today the term most widely used to describe this type of visual is filmstrip. Eastman Kodak in 1936, after producing a color and black and white film for 2×2 slides, used the same equipment and film to produce filmstrips. The picture areas measured 1×2 ins. or double the size of the picture area on earlier filmstrips. Thus, using the same photographic film—35 mm—it soon became possible to produce either 2 × 2 slides, double-frame filmstrips, or single-frame filmstrips.

Basic Design

Equipment manufacturers recognized the affinity between these above-noted materials and proceeded to design projectors that could accommodate all three. The optical elements of this projector are similar to those of the slide projector studied in the previous section. The reflector, the lamphouse, the condensing lens, and the projection lens are all identical to those of the 2 × 2 projector. The only variation is in the mechanism for channeling and moving the filmstrip through the projector.

Like the slide projectors, the filmstrip projectors may be equipped with any one of several types of switches: separate switches for fan and light and three position switches for OFF, FAN, and LAMP. Focusing of the projection lens is accomplished by turning the lens in the lens barrel; a few projectors use the rack-and-pinion arrangement. Filmstrip projectors can be elevated through a tilting mechanism or by releasing spring-loaded front legs.

The area of the aperture in the slide-filmstrip projector is most important because it is in this area that the modifications are effected. Attachment of accessories and movement of parts result in a single-frame filmstrip projector, a double-frame filmstrip projector, or a 2 × 2 slide projector.

By inserting a slide changer into the aperture area and locking it into position, the projector can be used with 2 × 2 slides. The changer is similar to the one described in the preceding section concerning slide projectors.

Filmstrip Carrier

The key to the use of the projector for filmstrips is the filmstrip carrier, (Figure 4.11), a rectangular tube with a curved metal container on one end to hold the roll of film.

The carrier has four distinct parts: the feed slot, two apertures, the motion sprocket knob, and the framer. The first of these, the feed slot, is an opening between two metal plates or pieces of glass. The plates are held together under pressure, and there is just enough space for the filmstrip to be inserted. The top of the channel has a slightly distended opening in order to facilitate the start of the film through the channel.

The apertures in the channel allow the directed light from the lamp to pass through the frame of the filmstrip. On one side the opening is large and unrestricted; the other side has an opening that can be adjusted through the movement or replacement of plates. This makes the carrier adaptable for use with either single-frame or double-frame filmstrips. For single-frame

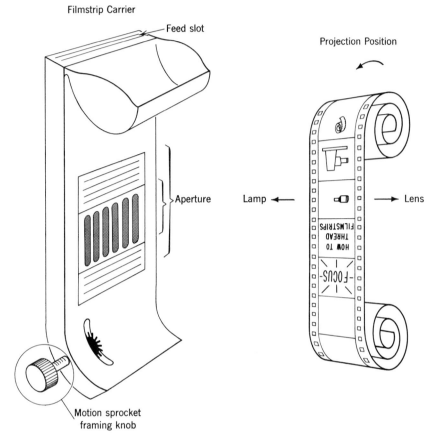

Figure 4.11   The filmstrip carrier is the key to the use of the projector with filmstrips. Sidney C. Eboch, *Operating Audiovisual Equipment*, **Chandler Publishing Co.**

filmstrips the second aperture is closed down to its smallest opening. For double-frame filmstrips, the aperture is widened accordingly. The filmstrip is fed vertically through the channel when the smaller opening is used. A locking-device can be released in some projectors to rotate the carrier to a horizontal position when double-frame filmstrips are used.

The motion-sprocket knob, also called the film-advance knob, is located either at the base of the carrier or is a fixed part of the projector positioned below the opening for the filmstrip channel. The knob turns a toothed wheel called a "sprocket." The sprocket teeth engage the holes in the film. Turning the knob pulls the film through the channel. The knob is spring-adjusted so that the film can be advanced one frame at a time. Two turns are needed to advance fully a double-frame filmstrip. The knob can be

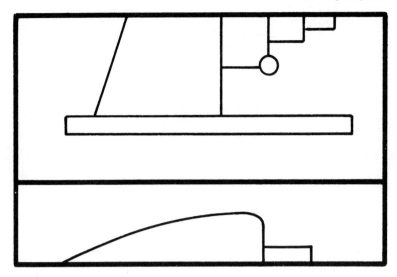

Figure 4.12 The framer is a device located near the film advance knob which allows for exact adjustment of the frame to the aperature in the plate.

turned freely in either direction, so it is possible to reverse as well as advance the filmstrip.

The framer is a device located near the film-advance knob which allows for exact adjustment of the frame to the aperture in the plate. Such an adjustment is necessary because it is not possible to align precisely the frame within the aperture. Without this control, the projection of split frames—the bottom of one and the top of another (Figure 4.12)—would result on the screen.[3]

Not all projectors are equipped wth a revolving turret for moving the filmstrip carrier from a vertical to a horizontal position. Those that have a turret can project the three types for visual materials: 2 × 2 slides, single-frame filmstrips, and double-frame filmstrips (Figure 4.13).

Operating the Filmstrip Projector

The successful use of any piece of audiovisual equipment requires knowledge and practice of certain basic rules of operation. They are simple and logical, and are easily mastered. The steps in the set-up and operation of filmstrip projectors, as given below, are general and refer to most models currently available to teachers.

[3]Sidney C. Eboch, *Operating Audiovisual Equipment*, San Francisco: Chandler Press, 1960, pp. 38–39.

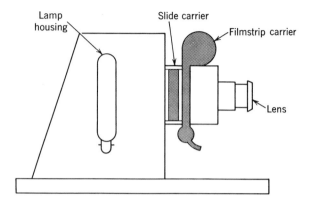

Lamp housing   Slide carrier   Filmstrip carrier   Lens

Figure 4.13   Sketch of combination slide-filmstrip projector.

Set up
1. Place the projector table at the approximate distance needed to obtain the desired screen size.
2. Remove the projector from the case and set it on the table. Loop the cord around the leg of the table (to prevent the projector from being pulled off the table by accident).
3. Plug the power cord into the wall outlet.

Prethreading Adjustments
1. Fix the aperture in the filmstrip channel for the correct frame size.
2. Insert filmstrip channel into the projector, vertically for single frame, horizontally for double-frame.
3. Turn on the fan switch and lamp switch.
4. Adjust the level of the projector so that the rectangular projection of light is perfectly aligned with the screen. Secure approximate focus by observing the sharp edges of rectangular light area.
5. Turn off the lamp, but allow cooling fan to operate (if the control allows for this.)

Threading
1. Check filmstrip. Be certain that the starting frames are on the outside winding.
2. Pace the filmstrip in the filmstrip holder so that the natural curl allows the leading edge of the film to be led over the top of the filmstrip roll into the filmstrip carrier channel.
3. Gently push the filmstrip through the channel, past the aperture, until the filmstrip comes in contact with the sprocket wheel. While maintaining this contact, turn the film-advance knob and move the film several turns.

3. Turn on the lamp. Advance the film until an image appears on the screen. Focus to obtain a sharp image.
4. Use framer to obtain complete picture on the screen.
5. Move filmstrip to starting frame.

Operate

1. Advance filmstrip by giving film-advance knob a quarter turn. Movement should be brisk. If moving rapidly through the filmstrip to preselected frames, turn off the lamp.
2. On completion of filmstrip presentation, turn off the lamp, but allow the cooling fan to run for several minutes.
3. Remove filmstrip from the projector; rewind and place it in the filmstrip container.
4. Turn off cooling fan.

Pack up

1. Remove power cord from wall outlet, and unwind from table leg.
2. Retract lens into its barrel and level the projector.
3. Place projector and attachments into carrying case.

Filmstrips are affected by heat in the same way that slides are: they can "pop" out of focus, so it is a good idea to protect them from overheating at all times. When rewinding filmstrips, start with a small roll rather than winding the film loosely and then drawing or "cinching" the film into a tighter roll. Such "cinching" could cause scratches to appear on the film.

Projection errors (Figure 4.14) can be eliminated by following carefully the rules stated above. One point that needs to be re-emphasized, however, is that the film must be inserted correctly. Pictures must be inverted; the filmstrip curls toward the screen above and below the channel.

With the filmstrip properly positioned between the plates and in the groove, it should move freely and be in constant focus throughout the presentation.

Filmstrip Projectors for Classroom Use

Because the filmstrip projector is one of the more popular pieces of equipment for use in the classroom, there are many different models of this projector from which the teacher may choose. Basic operating instructions for all such projectors are quite similar. A few examples of the more typical models are described below.

Bell & Howell Specialist 500. The Specialist 500 is a dual-purpose projector and can be used to project 2 × 2 slides as well as filmstrips. It uses a 500-W lamp, Code CZX. To remove the lamp, the entire lamp housing with the reflector and condensing lens can be lifted out. The lamp, with

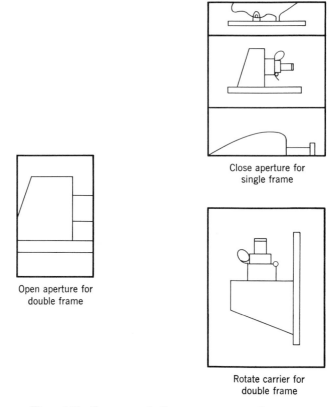

Close aperture for
single frame

Open aperture for
double frame

Rotate carrier for
double frame

Figure 4.14   Common projection errors as seen on the screen.

its medium prefocus base, is removed by depressing and turning it counter-clockwise one-quarter turn. Complete operating instructions are permanently mounted on the right side of the machine. The switch has three positions and must be moved to the extreme right position to turn on the lamp. The middle position activates the cooling fan only.

Bell & Howell Autoload.   The Bell & Howell Specialist Autoload filmstrip projector (Figure 4.15) has several distinctive features: it projects single-frame filmstrips with the easily inserted Autoload cartridge; it projects single frame filmstrips without a cartridge; it projects slides with a semi-automatic changer; and it projects single 2 × 2 35-mm slides. The Model 745C also is equipped for remote control operation.

The projector is plugged in and set up in much the same manner as is any other filmstrip projector. The leveling and tilting mechanism has been simplified and works in a positive manner. The filmstrip, however, rather than being directly threaded manually into the filmstrip channel, is tightened

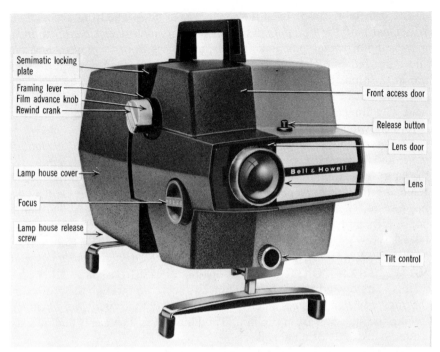

Semimatic locking plate

Framing lever
Film advance knob
Rewind crank

Front access door

Release button

Lens door

Lamp house cover

Lens

Focus

Lamp house release screw

Tilt control

Figure 4.15   Bell & Howell Specialist Autoload filmstrip projector. *Courtesy of Bell and Howell.*

into a 1-in. roll and placed into the cartridge. The filmstrip is so set in the cartridge that the leading edge feeds from the top toward the cartridge opening. To load the projector, the lens door is opened; the release button on the front of the projector is then pressed to free the front access door. Pulling down the cartridge lock allows the operator to slide the cartridge into position. The cartridge is designed to fit in only one way. (Without the filmstrip cartridge, the filmstrip is threaded into the channel and the roll set in the cartridge holder.) The cartridge lock is then replaced and the front access door closed.

By turning the film-advance knob in a counter-clockwise direction until an image appears on the screen, the operator can quickly thread the filmstrip through the channel. A rotating focus knob allows a sharp focus to be obtained. The framing lever positioned to the inside of the advance knob can be moved to either side to adjust the image in the screen. A rewind crank on the advance knob can be opened and used to rewind the film back into the cartridge. The crank is turned in a clockwise direction and should be rotated at least four turns beyond the point where nothing is projected on the screen to assure that the film strip has been returned completely to the cartridge.

The projector can be used for single 2 × 2 slides. The front access door is opened, and the film gate is moved from its locked vertical position to a locked horizontal position. The front access door is closed, and the slides are fed into the aperture from above and pushed down until they are in position. Each additional slide pushes out the preceding one. The last slide can be removed by pushing it out with another slide that is firmly held. The film gate should be returned to its original vertical locked position before showing any filmstrips.

Access to the lamp is achieved by loosening the screw on the lamphouse cover and drawing the cover back. A lamp ejector lever facilitates removal of the lamp. The lamphouse itself can be tilted back to ease further the task of removing the lamp. A new lamp is rotated on the socket until it fits into position and then is pressed down gently. It can only fit one way. The lamphouse is then tilted back into position, the lamphouse cover closed, and the release screw tightened. The lamp has a power output of 750 W, Code CWA.

Kodak Slide-Filmstrip Projection. Eastman Kodak offers the Signet 500 (Figure 4.16). One feature that distinguishes it from many other projectors is its rewind reel. After the film has been run through the projector, the film advance knob is maneuvered out of contact with the filmstrip, freeing the sprocket from the film. The filmstrip is then easily and quickly wound back to its original roll.

The 500-W lamp, Code CZX, can be replaced by removing the lamphouse cover, pushing down on the lamp, and turning it counterclockwise one-quarter turn. The complete condensing lens assembly can be removed through the lamp house. Access to the front condenser lens is possible by removing the filmstrip carrier.

Figure 4.16   Kodak slide-filmstrip projector.

Slides can be shown on this projector, and several attachments are available. The Kodak Signet Slide Changer moves the slides vertically past the aperture. The Airequipt automatic slide-changer with magazine can be adjusted to the side of the projector with slides moving horizontally past the aperture. The Readymatic and Universal slide changers can also be adapted for use with this projector.

Graflex, Schoolmaster. Graflex, Inc. is one of the major manufacturers of filmstrip projectors. One of its more popular models is the Schoolmaster 500, equipped with a 500-W lamp, Code CZX. Later models use lamps with the tube-type base, Code DAK.

A feature of this projector (Figure 4.17) is the automatic rewind mechanism that feeds the filmstrip into the can after the filmstrip emerges from the bottom of the carrier. The end of the filmstrip must be free of the carrier before the can is removed.

The slide changer is not removed during the showing of filmstrips. The changer handle is merely moved to either side, thus allowing the light to pass through the aperture of the filmstrip carrier. The filmstrip carrier is not removed from the projector when slides are shown. The film gate opens up, allowing the filmstrip carrier to be swung out and down. The film gate is then closed and the projection of slides is possible.

Access to the lamp is gained by raising a latch at the front of the lamp-

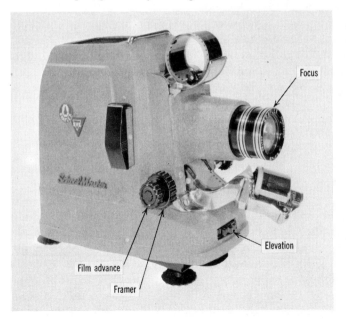

Figure 4.17 Graflex slide-filmstrip projector. *Courtesy of Graflex Inc.*

house. The top of the lamphouse, containing the reflector and condenser lenses, can then be readily lifted out.

Both the slide changer and the filmstrip attachment are left in the projector when it is packed. The changer must be centered, however, in order to allow the top of the case to fit over the projector.

SVE Filmstrip Projector. The Society for Visual Education, Inc., produced several popular models of projectors before it was purchased by Graflex, Inc. The Instructor uses a 300-watt lamp, Code CXK, and has no cooling fan. The hot air passes through the top of the lamphouse as cool air comes in through the bottom.

This machine can project single-frame and double-frame filmstrips as well as slides. It has a rotating turret which can lock the filmstrip carrier in either a horizontal or vertical position. Aperture plates in the carrier must be adjusted to the proper frame size. The filmstrip carrier must be removed when the slides are to be shown. The film channel is pressed down and pulled, bottom first, out of the projector.

The slide changer is placed in the space vacated by the filmstrip carrier. A pin, fixed to the changer, fits into a hole in the lens housing. It is held in position by a latch pin. The slide is placed in front of the changer handle and is moved into position by pushing the slide changer handle down and then up. When the next slide is positioned in the same way, the first slide is brought out behind the changer handle.

The lamphouse cover swings back, after the turret-set screw is loosened, to provide access to the lamp.

Standard Filmstrip Projector. Standard's Model 500-C2 (Figure 4.18) is typical of the several models of filmstrip projectors produced by the Standard Projector and Equipment Company. Four of its models also project 2 × 2 slides.

A feature of the Model 500-C2 is the pointer attached to the filmstrip carrier which allows the instructor to direct the attention of the students to specific details in a frame.

There are no lock-screws or latch pins required to fix the attachments in position. The filmstrip carrier is pushed down and is kept in place by friction with the sides of the projector. It must be removed when the slide changer is to be used. The slide changer is moved in from the right side and fits snugly in the space provided for it. Slides are loaded on the right side of the changer. A push-bar mechanism positions the slide in the aperture when the changer handle is moved in and out. Each succeeding slide pushes the preceding one out the left side of the changer.

Access to the lamp is gained by loosening two screws on either side of the lamphouse base and swinging back the lamphouse cover. The 500-W lamp, Code DAK, has a tube-type base and is removed by pulling straight up.

Figure 4.18 Standard filmstrip projector. *Courtesy of Standard Projector and Equipment Company.*

Victor Filmstrip Projectors. A remote control for advancing filmstrips is available with several filmstrip projectors (Figure 4.19) produced by the Victor Animatograph Corp, a division of Kalart.

To show slides, the filmstrip carrier is first drawn out of the projector. The changer is inserted into the opening from the right side of the projector, with the changer handle up and facing front. Magazines and trays of slides can be accommodated with special Airequipt semiautomatic and automatic slide changers.

The lamphouse cover can be removed by loosening the screw at the top front of the lamphouse. The lamp—which is a 500-W lamp, Code CZX—is removed by pressing down and turning it counterclockwise one-quarter turn.

An added feature with this model is an accessory record player (Figure 4.20), Victor Soundview, Model SA, which can be used with sound filmstrips. The filmstrip can be automatically advanced through inaudible 30/50-cycle signals or manually on cue from audible signals on the record.

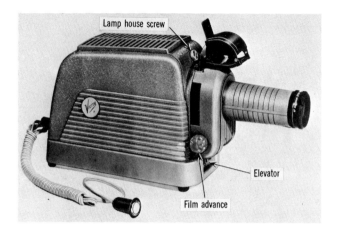

Figure 4.19   Victor filmstrip projector. *Courtesy of Victor Animotograph Corp.*

Figure 4.20   Victor automatic phonograph-projector combination. *Courtesy of Victor Animotograph Corp.*

Connecting cords between the projector and record player allow flexibility in the methods of advancing the filmstrip.

Viewlex Projectors. Viewlex, Inc., offers many popular filmstrip projector models (Figure 4.21), which can handle 2 × 2 slides, as well as single- and double-frame filmstrips.

A rotating turret allows the filmstrip carrier to be moved in a vertical or horizontal position for the single and the double-framed projection. The aperture plates must be positioned differently for each type of filmstrip. For double-frame filmstrips, the double-frame aperture plate only is placed in the rear slot of the filmstrip channel. For single-frame projection, both aparture plates are inserted into the slot next to the lens.

For slide projection the filmstrip carrier is removed and the slide changer is worked into the opening from the right side. It is locked in position by a set screw at the top of the turret.

The lamphouse cover can be lifted off after first loosening the set screw at the rear base of the lamphouse. The lamp is a 500-W lamp, Code CZX, and it can be removed by pressing down on it and turning it counterclockwise one-quarter turn.

Figure 4.21 Viewlex slide-filmstrip projector. *Courtesy of Viewlex, Inc.*

An attachment for the remote control of filmstrips is available for the Viewlex Model. This accessory, The Strip-o-Matic, is inserted into the projector in the same manner as the standard filmstrip carrier. The box containing the advance mechanism (Figure 4.22) rests against the case and is held in place by a set screw. The filmstrip is threaded and framed in the usual manner, but it is advanced by pressing a button switch at the end of the remote control cord. The mechanism must be plugged into an electrical outlet.

Accessories for Filmstrip Projectors

Specialized uses for projectors have resulted in the development of various accessory attachments. The need for flashing images on the screen at precisely controlled intervals of time led to the development of the tachistoscope or flash meter. This device is capable of allowing light to pass through in controlled intervals of from 1 second to 1/100 th of a second. An iris-type diaphragm can close or open the aperture, thus adjusting the brilliance of the light which is projected.

Another accessory, the Microbeam, makes possible the projection of microslides. It is fitted into the lens barrel in place of the objective lens. Spring clips permit the glass slide to be fixed in proper position for projection in the attachment. Magnification is as great as 100 diameters.

Specialized Filmstrip Viewers

DuKane Flipview. The filmstrip projectors considered above required that the image be directed against a screen surface placed some distance

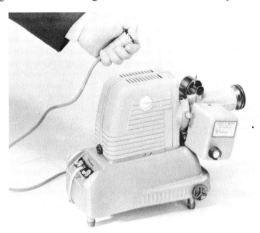

Figure 4.22 Viewlex electronic-advance mechanism. *Courtesy of Viewlex, Inc.*

from the projector. The DuKane Flipview (Figure 4.23) is one of several manufactureres' models that have the screen as part of the projection unit. It is used for individual or small-group viewing of filmstrips.

The screen, measuring approximately 8 × 10 in., is made of a translucent material. When the cover of the case is raised, the screen can be set in a tilted position for comfortable viewing. The image is directed against a mirror and reflected to the back of the translucent screen. The addition of the mirror cancels the inversion of the image; the filmstrip is fed into the unit right side up. This requires the winding of the filmstrip so that the start is on the inside of the roll. After passing through the Flipview, the filmstrip is wound correctly and ready for immediate showing again.

To obtain the enlargement of the image over such a short projection distance, a 2-in. focal-length lens is used. The light source is a 100-W lamp, Code CDX; it is convection cooled.

Viewers with Sound. Filmstrip projectors with attached record-playback equipment are available. Mention has already been made of the Victor Soundview Model SA. The record player is capable of using both standard and mirogroove records. Projection is for general classroom viewing.

Models such as the Viewlex TableTalk (Figure 4.24) are self-contained units that include the projector, screen, and record player—all in a small

Figure 4.23 DuKane Flipview, self-contained filmstrip projector and screen. *Courtesy of DuKane Corp.*

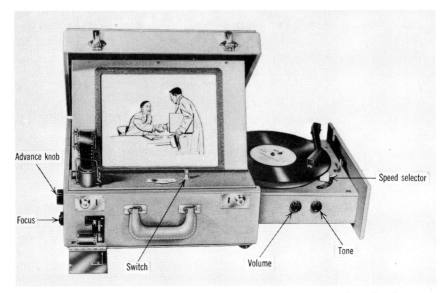

Advance knob

Focus

Speed selector

Tone

Switch

Volume

Figure 4.24   Viewlex sound-filmstrip, self-contained unit. *Courtesy of Viewlex, Inc.*

compact case. They are ideal for self-study or small-group viewing.

Individual Viewers. For individual study by students or for previewing by teachers, filmstrips can be viewed by using small self-contained units requiring no projection (Figure 4.25). The filmstrip is simply pushed through a slot; the frames are then illuminated by a lamp of low wattage, and a magnifying lens enlarges the image for easy reading. These viewers are produced by the major manufacturers of filmstrp projectors.

Determining Projection Distance

Filmstrip projectors are usually equipped with a 5-in. focal-length lens, but it is possible to obtain lenses ranging in size from a 2 to a 7-in. focal length. The 2-in. lens is used when a great enlargement over a short distance is required. The 7-in. lens is primarily for auditorium use, when the projector would be placed some distance away from the screen.

The accompanying table (Figure 4.26) indicates the various distances that the projector must be placed in order to fill standardsized screens. The distance depends on the focal length of the lens as well as on the size of the screen. For example, a projector with a 5-in. lens would have to be placed 28 ft. from a screen measuring 60 in.

Teaching with Filmstrips

Our attention has been directed primarily toward the use and operation of filmstrip projectors in the classroom. This equipment plays an important role because of the special advantages associated with teaching with filmstrips. The materials are compact, flexible, and easy to use. They lend themselves readily to group presentations as well as to individual study. They can be used to teach skills, to build vocabularies, and to present factual data in visual form. These materials help to direct the attention of students, focus their interest on specific subject matter, and tie together learnings from different sources.

Filmstrips are available in plentiful supply. Several reference guides provide helpful information for making the proper selection of teaching materials. The Filmstrip Guide is published by the H. W. Wilson Company, and the Educational Media Index began its publication in 1964. The careful classification of filmstrips helps the teacher in the selection of the correct filmstrip: correct in terms of vocabulary and conceptual level, educational and technical production, truthfulness and accuracy of contents, and stimulation of creative activity and discussion.

The values of filmstrips have been demonstrated in several research studies conducted in the classroom. The greatest gains in learning have resulted in instances in which filmstrips were used in combination with other media and teaching techniques (Figure 4.27). The worth of this medium, as with any other, however, is dependent upon the close adherence to the four-step plan for utilization of audiovisual materials: careful selection of the material, and preparation of the teacher; preparation of the student; presentation; and, finally, follow-up. If there is a breakdown in any of these steps, the value of the medium will be proportionally diminished.[4]

THE OVERHEAD PROJECTOR

One of the fastest-growing areas of projection involves the use of a comparatively new unit called the overhead projector (Figure 4.28). It was originally developed in the 1930's on the West Coast as a device for projecting bowling scores. The unique advantages of this projection method led to the development of projectors by the Charles Beseler Company that were extensively used during World War II. They filled the need for improved instructional devices for training the required large numbers of service personnel.

[4]William H. Allen, *Audiovisual Communication, Encyclopedia of Educational Research,* New York: Macmillan, 1960, pp. 120–121.

(a)

(b)

Figure 4.25   Typical filmstrip previewers and viewers.

82

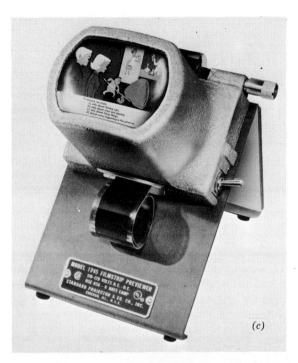

(c)

(d)

Figure 4.25 *(continued)*

Lens Focal Length	Screen Width												
	30"	40"	50"	60"	70"	84"	8'	9'	10'	12'	14'	16'	18'
3"	8'	11'	14'	17'	19'	23'	27'	30'	33'	40'	47'	53'	60'
4"	11'	15'	19'	22'	26'	31'	36'	40'	44'	53'	62'	71'	80'
5"	14'	19'	23'	28'	32'	39'	44'	50'	56'	68'	73'	89'	100'
6"	17'	22'	28'	33'	39'	47'	53'	60'	67'	80'	93'	107'	120'
7"	19'	26'	32'	39'	45'	55'	62'	70'	78'	94'	109'	125'	140'
8"	22'	29'	37'	45'	52'	62'	71'	80'	89'	107'	125'	142'	160'

Figure 4.26   Projection table for determining screen width for filmstrips.

Introduced into the public school systems after the war, the overhead projector was not readily accepted. Commercially-prepared slides were not being produced; techniques for the local production of slides were not sufficiently developed; and the equipment was not suited for normal classroom operation. In 1954, the Tecnifax Corporation developed a new printing process for the production of multicolor slides which simplified

Figure 4.27   The filmstrip can be used with good effect in conjunction with other instructional materials. *Courtesy Encyclopedia Britannica Films.*

Figure 4.28 The overhead projector is operated from the front of the room by the teacher under normal room-light conditions.

slide-making techniques; it also instituted a massive national training program for the instruction of school personnel. The design of the projector was radically changed to make its use more compatible with accepted classroom techniques. The passage of the national Defense Education Act in 1958 made more funds available to schools for the purchase of equipment and materials.

The combination of these factors has created a demand for overhead projectors that is greater today than ever before. In a survey conducted by the NEA, it was learned that in 1956 there was one overhead projector per 156 teachers in the public school system. By 1962 the ratio had been reduced to one projector for every 60 teachers[5] and, by 1964, one for every seven teachers.[6] Today the objective ratio is clearly defined, as set forth in a report of the New York City Board of Education:

".......The high schools now average 5 projectors per school (one school has 11, another 20). Junior high schools have all received at least one by the end of this year. The immensity of the task we face in various

[5]James D. Finn, Donald G. Perrin, and Lee E. Campion, *Studies in the Growth of Instructional Technology*, Technological Development Project, Washington, D.C.: National Education Association, 1962, p. 66.
[6]Eleanor Godfrey, *Use of Audiovisual Media*, Washington, D.C.: Bureau of Social Science Research, Inc., 1965.

schools is indicated by the fact that we ordered 500 projectors for the elementary schools alone, during the past year. This hardly scratches the surface, when one feels that there ought to be an overhead projector in each classroom . . . ."[7]

Advantages

There are many reasons for the rapidly increasing use of the technique known as overhead projection. Whereas most projection techniques tend to replace the teacher while they are in use, the overhead projector complements his efforts. At all times the teacher controls this mechanical assistant and takes a prominent part in the presentation. There is no need for a separate projector operator or the accompanying instructions from teacher to assistant.

The optical system of the projector permits placing the projector close to the screen, thereby making it possible to project slides from the front of the room. Since the image is projected over the shoulder of the teacher, he faces the class at all times. A high light output provides excellent screen visibility, without darkening the room or impairing ventilation. With his class in full view the teacher can observe reactions and adjust his program to meet the response of viewers. He selects his own pace, extemporizing as he wishes, and commenting before, during, and after projection of a slide. He can alter the sequence of slides or return to a previously shown slide without awkward instructions to an assistant or cumbersome manipulation of materials.

A large, horizontal projection "stage" permits the classroom teacher to use the screen as a "blackboard." He can write or draw at will with a "grease pencil" on slides or sheets of transparent plastic, without turning away from the class. He can also use a pointer or pencil to point out important details of a slide.

Several sheets of film are easily superimposed on the stage (Figure 4.29), permitting many colors to be used to identify the different elements of the projected image. The teacher can unmask transparencies in progressive disclosures of information or build up several components into a composite image.

Slides are large—$7\frac{1}{2} \times 10$ in. and 10×10 in.—a fact which simplifies the preparation of artwork for slides. In most cases photographic reduction of original artwork is not necessary. Rudimentary art skills can produce dramatic, colorful, and professional-looking slides.

[7]Eugene J. Erdos, *Developing Services for Overhead Projection*, 1965 Educational Communications Convocation Proceedings, Albany: New York State Education Department, 1965, p. 196.

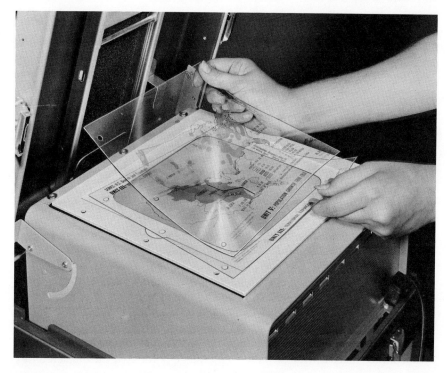

Figure 4.29 With overhead projection slides and other materials are placed on the flat glass aperture called the stage.

Design

In studying the design of the overhead projector we find that there are the usual optical elements of any projection system: the lamp, reflector, condensing lens, and objective lens. But there are modifications as well that add to the uniqueness of this projector. Instead of the straight-through horizontal path of light that was noted in the earlier projectors, there is an area of vertical projection. Reference to the diagram (Figure 4.30) will illustrate that the normal path of light from the lamp is intercepted by a mirror placed at a 45° angle. As a result, the light rays are reflected upwards through a condensing lens system, through a plate glass aperture, and through the objective lens. The light rays, still traveling vertically, at this point are reflected from another mirror placed in the head of the projector at a 45° angle. The path of light rays is changed to a horizontal one and continues over the shoulder of the speaker to the screen.

The slides and other visual materials are paced on the flat glass aperture.

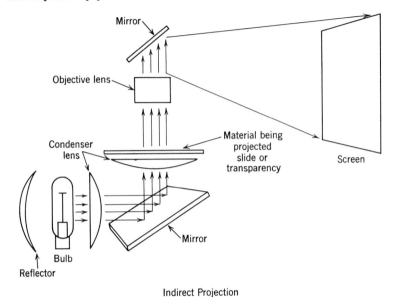

Indirect Projection

Figure 4.30 The direction of light in the overhead projector.

The opening is 10×10 in., although the rectangular opening ($7\frac{1}{2} \times 10$ in.) is becoming increasingly popular. The image is focused on the screen by moving the projection head (containing the objective lens and mirror) vertically by means of a rack-and-pinion device. The projected image can be raised or lowered by tilting the mirror in the projection head or by adjusting the front legs of the projector. A cooling fan in the base of the projector provides a constant flow of air past the lamp.

Operating Overhead Projectors

Most overhead projectors are set on tables, ready for instant use. For that reason, storage cases are rarely used. Instead, protective plastic covers serve to minimize the problems of dirt, dust, and careless handling. Overhead projectors are placed on projector dollies (small tables with casters) 16 or 26 in. high. The 16-in. dolly allows the teacher to work comfortably at the projector from a normal seated position. The 26-in. dolly raises the level of the stage for ease of operation while standing. Current light-weight models of projectors are being designed to be placed on the teachers's desk or table.

The projector is easily operated. Its power cord is plugged into a wall outlet, the power switch is turned on, the slide is placed on the projection stage, and the image is focused on the screen. The image is raised or lowered by tilting the mirror in the projection head or by adjusting the front legs. Special roll film attachments are available for some models. These allow a continuous 50-ft. length of film to be drawn across the projection stage; they also provide the teacher with a surface for writing and drawing for immediate projection.

Most projectors are equipped with a 14-in. focal-length lens. This fact simplifies the determination of projection distance. A general rule that is accurate enough for practical use states that the overhead projector should be placed $1\frac{1}{2}$ times the width of the screen away from the screen in order to fill the screen. For example, the overhead projector should be placed approximately 9 ft. away from a 6-ft. screen ($1\frac{1}{2} \times 6$ ft. = 9 ft).

The 14-in. focal length means also that there is a distance of about 14 in. between the projection stage and projection head. This distance is adequate to allow a teacher to work comfortably with the projector as far as the placement and manipulation of visual materials is concerned.

After its use the projector switch is turned off, the power cord removed from the wall outlet, and the projector wheeled to a corner of the room or to another location. When the projector is used frequently it is usually permanently located in the classroom.

Typical Overhead Projectors

As mentioned earlier, the production of overhead projectors has increased tremendously in the past few years and so has the number of manufacturers and manufacturers' models. In this section only representative models will be described. No attempt will be made to list all the manufacturers or all the presently available models.

Beseler Master Vu-Graph. One of the earliest models, still widely used, is the Master Vu-Graph (Figure 4.31 and 4.32), produced by the Charles Beseler Company. Its arrangement of optical elements follows closely the standard pattern. The condensing lens is a flat piece of plastic with grooves drawn in concentric circles on one surface. The angles of the grooves vary, causing changes in the angle of refraction. This type of lens is called the fresnel lens.

The projection stage handles slides up to an aperture of 10×10 in. The objective lens has a focal length of 14 in. The lamp is a 1000-W, Code DRS, medium prefocus base. Access to the lamp is gained by loosening a thumbscrew at the top of the door at the rear and then opening the door. Raising a latch inside allows the metal plate, to which the reflector is attached, to swing backward and reveal the lamp. The lamp is pressed down and turned counterclockwise in order to remove it from the socket.

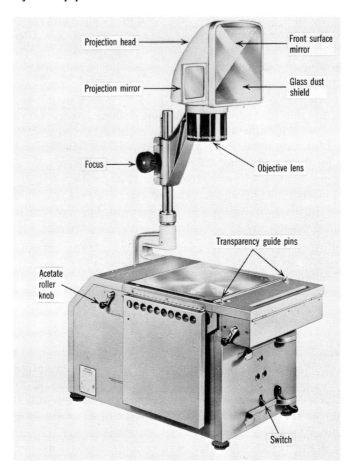

Figure 4.31 Beseler Master Vu-Graph overhead projector. *Courtesy of the Charles Beseler Co.*

The switch is two-way: *ON* and *OFF*. The image is raised or lowered on the screen by moving a lever on the rear of the projection head. The lever is connected to the mirror. Two pins on the stage of the projector are used to steady transparencies that are set over the pins.

Keystone Model 105S. The Keystone View Company produces a projestor that is properly called an overhead projector (Figure 4.33), but has several distinctive features: lantern slides are most frequently used, although smaller slides can be used as lenses are easily interchanged. The aperture measures 5 × 5 in. The projector is equipped with a standard 6½-in. lens; available also are 3-in. lenses and microprojection lenses. Special attachments permit the showing of 2 × 2 slides, filmstrips, and microslides.

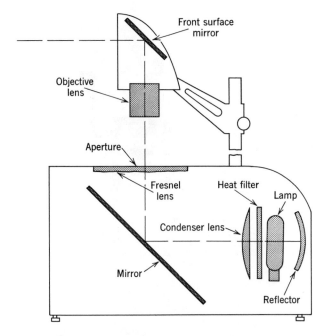

Figure 4.32   Schematic drawing of Beseler Vu-Graph overhead projector.

The tachistoscope, or flashmeter, is especially well-suited for use on this projector.

There are two focusing adjustments necessary (Figure 4.34). The projection head can be raised or lowered on its supporting shafts in order to obtain a rough focus. Fine focus is then achieved by turning the fine-focus knob. The image is adjusted on the screen by tilting the front-surface mirror in the projection head.

Lamps with a medium prefocus base of 500, 750, or 1000 watts can be used. The distribution of light on the screen is adjusted by movement of a knob that controls the positioning of the lamp and reflector.

The Transpaque Auto-Level.   The Projection Optics Company produces several models of overhead projectors (Figure 4.35). Among these is the Transpaque Auto-Level, which has several interesting features. For one thing, the functions of the condensing lens and the mirror in the base of the projector are combined into a single element—a parabolic, or saucer-shaped, mirror. This mirror gathers light rays emitted by the lamp and directs them upward through the stage of the projector with great efficiency.

Another feature of this projector has to do with the projection head. The mirror in the head is placed before the objective lens, a fact which

Figure 4.33 Keystone overhead projector. *Courtesy of the Keystone View Co.*

permits a reduction in the size of the head and reduces the height of the head. The lower silhouette also reduced the chances of the students' view being obscured by the bulk of the projector.

The image can be raised or lowered on the screen either by turning an adjustment knob in the head of the projector or by adjusting the front legs of the projector. Provision is also made for use of cellophane rolls. A slide guide fastened to the stage of the projector is adjustable to the various sizes of slide mounts. In addition a special microswitch can be attached that will turn on the lamp with the placement of a slide and will turn off the lamp automatically when the slide is removed.

The lamp has a medium prefocus base of 1000 W, Code DRS. It can be removed by swinging back the metal door at the top rear of the projector base, pressing down on the lamp, and turning it counterclockwise. It has a three-position switch: *OFF*, *FAN*, and *LAMP*.

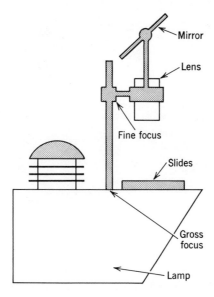

Figure 4.34   Schematic drawing of Keystone overhead projector.

The Travel-Graph overhead projector (Figure 4.36) is a lightweight, inexpensive unit that can be adapted for use in any classroom. It utilizes a 600-W quartz-iodide lamp located in the base of the projector directly beneath the stage. The stage is a hinged cover, permitting instant access to the interior for maintenance and lamp-changing. Fingertip tilting of the front lens element raises the projected image up to 30°. The bottom element always remains in the center of the optical path.

The unit is equipped with a three-position switch: *OFF, FAN ONLY* (for quick cooling), and *FAN AND LAMP* (for projecting). Interior storage space is provided for an extra lamp.

Tecnifax Visucom Projector. Tecnifax Corp. produces the Visucom Overhead Projector (Figure 4.37). This projector is equipped with a condensing mirror that directs the light through a stage opening that is $7\frac{1}{2} \times 10$ in. The molded fibreglass case reduces the weight of the projector and facilitates its cooling. Special vents and channeling beneath the stage eliminate any problems that might arise from heat buildup.

The lamp has a medium prefocus base, 750 W, Code DDB. Access to the lamp is achieved by turning a knob at the rear of the projector and swinging open the door.

The objective lens in the projection head has a focal length of 14 in. The image can be raised or lowered on the screen by a lever on the side of

Figure 4.35 Projection Optics Auto-Level overhead projector. *Courtesy of the Projection Optics Co.*

the projection head. A maximum tilt angle of 25° is possible with this control, although further adjustment can be accomplished by extending the front legs of the projector. The focus knob uses a friction drive rather than a rack-and-pinion mechanism and, as a result, a much finer and more accurate focus can be achieved.

A transparency guide is set on the stage of the projector: it ensures the accurate placement of the slide on the stage without needless fumbling and manipulations, which usually are distracting to the class. The switch has two positions: *on* and *off*. The power cord is permanently attached to the unit and can be wound around the base of the projector when it is not in use.

3M Company Overhead Projector. The 3M Visual Products Company offers several projectors of distinctive design. The Model 66 (Figure 4.38*a*), with its revolutionary optical elements, was introduced several years ago and continues to be a popular projector. The lamp is 600 W, Code FAL. It is a new quartz-iodide lamp—short and slender—is positioned between two electrodes at the base of the projector, directly below the aperture. A reflector behind it helps to direct the intense light through the fresnel lens, through the slide aperture, and up to the projection head. The objective lens and the mirror are completely sealed to protect them from dust and dirt. The entire head can be tilted to adjust the image on the screen.

A knob with friction drive is used to focus the image. The lens has a focal length of 14 in. Access to the lamp is gained through a door at the front of the projector. The lamp is easily removed from the two spring-clip electrodes holding it in position. The cord is attached to the projector.

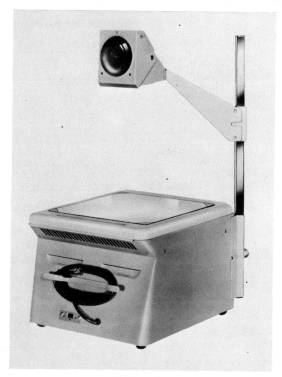

Figure 4.36   Projection Optics Travel-Graph overhead projector. *Courtesy of the Projection Optics Co.*

The switch has two positions: *on* and *off*. The weight of the projector is 15 pounds.

The 3M Visual Products Model 88 (Figure 4.38b) is an overhead projector of radically new design. It has literally no base when compared with those of other projectors. Features include a lens that is both a lens and mirror, a new high-efficiency projection lamp, a "tilt" projector head for projecting images at angles up to 35°, and low silhouette to provide minimum obstruction of view when used on a desk. The unit has no moving parts or blower, allowing for completely silent operation. Other features include a single *on-off* switch, and a self-positioning focus knob. The unit operates on standard household-line voltage of 110 to 125 volts, ac.

The slide is positioned on the stage as it would be with any overhead projector. By means of a reflection process the image is directed through the objective lens onto the screen. The film must lie flat against the stage to minimize the projection of double images. Colors project well only under subdued light conditions. The lines had a focal length of

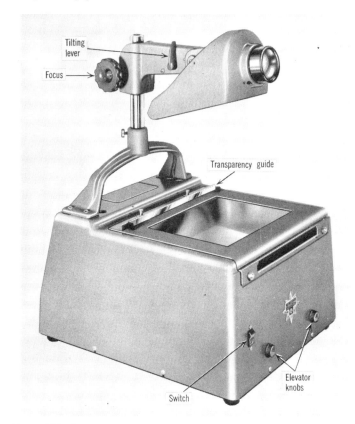

Figure 4.37   Tecnifax Visucom overhead projector. *Courtesy of Tecnifax Corp.*

$12\frac{1}{2}$ in.; the projection distance is, therefore, reduced as compared with a standard 14-in. lens. A high tilt angle makes possible close range projection.

Overhead Projector Teaching Centers

The concept of keeping the overhead projector in a fixed position in the classroom has led to the design of desks with built-in projectors. The Beseler Porta-Scribe Teaching Center (Figure 4.39) is typical. This is an all-metal desk that measures 30×60 in., has a standard 29-in. height, a center drawer, and left-hand drawers. The projector is fitted into the right-hand side of the desk and has a 10×10 in. aperture. The image can be raised to a maximum angle of $30°$.

The projector is quiet and vibration-free; it has efficient fan-cooling with pass-through vents to inhibit collection of heated air. There is easy

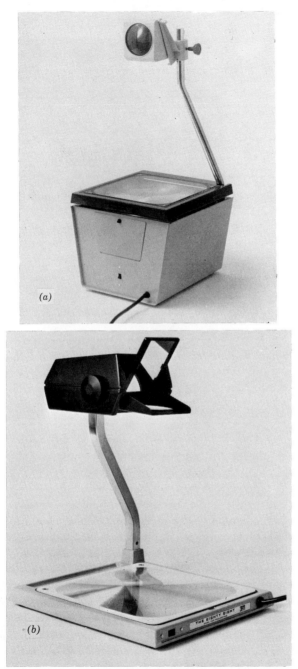

Figure 4.38 Two types of overhead projector produced by the 3M company. (*a*) Model 66; (*b*) **Model 88.** *Courtesy of 3M Visual Products Co.*

Figure 4.39 Beseler Porta-Scribe teaching center. *Courtesy of the Charles Beseler Co.*

access to the interior for routine maintenance and cleaning. Important also is the fact that the projector can be lifted out of the desk and used at another location without necessarily moving the desk.

The overhead projector has become a popular teaching tool because it can be so readily adapted to the specific needs of the teacher. The teacher always has control over the medium and, subsequently, control over the class while this machine is being used. Most important, its use saves teaching time. Experimental studies both at the University of Texas[8] and Kansas State University[9] first established this fact, but it has been confirmed in numerous studies since then. The amount of detail that can be projected, and its relationship to other factors, is depicted in Figure 4.40.

[8]Clayton W. Chance, *Experimentation in the Adaptation of the Overhead Projector Utilizing 200 Transparencies and 800 Overlays in Teaching Engineering Descriptive Ceometry Curricula*, Austin: University of Texas, 1960.
[9]H. M. Neely, *Design and Development of Transparent Overlay Visual Aids for Teaching Basic Principles of Engineering Graphics*, Manhattan, Kansas: State University, 1960.

	Projector-to-Screen Distance (ft)	10 × 10 Image Size (in.)	8 × 10 Mask (in.)
	4	32 × 32	26 × 32
Overhead Projector	6	48 × 48	38 × 48
For each foot of screen-to-	8	64 × 64	50 × 64
projector distance, the ob-	10	80 × 80	64 × 80
ject is magnified 0.8 times.	12	96 × 96	76 × 96
(14 in. focal length lens)	14	112 × 112	90 × 112

NOTE: An object 1 in. high will magnify to 4.8 in. when projected from a distance of 6 ft.

Figure 4.40   Projection table for use with overhead projector.

The use of the projector is not limited by subject matter. In social studies classes maps can be quickly prepared and projected for viewing by everyone in the class; special map features can be highlighted. Before or during music classes, notes can be written on permanently drawn lines.

In art classes most of the graphic techniques and methods of drawing can be used on the stage of the projector. Paints, inks, water colors, brush strokes, plastic templates—all these materials can be projected onto the screen.

In the sciences meters with transparent dials allow everyone to observe measurements. The vein pattern in leaves can be shown once the chlorophyll is removed. The lines of force in a magnetic field can be shown with the use of iron filings and magnets on the stage of the projector.

More than any other technique, the use of the overhead projector involves all the factors in the teaching-learning situation: the teacher, the student, the classroom, and the materials. (A later chapter will consider in greater detail the preparation of materials for use on the overhead projector.)

THE OPAQUE PROJECTOR

In the study of projection of still pictures there is one more type of projector to be considered: the opaque projector. Although this projector is old—its origins can be traced to the work of Athanasius Kirscher in 1646—it has maintained its popularity because of its capability of projecting anything, either opaque or transparent, that can be positioned into the projection area. Materials that can be used in the opaque projector include such items as pupil work papers, pictures, pamphlets, textiles, biological or physical specimens, textbooks, test papers, and various objects.

A survey conducted by the United State Office of Education in 1960 indicated that there was an average of one opaque projector for every 45 teachers—approximately 39,000 projectors—but that there was an immediate need for an additional 23,000 units.[10] This demand will continue to increase as the light output of the projector increases and the size of the projection area increases. Early models of the projector were limited to handling materials of postcard size. The projection aperture in current models, however, has been increased to 10 × 10 in.

Basic Design

The opaque projector depends on reflected light (Figure 4.41) for its operation rather than on the direct light transmission used for the projection

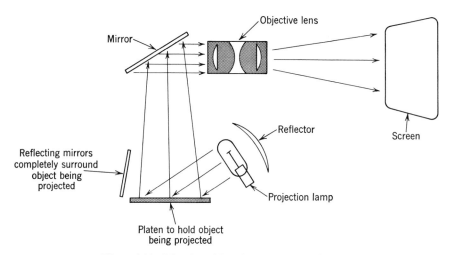

Figure 4.41   Direction of light in the opaque projector.

of transparent materials. The basic construction of the opaque projector is designed to maximize the output of reflected light.

The projection area is located at the base of the projector. Materials inserted into the projector are positioned on an adjustable board called the platen. The lamp and reflector are located at the front of the projector and inclined toward the projection area at an angle of 30°. The interior of the projector is lined with highly polished metal, thus providing a mirror surface. The light rays from the lamp and mirror surface are reflected upward by the material in the projection aperture to the top of the projector. A large front-surfaced mirror, set at an angle of 45°, directs

[10]*Audiovisual Equipment and Materials in U.S. Public School Districts, Spring 1961*, Washington, D.C.: U.S. Dept. of Health, Education and Welfare, USGPO, 1962.

the light horizontally at that point through the objective lens and onto the screen.

Some features of the opaque projector are illustrated in Figure 4.42. A door at the rear of the projector allows easy access to all parts inside the projector. A cooling fan is located either at the front of the projector (near the lamp) or under the platen. The lamp usually recommended for use in the projector is rated at 1000 watts. There is no condensing lens system to gather and concentrate the light; instead, the interior reflecting surfaces themselves play an important role in directing as much light as possible onto the projection area. Even so, much light is lost in the projector and, therefore, the classroom must be almost completely darkened for effective use of the opaque projector.

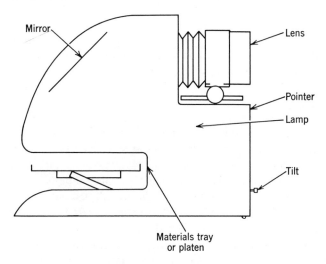

Figure 4.42   Principal features of the opaque projector.

All visual materials are positioned in the projector with the bottom toward the screen on which the image is to be projected.

Operating the Opaque Projector

The four major headings governing the operation of all audiovisual equipment will aid in the understanding of the opaque projector and its use. The projector has few moving parts and requires little maintenance for efficient operation:

Set up
1. Wheel the projector into position and plug in the cord. (Because

of its bulk, the opaque projector is usually set on a projection table and is transported from location to location while on the table.)

2. Place the projector on a sturdy table if no projection table is available.

Adjust

1. Place a picture in the projector by lowering the platen. The bottom of the picture is set toward the front of the projector.
2. Raise the base or platen against the aperture.

Operate

1. Change pictures either by lowering the platen for each illustration or by turning a belt that transports individual pictures into position. If the platen is lowered and raised for individual pictures, it is recommended that the lamp be turned off during changes.

Pack Up

1. After the last picture has been shown, turn off the lamp, level the projector, and draw back the projection lens into the lens barrel.
2. Unplug the power cord and wind around projector. Place dust cover on projector (if available) and wheel it to the side of the room.

Current Models

The concept and design of the opaque projector is basic and has had few modifications over the years. The projectors of several producers, however, are described below with emphasis on the accessories and attachments.

Opaque Delineascope. The American Optical Company offers its Opaque Delineascope.(Figure 4.43). All controls and adjustment knobs are located on one side of the projector to facilitate handling and operation. Focusing of the objective lens is accomplished with a rack-and-pinion mechanism. The lamp is of 1000 W, Code DRS, with a medium prefocus base. The lamp can be removed by pressing it down and turning it counterclockwise one-quarter turn. A door at the rear allows access to the interior for lamp changes, cleaning, and for the placement of bulky materials into the projection aperture. The lens has a focal length of 18 in.

An optical pointer that directs a bright arrow of light anywhere on the screen surface is available. The elevating legs are independently operated and can be individually locked into position. The platen can be adjusted and locked at any level; the maximum opening, however, is $2\frac{1}{2}$ in. wide.

Accessory items include a glass pressure plate which is used to hold thick copy – such as open books—flat for accurate projection. It also keeps individual photographs and pictures from curling and fluttering. A roll-feed attachment, a black nylon covered belt, is especially convenient for long copy in scroll form. Copy is inserted into one side and rolled out on the other side. This facilitates the projection of a series of flat pictures.

Figure 4.43   The American Optical Co. Opaque 1000 Delineascope. *Courtesy of the American Optical Co.*

Bausch & Lomb Opaque-Slide Combination.   Bausch & Lomb produce several models of combination opaque-slide projectors. With a single machine it is possible, through separate optical systems, to project lantern slides or to project opaque materials no larger than 6 × 7 in. A special control knob allows quick conversion from one method of projection to another. A single 500-Watt lamp, Code CZX, is used for both systems.

A wooden slide changer is used for the $3\frac{1}{4}$ × 4 slides. A platen arrangement at the base of the projector is used for holding opaque materials in position for projection.

Beseler Vu-Lyte II.   The Charles Beseler Company produces several models of opaque projectors. The Vu-Lyte II (Figure 4.44) features the Vacumatic platen, a unique arrangement whereby the direction of the air flow caused by the cooling fan is used to hold flat single sheets of copy

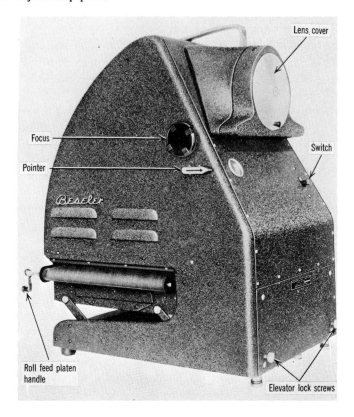

Figure 4.44 **The Beseler Vu-Lyte II opaque projector.** *Courtesy of the Charles Beseler Co.*

without flutter, thus eliminating the need for copy holders. The platen lowers itself parallel in the desired copy plane.

The projector has individually suspended, spring-loaded elevating legs for elevation and compensation of uneven table surfaces. It has a built-in drawer designed to accept a glass plate in order to facilitate projection of books and glossy photographs.

It also has a large rear door which provides for insertion of large specimens and easy access to the lamp; a permanently attached 15-ft. heavy-duty power cord; a permanently attached lens cap; and a 1000-W lamp, Code DRS. The projector has an 18-in. focal-length lens with an aperture of 5 in. The lens system plus the use of a highly reflective material called "Alzac" on the interior surfaces combine to produce a light output of a comparatively high intensity. An optical pointer that directs a brightly-lit arrow on the screen is also available.

Beseler Vu-Lyte III. The Beseler Vu-Lyte III (Figure 4.45) is a smaller, more compact unit than previous models. The lamp is of 1000 W, Code DRS The improved reflection system and lens of this projector delivers more light to the screen than does the earlier model described above.

The unit has a projection aperture of 10 × 10 in. It projects all opaque subjects up to 2½ in. in thickness. The base remains fixed as a special knob increases copy space. Individual sheets can be fed into the projector on a continuous copy conveyer belt called the "Feedomatic."

There is a large door at the rear of the projector for easy placement of oversize specimens in the projection aperture and for easy access to the lamp. The mechanism for adjusting the focus is completely concealed, center-driven, and nylon-guided. A metal knob can be turned with the thumb for precise focus.

The legs are individually spring-loaded. To raise the projector, the spring lock should be released first. The spring action in the legs gently elevate the projector.

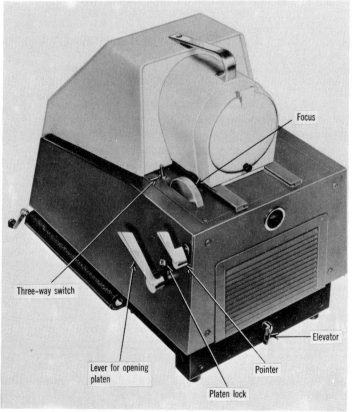

Figure 4.45   The Beseler Vu-Lyte III opaque projector.

Projection Screen and Distance

The light that is directed onto the screen by the opaque projector is less than the light from any other units. For that reason, the room must be darkened for greatest visibility, or the projected image should be kept small in order to concentrate as much light as possible in the limited area. The larger the projected image, the dimmer it appears.

The typical lens used in this projector has a focal length of 18 inches, but other lenses are also available. The relationship between lenses, screen widths, and projection distances are shown in Figure 4.46. An easily remembered rule states that for each foot of projection width, the standard opaque projector (18-in. lens) must be placed slightly more than 2 ft. away from the screen.

Opaque Projection	Lens Focal Length	Projector-to-Screen Distance											
		10'	15'	20'	25'	30'	35'	40'	45'	50'	60'	70'	80'
		Square Screen Size											
Maximum	14"	60"	7'	9'	12'	14'	16'	18'	20'				
Aperture	16"	50"	70"	8'	10'	12'	14'	16'	18'	20'			
6 × 6 in.	18"	40"	60"	7'	9'	10'	12'	14'	16'	18'	20'		
	25"	40"	50"	60"	7'	8'	9'	10'	12'	12'	16'	18'	20'

Opaque Projection 10 × 10 in. Copy	Focal Length (Inches)	Projector-to-Screen Distance (Feet)								
		5	7½	10	12½	15	17½	20	22½	25
		Image Size (Inches)								
	18	24	42	58	75	90	105	125		
	22		34	48	64	75	90	105	125	
	26			34	45	60	70	80	94	105

Figure 4.46   Projection table for determing screen size or projection distance with the opaque projector.
1. Room should be as dark as possible.
2. Keep screen image small if room cannot be adequately darkened.
3. Size of image should be suited to the distance from which it is to be viewed. The relationship should be such that the entire picture can be seen without shifting the eyes over too wide a range.
4. Select stand or table high enough to throw image above heads of spectators. Do not use low tables as they require excessive elevating of projector, thereby producing a distorted image on the screen.
5. Determine the projector-to-screen distance from one of the two tables above.

One of the principal advantages of the opaque projector is that teachers and pupils have an unlimited supply of materials easily available. Magazines, cartoons, books, pamphlets, and newspapers all contain desirable material. Snapshots, fabrics, coins, flowers, and insects are readily available. Discarded books and encyclopedias are filled with valuable pictorial material. The research, planning, and preparation of material for the opaque projector can be valuable activities for students.

Some of the uses of the opaque projector involve projecting outlines of maps and other graphics onto the chalkboard or onto large sheets of paper for tracing; use of this projector allows for group critiques of individual samples of handwriting, art, lettering, or mechanical drawing. Postage stamps and rare coins can be shown to the group as a whole; simple chemical reactions can be seen by large groups if performed in a shallow dish; reading-readiness may be tested and improved by projecting planned picture-and-word combinations; identification of birds, plants, and flowers may be learned quickly through the use of the opaque projector.

It is evident that the uses of the projector are many. But a word of caution is necessary for those who believe that this equipment may be the answer to all their projection problems. The readability of the projected image is poor unless the room is almost completely darkened. A darkened room is difficult to achieve and the students in it are more difficult to control. There is also the tendency to project all materials even though some are too small to be identified and understood from all parts of the room.

SELECTED REFERENCES

Allen, William H. "Audio-Visual Communication," in *Encyclopedia of Educational Research*. New York: Macmillan, 1960.

Audio-Visual Equipment Directory (Annual Edition). Fairfax, Virginia: National Audiovisual Association 1966 (and annually).

Brandon, Leonie. "Filmstrips Gave Ancient History Reality," *Instructor* 65, 22–23 (January, 1956).

Brown, James W., Richard B. Lewis, and Fred F. Harcleroad. *A-V Instruction, Materials and Methods* (2nd ed.), New York: McGraw-Hill, 1964.

Cypher, Irene. "Perspective for Learning through Filmstrips," *Educational Screen and Audiovisual guide*, 36, 72–73 (February, 1957).

Dale, Edgar. *Audio-visual Methods in Teaching* (rev. ed.), New York: Holt, Rinehart, and Winston, 1961, pp. 258–275.

Davidson, Raymond L. *Audiovisual Machines*, Lubbock, Texas: Texas Tech Press, 1964, Chapters 3, 4, 5, and 6.

Dworkin, Solomon, and Alan Holden. "An Experimental Evaluation of Sound Filmstrips vs. Classroom Lectures." (Abstract). *AV Communication Review*, 8, 157 (May–June, 1960).

Eboch, Sidney C. *Operating Audio-visual Equipment*. San Francisco: Chandler, 1960, Chapter 3.

Erickson, Carlton W. H. *Fundamentals of Teaching with Audiovisual Technology.* New York: Macmillan Company, 1965, Chapter 1.

Finn, James D. *The Audio-visual Equipment Manual.* New York: Holt, 1957.

Haas, Kenneth B., and Harry Packer. *Preparation and Use of Audio-visual Aids* (3rd ed.), Englewood Cliffs, N. J.: Prentice-Hall, Inc., 1955, Chapters 2–4.

Kinder, James S., *Audio-visual Materials and Techniques* (2nd ed.), New York: American Book, 1959, Chapter 5.

Mannino, Philip. *ABC's of Audio-visual Equipment* (rev. ed.) University Park, Pa.: M. O Publishers, 1959.

McBeath, Ronald J., "A Comparative Study of the Effectiveness of the Filmstrip, Sound Filmstrip and Filmograph for Teaching Facts and Concepts." (Abstract) *AV Communication Review*, **9**, A-24–25 (July–August, 1961).

Sands, Lester B., *Audio-visual Procedures in Teaching*, New York: The Ronald Press Co., 1956, Chapters 17–19.

Schultz, Morton J. *The Teacher and the Overhead Projector.* Englewood, N. J.: Prentice-Hall, 1965.

Teaching and Training with Filmstrip and Slides (Booklet) Chicago, Ill.: Bell & Howell Co.

Wittich, Walter Arno, and Charles Francis Schuller, *Audio-Visual Materials, Their nature and use* (2nd ed.), New York: Harper and Row, 1962, Chapter 12.

Wyman, Raymond. *Audiovisual Devices and Techniques.* Amherst, Mass.: University of Massachusetts, 1960, Chapter 5.

INSTRUCTIONAL MATERIALS

"Adventures in Slidefilm," 14 min., DuKane Corporation.

"Enriching the Curriculum with Filmstrips," 60 frames, silent, b & w, Society for Visual Education, 1952.

"The Filmstrip Projector," 35-mm. filmstrip, 32 frames, silent, color, McGraw-Hill, 1962.

"Filmstrips and the Teacher," 35-mm. filmstrip, 32 frames, silent, color, McGraw-Hill, 1962.

"How to Get the Most Out of a Filmstrip." 52 frames, sound, color, Eyegate House, Ind., 1959.

"The Opaque Projector," 46 frames, silent, color, Columbus, Ohio: Ohio State University.

"The Opaque Projector—Its Purpose and Use," 6 min., sound, b & w, Iowa City, Iowa: State University of Iowa, Bureau of Audiovisual Instruction.

"Projecting Ideas—on the Overhead Projector," 17 min., sound, color, Iowa City, Iowa: State University of Iowa, Bureau of Audio-Visual Instruction, 1960.

"Teachers Consider Filmstrips," 27 frames, silent, color, Eyegate House, Inc., 1950.

"Teaching Drafting with Transparencies," 9 min., sound, b & w, State University of Iowa, Bureau of Audiovisual Instruction, 1957.

"Teaching with a Filmstrip," 59 frames, silent, b & w, Society for Visual Education, 1953.

5

MOTION-PICTURE PROJECTION

A medium of classroom communication that has shown considerable growth and popularity in recent times is that of motion-picture projection. A survey conducted in 1961 by the United States Office of Education indicated that there were 125,500 16-mm sound projectors then being used and an additional 25,700 being purchased. The total number of 16-mm sound films owned exceeded 752,000, and 495,700 were planned for purchase in the near future. The number of projectors and equipment has increased (Figure 5.1) by almost 30% in the period 1961–1964.[1]

This endorsement for motion-picture projection is the culmination of an extensive series of studies dating from 1918 and dealing with the effectiveness of the motion picture as a teaching tool. Men such as Weber, McClusky, Freeman, Wood, and Kowalter were poineers in the development of effective silent classroom films. In the 1930's, with the advent of sound motion pictures, classic studies by Roulon, Clark, and Westfield demonstrated that information specially adapted to sound and motion could be effectively presented on film. Studies conducted during World War II and in the years immediately following were designed to determine the effectiveness of films in achieving various degrees of learning; some dealt with the organizational aspects of film utilization, motivational effects of film, and the influence of films in changing attitudes. A current study, called Project Discovery, is a cooperative endeavor by a film producer and an equipment manufacturer to test the further integration of motion-picture film with the curriculum in the classroom.

The findings of research conducted over the years have established several key points:

1. Good films can be used as the sole means of imparting certain factual information and developing performance skills.

[1] Eleanor, Godfrey, *op. cit.*, p. 7.

Figure 5.1   The increased use of motion picture projection in the classroom attests to its value as an instructional aid. *Courtesy of Graphlex, Inc.*

2. Pupils can change or develop attitudes and opinions as a result of viewing films.

3. Pupils will learn more from films if they are properly prepared and motivated. Testing is a valid method of motivation.

4. Learning will increase with repeated showings of a film. Short single-concept films, run in a continuous loop, have definite advantages.

5. Pupils can develop the skill of problem-solving by viewing well-produced films.

6. Ability to learn from films will increase with practice.

7. Films with built-in viewer participation, and repetition of key points increase learning. When these factors are lacking in a film they should be supplied by the teacher during, or immediately after the showing of the film.

8. It should not be assumed that learning has occurred from one showing of a film. Method of presentation may be inadequate; the film may not be suited for the age-level of the students.[2]

[2]Charles F. Hoban, and Edward B. van Ormer, *Instructional Film Research, 1918–1950.* Technical Report No. SDC 289-7-19, Port Washington, N.Y.: Special Devices Center, 1951.

Teachers are encouraged to use films and projection equipment because such studies have demonstrated that if the four-step plan of audiovisual utilization is followed, learning is more rapid and retention is increased.

THE MECHANICS OF MOTION-PICTURE PROJECTION

The combination of sound and motion with the projected picture is the result of perfect synchronization of the film with the projection equipment. Advancements and improvements in one often led to the increased effectiveness of the other. Our study of motion-picture projection will be concerned with both the film and the projector.

MOTION-PICTURE FILM

Motion-picture film is a strip of clear, transparent cellulose-acetate of varying length (Figure 5.2). One side has an emulsion coating within which are light-sensitive chemicals. When this film is exposed in a camera and developed, the result is a series of pictures, black-and-white or colored, printed in the emulsion layer. Since the base is transparent, light can be directed through the film and can project the images on the screen.

The film has three elements which give it its specific identity: a sound

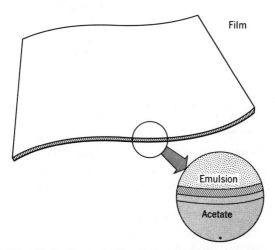

Figure 5.2 Motion picture film is a strip of clear, transparent, cellulose-acetate. One side has an emulsion coating, within which are light-sensitive chemicals. Sidney C. Eboch, *Operating Audiovisual Equipment,* **Chandler Publishing Co.**

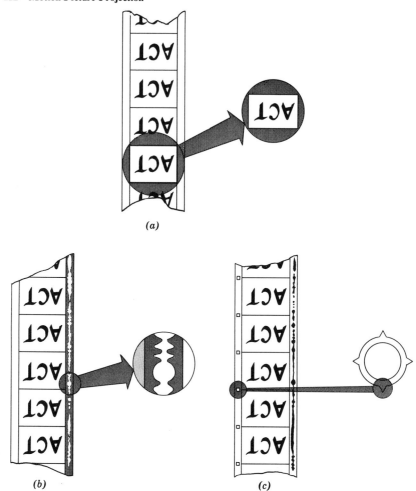

Figure 5.3 **Sound motion picture film has three distinguishing features:** (*a*) **individual frames or pictures;** (*b*) **a sound track;** (*c*) **sprocket holes. Sidney C. Eboch,** *Operating Audiovisual Equipment,* **Chandler Publishing Co.**

track, individual frames or pictures, and sprocket holes (Figure 5.3). The sound track appears along one edge of the film as a wavering white line on a gray background. It is a visual recording of sound produced by transforming sound waves into light waves which are directed against photographic film. The line continuously varies in width, according to the sound recorded, and is called a *variable area sound track*

Much of the width of the film is taken up by individual frames or picture areas. In normal motion-picture photography there are 24 frames or pictures per second in a sound film.

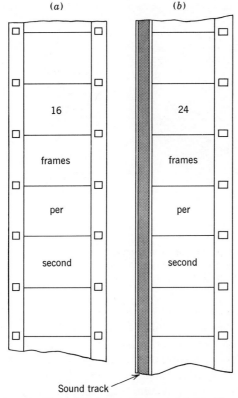

Sound track

Figure 5.4   (*a*) **Silent film runs at a slower speed than** (*b*) **sound film.**

Movement of the film through the projector which occurs at a slower speed in silent films, as noted in Figure 5.4 is made possible by engaging the teeth of gears called "sprockets" into a series of perforations along the edge of the film opposite the sound track. These perforations are called sprocket holes.

One of the values of sound motion pictures lies in its capability of showing movement. Yet there is no motion in the individual frame or picture. Movement is obtained by photographing an action as a series of still-pictures. The film, when drawn past an aperture through which a light is directed, recreates this action on the screen (Figure 5.5). The movement of the film through the projector is at the same rate as the movement of film through the camera (24 frames per second) in order to effect exact recreation of the action.

This "illusion of motion" can be modified to produce some unique effects. For example, it is possible to photograph an action such as a golfer hitting a ball at 96 frames per second. When this film is projected at

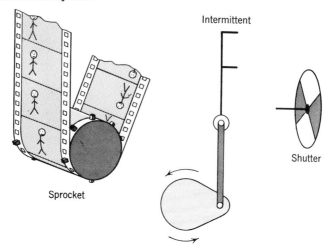

Figure 5.5   Movement of the film is accomplished by the action of the sprockets. The intermittent draws each frame past the aperture of the projector. Raymond L. Davidson, *Audiovisional Machines*, Texas Technological College.

the standard speed of 24 frames per second the movement is much slower—one fourth as fast as the original action. Through this technique the basic elements of an operation or an activity can be more closely analyzed.

Similarly, activity occurring over a long period of time can be compressed onto motion-picture film through a technique known as time-lapse photography. For example, a tulip bud takes three days to develop into a full flower. A motion-picture camera directed at the bud and taking one picture every 10 minutes will have 432 pictures at the end of three days. The blooming of the tulip can then be projected onto the screen in 18 seconds at the standard speed of 24 frames per second.

"Stop-motion" can be accomplished in the processing of the film by reprinting one frame many times. When this segment is spliced into the film, it produces the illusion of suspending motion at that point. This technique is particularly useful in demonstrating sports and games with fast action.

In order to achieve the illusion of motion each frame is moved in front of the aperture, held there for a fraction of a second, and is then moved on while the next frame is brought in front of the aperture. The movement or transport of the film past the aperture (Figure 5.6) is accomplished by a claw or an "intermittent." A shutter intercepts the light during that split second when one frame is moved out of the aperture and another one is moved in. The shutter and the intermittent are in perfect synchronization. If the sprocket holes are not engaged exactly by the intermittent, the result is evident on the screen as a fluttery picture.

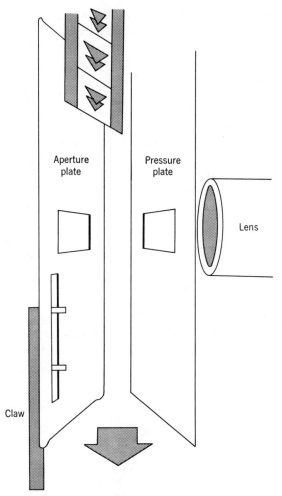

Figure 5.6   The motion picture film is positioned between the aperture plate and the pressure plate. Note the location of the claw or intermittent. Sidney C. Eboch, *Operating Audiovisual Equipment,* **Chandler Publishing Co.**

The sprockets transport the film through the projector at a uniform rate of 24 frames per second. The intermittent moves the film past the aperture in quick, short jerks at the same rate. A loop in the film before and after the aperture facilitates the free movement of the film past the aperture.

Thus, in motion-picture film there are still pictures which possess all of the qualities and characteristics of photographs in general: reduction or enlargement of subject matter, or selection of certain elements for emphasis. Yet there are the unique characteristics that lend the film its special value: the illusion of motion created by the rapidly projected series of still pictures, and the time distortion created by varying speeds of photography within standard projection speeds.

The auditory portion of the sound motion-picture film is the optical sound track and the sound system. The film, as it passes through the projector, is fitted snugly over a heavily-weighted, perfectly balanced roller called the sound drum. It is at this point that a fine beam of light from a light source called the exciter lamp (Figure 5.7) is directed through a miniature condensing lens system and through the optical sound track. The film, moving at a constant rate of 24 frames per second, intercepts the beam of light in an irregular manner. The blinking or intermittent flashes are the result of the irregular wave pattern of the sound track, blocking or intercepting the light.

The intermittent light pattern is directed against a photoelectric cell. The photoelectric receives the light impulses and converts them into electric energy. The electrical signals are strengthened by passing through several stages of amplification. When fed into a loudspeaker, the electrical signals are strong enough to cause the paper cone of the speaker to vibrate, thus creating the sound waves which we hear and interpret as the audio portion of sound motion-picture film.

Sound can be incorporated with the visual element on film by placing a coating of iron oxide on the edge of the film in place of the optical sound track. Magnetic recordings can be easily made on this track and played back. The audio frequency response and fidelity of sound on such

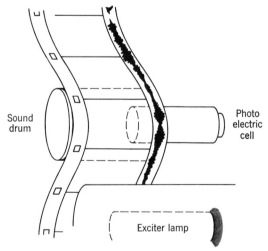

Figure 5.7 The light from the exciter lamp is intercepted by the sound track on the film. The intermittent pattern is directed against the photo-electric cell, which receives the light impulses and converts them into electrical energy. Sidney C. Eboch, *Operating Audiovisual Equipment,* Chandler Publishing Co.

recordings is much greater than with the optical sound track. The methods of recording and playback are similar to those for tape recording. (Further details on this process are contained in Chapter 7.)

Our consideration of films so far has been concerned with sound film. both optical and magnetic. It is even possible to have both methods used on the same film, offering greater flexibility in the treatment of the audio portion. The earliest films, however, were silent; sound tracks were provided separately. Because of this, there are two outstanding differences between the earlier silent films and the later sound films. The silent films have sprocket holes along both edges. Also, the films are produced and projected at a speed of 16 frames per second. However, silent films can be shown on current projector models, because there is usually a control provided for slowing the projector speed to 16 frames per second. Sound motion-picture films, however, should not be shown on old silent projectors as these projectors have teeth on either side of the sprockets, which would cause holes to be punched through the sound track of the film.

The width of sound motion-picture films used in the classroom is 16 mm. Other widths are available: 35 mm is primarily for professional or theater use; 8 mm has long been popular for making home movies. In the last several years increasing interest has been shown in 8-mm films for classroom use, but, unless otherwise noted, the classroom film referred to in this text is 16 mm in width.

The length of film used in the classroom will vary from segments several feet long to those that are 1200 ft long. This film is rolled on spools called reels. The reels are designed to accommodate standard lengths of 400, 800, 1200, and 1600 ft. A 400-ft reel of film has a playing time (Figure 5.8) of approximately 11 minutes.

16-mm Sound Footage	Time
400	11
600	17
800	22
1000	28
1200	33
1400	39
1600	44
1800	50
2000	56

Figure 5.8 Film running time. A good projectionist keeps on his schedule by knowing the running time for the film he is showing. Sixteen millimeter film has 40 pictures or frames to the foot. Sound equipment operates at the rate of 24 frames or pictures per second. Silent films should be projected at the rate of 16 frames per second. If the projector operates at sound speed only, silent pictures, if used, will run faster than normal.

THE MOTION-PICTURE PROJECTOR

Basic Design

The basic elements of any projection system are found in motion-picture equipment (Figure 5.9). There is the lamp, reflector, condensing lens system, film aperture, and objective lens. Two other systems are present: a motion system for transporting the film, and the audio system for

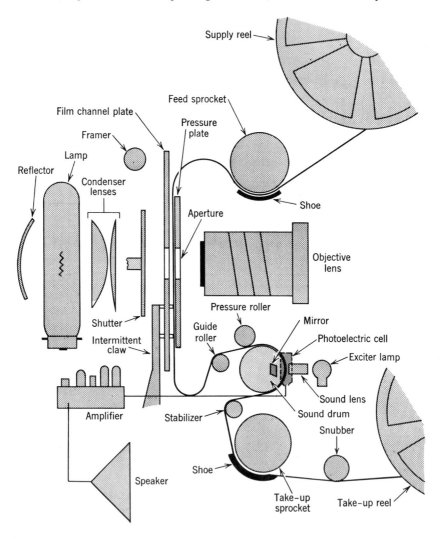

Figure 5.9 Schematic diagram of essential parts of motion picture projector.

producing the sound. Current models of projectors have all three systems enclosed in one container. In some instances, the speaker is contained in the cover of the unit. Its location is marked by a metal or cloth screen covering the face of the speaker.

A sound motion-picture system packed in two cases indicates that the speaker, and possibly amplifier, are in one case, while the motion and projection system are in the second case. Connectors are provided to join all systems. These connectors vary with the models and should be carefully inserted into the proper outlets to guarantee effective use of the equipment. The variations are designed to prevent improper connections.

The combination of the three systems in the sound–motion projector requires several controls and the identification of the specialized functions of its various parts. There is, first of all, the switch for the motor and the switch for the lamp. The lamp cannot be turned on alone; the motor switch must be on as well because it usually controls a cooling fan.

The amplifier switch controls the flow of power into the sound system. On some projectors this is an ON-OFF switch. With others, the knob also controls the volume; turning the knob clockwise increases the volume. With most projectors the amplifier switch should be turned on before threading because of the warm-up time required for the audio system.

Separate volume and tone controls may be included on the control panel. The sound can be critically tuned to fit both the acoustical characteristics and the dimensions of the room.

Mention was made earlier of the fact that current models of projectors can handle silent as well as sound film. The difference in speed can be effected through use of the SOUND-SILENT switch. Switching to SILENT slows the speed of the film to 16 frames per second and usually cuts out the audio system.

A great convenience for those wishing to return to earlier portions of a film is the REVERSE switch. The movement backward is at the same speed as the forward movement. This switch is not, however, to be confused with the rewind function.

The REWIND function is one that all projectors can accomplish. The controls vary—switches, levers, hooks—but the effect is to wind the film back onto the original reel quickly. The film is always first removed from the threading path.

A focus control for the projection lens is present on all projectors. The latest models have fine-focus systems that stay locked in position. Earlier models have rough as well as fine-focus controls with set-screws for holding the lens at a fixed distance from the film.

Sometimes, in passing through the aperture, parts of two image areas may be projected onto the screen instead of a single full image area. the FRAMER is the control that is used to adjust the aperture so as to insure that only complete frame appears on the screen.

Individual models of projectors may have other controls. One is the HAND-TEST knob that allows a person manually to operate all the moving parts of the projector after threading to make sure that the film is being properly transported. Another control is the CLUTCH, which disengages the gears of those parts transporting the film. This allows the showing of still pictures. Another control is sometimes used in connection with the showing of single frames; the SINGLE-FRAME switch may increase the speed of the cooling fan or it may drop a heat-absorbing filter between the lamp and the film.

Operating Parts

Before discussing the general procedures for threading and rewinding the film, there should be a brief description of the basic operating parts of the projector. Film is initially moved into the threading path, and is finally drawn out of the threading path, by means of sprockets. Sprockets are wheels with teeth on one side so spaced that they fit the holes in the side of the film. The film is carefully positioned over the sprockets and then locked into place by clamps or rubber "shoes" that fit over the spocket.

The film is drawn past the aperture by a claw that moves in an intermittent manner. This claw is a forked device that fits into two sprocket holes, moves downward exactly one frame, is withdrawn from the sprocket holes, moves up exactly one frame, is inserted in two sprocket holes, moves down exactly one frame, and so forth—24 times per second. As the claw is withdrawn from the sprocket holes it disappears in the projector, only to appear above to move the film down another frame.

The sound drum is a heavy roller around which the film must be tightly, or at least snugly, fitted. Film loosely wound around the drum will result in a "mushy" quality in the sound.

Several roller wheels are used on the projectors to guide and direct the film along its proper path through the projector. These rollers are identified by different manufacturers as snubbers, stabilizers, guides or pressure wheels. They keep the film taut and prevent the film from rubbing against the projector.

General Operating Directions

Identification of the various switches, controls, and parts that are specific to the motion-picture projector facilitates understanding of the following instructions for the set-up and operation of the projector.

Set up
  1. Open cover to control panel after setting projector on a sturdy, level surface.
  2. Set the speaker at front of room near screen (provided it is detachable).
  3. Connect power and speaker cords.
  4. Mount feed-reel arm and take-up reel arm to the projector.
  5. Attach spring belts to pulleys.

Adjust
  1. Turn on motor and lamp.
  2. Turn on amplifier switch.
  3. Loosen lens locking screw (if any) and move lens in and out until image of aperture is sharply defined on the screen.
  4. Turn up volume control until there is a faint hum in the speaker.
  5. Check the sound system by moving a card back and forth between the sound lens and the sound drum. A thumping sound will be heard if the (system is operating properly).
  6. Check all other switches and controls: SOUND-SILENT, REVERSE, MAGNETIC-OPTICAL, SOUND.
  7. Turn off lamp and motor switch.

Thread
  1. Place empty reel (of same size as feed reel) on take-up spindle.
  2. Place feed reel on feed spindle. Unwind about 3 ft. of film. Film should unwind from reel in a clockwise direction. Sprocket holes should be on the right (next to operator). Images on the frames should be upside-down and reversed.
  3. Place film over sprocket. Make certain that sprocket holes fit over the pins. Lock in place with clamp of shoe.
  4. Set film in film channel. Close film gate over it. Make certain that there is a loop at least two fingers wide above and below the film channel.
  5. Pass film around sound drum.
  6. Place film over sprocket. Draw tightly to assure snug fit of film over sound drum. Lock in place.
  7. Wind film on take-up reel. Reel should turn in a clockwise direction.

Operate
  1. Turn on projector motor and lamp.
  2. Center and frame image on screen.
  3. Adjust volume control until sound is at desired level.
  4. Observe that loops are maintained and film is winding on take-up reel.
  5. Turn off lamp and motor at end of showing.

Rewind and Pack up
1. Rewind the film (if it is to be used again) according to the instructions for the model projector being used.
2. Unplug power and speaker cords.
3. Remove feed reel arm and take-up reel arm.
4. Place cords and arm assemblies in the case or cases.
5. Lower front of projector to level position.
6. Close cover on case (or cases.)

The successful operation of the sound motion-picture projector depends on the correct placement of the film in the projector. The film reel is placed on the spindle of the reel arm. The spindle is joined to a pulley, which is connected to the motor drive by means of a spring belt. The spindle should be correctly faced toward the operator if the arms are of the loose type and need to be fastened before projection.

Film reels have openings running through the center core. The opening is square at least on one end, enabling the reel to be slipped over the square shaft of the spindle. If the other opening of the center core is circular, the likelihood of error in the placement of the film reel is lessened. The reel is locked onto the shaft either by means ot a swivel on the end of the shaft that can be moved into a vertical position or by means of a button or ball spring located on the shaft. As the reel is slipped over the shaft, the ball is depressed; but it then pops up and holds the reel firmly in position.

Locking devices for reels are important. A reel that works loose during operation could cause personal injury and certainly would cause damage to the film.

When film is passing through the projector during normal operation, both the feed reel and take-up reels are rotating clockwise. The sprocket holes are toward the operator, and the image is upside down and reversed. In most instances the feed-reel will have the film correctly wound and oriented (Figure 5.10). Films should be checked carefully before class showing to detect any exceptions where the film may have been improperly wound on the reel. If the film is not ready for projection, it must be rewound with full attention being given to the end of the film which faces out; the position of the picture and the sprocket holes and the direction of rotation are also important. Adjustments sometimes call for twisting the film or for the removal of one of the spring belts to facilitate correct winding.

It is important to note that a correct rewind operation has both the take-up reel and the feed reel moving in the counter clockwise direction.

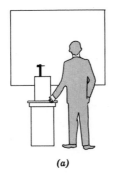

(a)

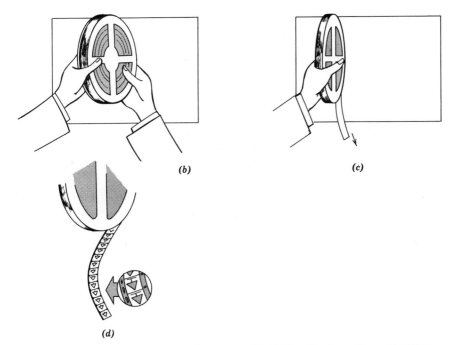

(b)   (c)

(d)

Figure 5.10   How to load a reel. (*a*) **Face screen.** (*b*) **Hold reel in front of you.** (*c*) **Pull film down from reel on side nearest the screen.** (*d*) **Picture is upside down; sprocket holes are on right side of film: if both are true, place reel on projector with right hand; if either is not true, film must be rewound.** Sidney C. Eboch, *Operating Audiovisual Equipment,* **Chandler Publishing Co.**

Specific Operating Directions

Sound motion-picture projectors produced by the various manufacturers are similar only in that they contain the three basic systems: sound, motion, and projection. Mastery by the teacher of several of these models should establish the pattern for understanding the operation of all other projectors. Representative models of available classroom projectors are described below.

Bell & Howell Motion-Picture Projectors. The Bell & Howell Company has supplied projectors for the classrooms for many years. In its design and operation, model 385 is typical of several of the earlier models. The instructions given below can be applied to all the models. It is well for the teacher to understand that effective use of the projectors depends on systematic adherence to certain steps in the operation of the projector.

Set up

1. Place the projector on a sturdy table. (Mobile projection tables are highly recommended.) Open all doors in the case—two on right and one in the front of the projector.
2. Remove the two reel arms from their stored position inside the case. The arms should be positioned in with the spindles facing the operator.
3. The spring belts should be drawn through the openings of the case and slipped over the pulleys. Do not twist the belts.
4. Remove the power cord from the case. Plug one end into the power outlet and the other into the socket on the left side of the projector.
5. Open the speaker door on the left side of the case. Unwind as much of the speaker cord as may be needed and plug into the speaker outlet on the left side of the projector.
6. The speaker may be removed from its hinges and may be positioned away from the projector, the limiting factor being the length of the cable.

Adjust

1. Locate the clutch knob; turn it clockwise as far as it will go.
2. Position the FORWARD-REVERSE switch at FORWARD.
3. Set the SILENT-SOUND switch at SOUND; if the film is a silent one, set the switch at SILENT.
4. Turn the amplifier control knob to ON.
5. Push the line switch up, starting the motor.
6. Make certain the film gate is closed by pushing down on film-gate lever at the rear-left of the objective lens.
7. Push the lamp switch up.
8. Direct the light onto the screen. Raise the lighted area by turning the elevator knob at the front of the projector. Move the projector right or left as may be needed. Move the projector forward toward the screen or backward away from the screen to reduce or enlarge the lighted area.

9. Focus the edges of the lighted area on to the screen. Loosen the lens lock screw; rotate the objective lens until edges appear sharpest; and lightly tighten the lens lock screw.
10. Push down on the lamp switch and the motor switch.
11. Check on the operation of the amplifier by turning the volume control clockwise and listening for a "hiss" from the speaker. Then turn the volume control knob back to zero.
12. Adjust the tone control knob at midpoint.

Threading (Figure 5.11)
1. Place a reel of film on the feed reel spindle. Push it on as far as it will go. Be certain the reel unwinds in a clockwise direction.
2. Place an empty reel on the take-up arm spindle. Press the rewind gear at the side of the pulley to make certain that rewind gears are not engaged.
3. Draw off about 5 ft. of film from the feed reel and set it through the slot in the projector case. Allow the film to hang freely.
4. Grasp the film above the objective lens and place it under the feed sprocket. Be sure that the sprocket holes in film fit over the sprocket teeth. The sprocket shoe (lock) must be raised for this operation and then lowered to fix the film.
5. Open the film gate by raising the lens lock lever.
6. Place the film between the film channel and film pressure plate, leaving a one-in. loop above the film channel. Draw down on the lens lock lever.
7. Place the film over the second sprocket, using the sprocket shoe to lock the film into position. Be sure to allow a one-in. loop below the film channel.
8. Thread the film (Figure 5.11) under the upper oscillating stabilizer, around the sound drum, under the lower stabilizer and over the take-up sprocket. Draw the film snugly over the sound drum before locking the film with the sprocket shoe. The stabilizing rollers should absorb the tension being placed on the film.
9. Set the film under the snubber roller, through the slot in the projector case, and onto the take-up reel. Turn the reel clockwise to absorb the slack in the film.
10. Test the threading of the film by turning the manual control knob located behind the objective lens. Turn the clutch counterclockwise first. Return the clutch to original position after the test.

Operate
1. Push up on line switch and lamp switch.
2. Adjust fine focus of image on screen by loosening lens-lock screw,

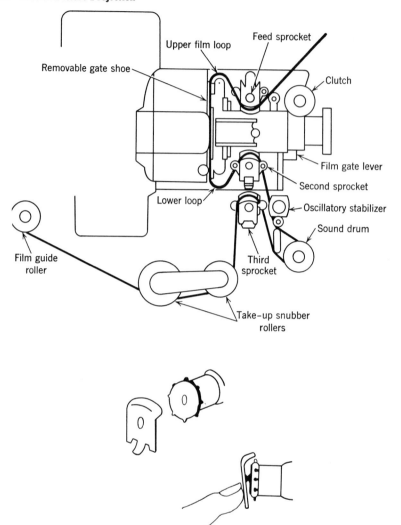

Sprocket and shoe detail

Figure 5.11   Threading diagram for Bell & Howell sound motion picture projector.

turning the objective lens to the desired point, and then retightening the lens-lock screw.

3. Turn volume control knob clockwise until desired level of volume is reached. Adjust tone.

4. The framing knob should be turned if part of a second frame needs to be eliminated.

5. Keep checking the following during the showing of the film: (a) film being wound on take-up reel; (b) synchronization between picture and sound; (c) maintenance of loops above and below film channel; and (d) proper volume and tone settings.
6. Reshow a portion of the film by stopping projector motor, pushing up the switch to REVERSE position, and restarting motor; the film will run backward to the desired point. Controls are then reset for regular projection.
7. As the film comes to a close, switch off the lamp, turn down the volume, run the end of the film onto the take-up reel, turn off the motor.

Rewind
1. Remove the take-up reel and place it on the feed arm spindle; take the empty reel and place it on the take-up spindle.
2. Wind the film over the top of the full reel to the top of the empty reel.
3. Turn the clutch counterclockwise to disengage the transport mechanism from the motor.
4. Lift the empty reel $\frac{1}{4}$ in. and press the rewind lock lever so as to engage the two gears on the rear reel arm. The fabric belt on the reel arm should be slack.
5. Push up on the line switch starting the motor. Allow all the film to be rewound, and then push down on the line switch.
6. Disengage the rewind gears by pushing the rewind lock lever. Turn the clutch clockwise to re-engage the gears in the drive mechanism.

Pack up
1. Turn off amplifier.
2. Slip off the spring belts from the pulleys and draw the spring belts back into the projector case.
3. Remove the arms and position them in the case. Be sure that the straps are securely fastened.
4. Unplug the speaker cable, wind the cable, and replace the speaker in the projector case.
5. Remove power cord from electrical outlet and from projector plug, wind, and place in projector case.
6. Lower front of projector by turning elevator knob counterclockwise.
7. Close all the doors of the projector.

The need may arise for stopping the action of the motion-picture film while still holding the image on the screen. This can be accomplished by turning the clutch counterclockwise, thus disengaging the drive mechanism. If the shutter interrupts the light, it can be moved out of the way by turning the manual drive knob.

The projected still picture is dimmer than the motion-picture projection because of a metal screen that falls into position between the lamp and the film. Without this screen, the intense heat from the lamp would burn and blister the stationary film. The picture usually needs to be refocused during still projection.

Most sound motion-picture projectors have several items that need to be replaced after a period of usage; one of these is the projection lamp. The lamp in the Model 385 projector is rated at 750 W, Code DEJ; a 1000-W lamp can also be used, Code DFY. Both lamps have a medium prefocus base with a large ring and prong attached to the base. The lamp is replaced by turning the cap at the base of the lamphouse. The old lamp drops down, and the new lamp is inserted into the lamphouse with the metal base prong positioned toward the front of the projector. The cap is then replaced.

If the exciter lamp fails to light, it may need replacement. To do this remove the cover over the exciter lamp; then press down on the lamp and turn clockwise until the lamp is freed from the base. Position and lock the lamp into place by reversing the process.

There is one other item that may need replacement, especially if there is an electrical malfunction in the projector or electrical disturbance outside of the projector: this is the fuse, which is located at the rear of the projector to the right of the speaker output plugs. To move the fuse, turn the cap to the left, and draw it out. The fuse will be attached to the cap.

In its Model 542, Bell and Howell has simplified the operation of the motion-picture projector (Figure 5.12). Half of the projector case can be removed, making the controls more readily accessible and the threading operation easier. The reel arms are permanently attached; they can be raised into position and locked by means of lock buttons. The threading path is the same, but the lens housing swings away from placement of the film in the film channel.

The speakers are permanently mounted inside the front portion of the projector case. A single switch controls the lamp and the motor. The film is rewound without changing reels. The take-up arm is raised to a vertical position by pressing an arm-lock button. The film is attached to the empty reel and a few counterclockwise turns are made with the reel. The switch is then set at the first position which starts the rewind action without turning the lamp on. The rewind button is pressed to speed the transfer of film from the take-up reel to the feed reel.

The Model 542 uses a 1000-W lamp, Code CTS, or a 750-W lamp, Code CWA. The front panel can be moved aside for easy access to the lamp and condensing lens.

Sound-silent switch

Framer

Retaining pin for
take up arm

Still picture
switch

Forward–
reverse

Volume

Tone

Rewind button

Focus

Elevator control

(a)

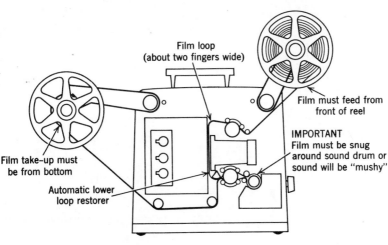

Film loop
(about two fingers wide)

Film must feed from
front of reel

IMPORTANT
Film must be snug
around sound drum or
sound will be "mushy"

Film take-up must
be from bottom

Automatic lower
loop restorer

(b)

Figure 5.12 (a) **Bell & Howell motion picture projector Model 542 and** (b) **threading diagram.**
Courtesy Bell & Howell.

Bell & Howell's most recent model, the Specialist Autoload (Figure 5.13), incorporates the features of the Model 542 plus the added advantage of a self-threading mechanism. To use this feature, the film leader is first neatly clipped by means of a trimmer located at the front of the projector below the elevator knob. The threading guides are positioned by pushing the autoload lever, located below the lens, to the right. With the motor switch turned on, the film is inserted into the threading slot and feeds itself through the projector and around the snubbing rollers. After several feet of film have passed through the projector, the motor switch is turned off. The end of the film is next wound around the take-up reel, and the projector is ready for normal operation.

The resetting of film loops, if necessary, is accomplished by pressing down on the loop setter, located above the lens, for about one second. Rewinding is accomplished in the same way as with the Model 542. The film can be manually unthreaded by removing the protective panel and unlocking the threading guides.

Eastman Kodak Motion-Picture Projectors. Eastman Kodak produces

Figure 5.13 Bell & Howell Specialist Autoload projector. *Courtesy of Bell & Howell Co.*

several models of sound–motion picture projector (Figure 5.14). The instructions listed below can be used for most of the models as well as for the AV-085.

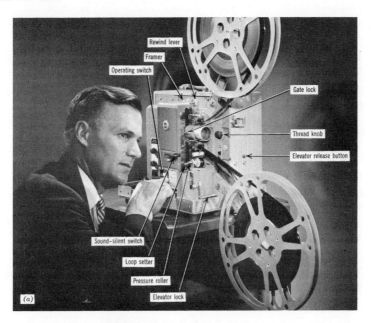

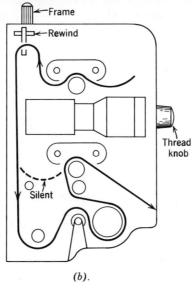

(b).

Figure 5.14 (a) Eastman Kodak motion picture projector and (b) threading diagram.

Set up

1. Place the projector on a sturdy table surface with the front of the projector close to the leading edge of the table.
2. Unhinge the cover and remove the power cord that is wound inside.
3. Unfold the supply arm and the takeup arm. Make certain that the drive belts are set on the pulleys of the reel arms.
4. Plug the power cord into an electrical outlet.
5. Unwind as much of the speaker cable from the speaker case (front cover) as is necessary. Connect the cable to speaker outlet at base of the projector.

Adjust

1. The single switch control has four positions: OFF, THREAD, MOTOR, LAMP. Turn the switch slowly to the lamp position.
2. Direct the light on the screen. To raise the front of the projector, turn the elevator lock lever to the right and press the elevator release button on the front of the projector. The elevating device is spring-loaded. It can be held at any point by turning the lock lever to the left.
3. Adjust rough focus by turning lens until edges of lighted area are sharp.
4. Turn off the lamp and motor by placing switch on THREAD position.
5. Test the response of the amplifier by turning the volume control knob clockwise; there should be an audible "hiss" from the loudspeaker. Turn the volume control knob back to the left.
6. Set the following controls: TONE CONTROL at midpoint; SILENT-SOUND switch at SOUND; push in the rewind lever.

Threading

1. Place a full reel of film over the feed-arm spindle; lock the reel on the spindle by turning up the end-catch; unwind, clockwise, about 5 ft. of film.
2. Push film gate open and latch it to front of projection lens.
3. Place film over the feed sprocket by first raising sprocket shoe. Lock film into place with the sprocket shoe when perforations are fitted over sprocket teeth.
4. Place film in film channel, allowing a loop in the film equal in height to the red handle of the rewind lever; unlatch the film gate and lock film in film channel.
5. Position the film just under the loop setter located below the film channel.
6. Move back the pressure roller resting against the sound drum. Place the film over the pressure roller, and under and over the sound drum.

7. Lead the film around the stabilizer roller, place it on the take-up sprocket and lock it in place by drawing down the sprocket shoe.
8. Place empty reel on take-up arm spindle; attach film; wind up slack.
9. Push down on loop setter to form correctly the loops above and below the film channel. Turn the thread knob at the front of the projector to test manually the threading of the film.

Operate
1. Set the operating switch at MOTOR and the at LAMP.
2. Focus the image on the screen by turning the projection lens; turn the volume control knob and set the sound at optimum level.
3. Use framer, located on top of lamphouse, if picture area needs to be adjusted.
4. Sound can be adjusted by using the fidelity lever and the tone control.
5. Reset loops, if necessary, by depressing loop setter.
6. As final frames of film are shown, turn control switch to MOTOR, turn volume control knob counterclockwise; allow film to run through projector completely before switching to THREAD.

Rewind
1. Fix the end of the film from the take-up reel onto the hub of the empty feed reel. Rotate the reel a few turns counterclockwise.
2. Pull out rewind lever and set operating switch at MOTOR.
3. After film has been rewound, push in rewind lever and set operating switch at THREAD.

Pack up
1. Retract the elevator foot by moving elevator lock lever forward and pressing down on front of the projector. The elevator foot will lock into position. Move elevator lock lever backward.
2. Turn the operating switch to OFF position.
3. Unplug speaker cable and wind it around brackets in the speaker case.
4. Unplug the power cord from outlet and wind cord into the speaker case.
5. Fold down the two reel arms against the projector.
6. Hinge the speaker lid onto the projector, close, and fasten latches.

A feature of this projector is its capability of increasing the light output through mechanical adjustment of the shutter blades. To accomplish this the lamphouse cover is removed and the shutter set in a two-blade position. Conversely, if it is necessary to cut down on screen illumination, the shutter can be set in a three-blade position.

The lamp is changed by removing the lamphouse cover, pushing down on the lamp, and turning it one-quarter turn counterclockwise. The lamp used has an output of 750 W, Code DDB.

The exciter lamp, Code BTD, can be reached by removing the exciter lamp cover. To remove the lamp, the release lever is depressed and the lamp turned to the left.

Lubrication for all movable parts of the projector is sealed in at the factory and is guaranteed for the life of the projector.

The use of the transistor in place of the vacuum tube is affecting the design and performance of motion picture projectors. Eastman Kodak's Model AV-126-TR, using transistors, has a sound system that delivers 50% more power with higher fidelity. Yet it is as compact as earlier models.

The threading path (Figure 5.15) has one basic change. After passing over the take-up sprocket, the film is led by means of snubber rollers to the back of the projector and onto the take-up reel. The take-up reel is on the same level as the feed reel but is located at the rear of the projector.

A horizontal switch control provides for motor and lamp operation in both the forward and reverse directions. Audio controls, including microphone and phono-input jacks, are located on a panel at the base of the projector.

Graflex Motion-Picture Projectors   Graflex, Inc. currently is offering several models of improved projectors in its series called the Graflex 16 models. Its features include push-button controls, a new 250-W lamp that delivers more light to the screen than conventional 1000-W lamps, a 2-in. f/1.6 field flattener lens that provides for greater corner to corner sharpness, and an amplifier with peak output of 30 W. The Graflex Model 820 and its operation will be considered in detail, since an understanding of this unit will facilitate operation of any of the Graflex projectors (Figure 5.16).

Set up

1. Set the projector on a flat sturdy surface with the front facing the screen.
2. Lift off the cover. It contains the speaker and the speaker cable. Unwind as much cable as is needed and plug in speaker cable to outlet located on the control panel.
3. Unwind power cord from rear of projector and plug it into an electrical outlet.
4. Swing reel arms into position. They will lock firmly when correctly placed.

Adjust

1. Switch on amplifier and move master control lever to FORWARD.
2. Push down on green button to activate the projector mechanism.
3. Press down on the yellow button marked NORM to switch on the lamp.
4. Center the lighted area on the screen. To raise the front of the

(a)

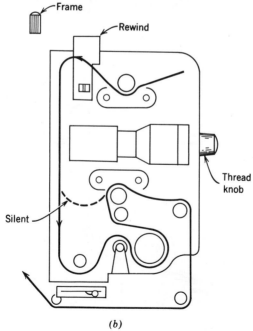

(b)

Figure 5.15 (a) **Eastman Kodak motion picture projector Model AV-126 TR and** (b) **threading diagram.** *Courtesy of Eastman Kodak.*

Reel arm lock

Snubber

Framer

Rewind lever

Take up sprocket

Sprocket shoe lever

Amplifier switch

Feed sprocket

Manual advance knob

Elevator lock

Film gate lock

(a)

Push button switches

Master control

Sound head

Loop synchronizer

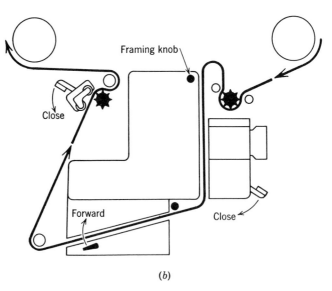

Framing knob

Close

Forward

Close

(b)

Figure 5.16 (*a*) **Graflex motion picture projector and** (*b*) **threading diagram.** *Courtesy Graflex, Inc.*

projector, turn the elevator lock to the left, lift the front, and then turn the elevator lock lever to the right.

5. Check the operation of the sound system by turning the volume control knob clockwise until a "hiss" is heard; then turn it back to the left.
6. Set the SOUND-SILENT switch at SOUND.
7. Push down the black button to turn off lamp; push down the red button to stop the projector.

Thread

1. Set a roll of film on feed arm spindle. Lock it into place by moving the catch at the end of the spindle. Unwind 5 ft. of film in the clockwise direction.
2. Set the take-up reel on the spindle of the take-up arm. Lock it in place.
3. Open the feed sprocket shoe and film channel by moving film-gate lever forward. It is located below the projection lens.
4. Place the film under and around the feed sprocket and into the film channel. Allow a loop of $1\frac{1}{2}$ in. in the film above the film channel. Move back the film-gate lever to close film channel and feed-sprocket shoe.
5. Move master control lever to the THREAD position; slide the film into the wide diagonal slot.
6. Open the take-up sprocket shoe, above the FORWARD position, by moving the lever to the left. Fit the film carefully on the sprocket to be certain that teeth are set in the film perforations. Work the film around the snubber roller, then toward the rear of the projector. Move lever to the right to close sprocket show over the film.
7. Attach film to empty reel, and make several turns of the reel, clockwise, to take up the slack film.
8. Move the master control lever to FORWARD position. Set the correct-size bottom loop by moving the sound loop synchronizer to the right and downward. This control is located below and to the left of the film channel.
9. The threading of the film can be tested by turning the manual advance knob located just above the projection lens.

Operate

1. Press down on the green button to start the projector; press down on yellow button to turn on lamp at normal intensity. The white button can be pressed for higher light intensity.
2. Adjust focus by turning the objective lens; bring up volume to optimum level by turning volume control knob.
3. Two knobs marked BASS and TREBLE, allow for fine, tone-control tuning. The framer knob is located just above and to the left of the

film channel. It should be turned if adjustment of picture area is required.

4. Film can be reversed by moving the master control knob to the REVERSE position.

5. At end of film, turn down volume, and push down black button turning off the lamp. When all the film has run through the projector, push down the red button stopping the projector mechanism.

Rewind

1. Attach the film to the empty feed reel; turn the reel several times counterclockwise.

2. Move the master control lever to REWIND. Move rewind lever, above film channel, to the right. Press down on green button. Release rewind lever.

3. Push down on red button when film has been completely rewound.

Pack up

1. Unlock and remove the supply and take-up reels. Fold the reel arms into the projector by pushing the lock release buttons at the base of the arms.

2. Switch off the amplifier; unplug the power cord, coil it, and set it into the storage compartment at rear of the projector case.

3. Unplug speaker cable. Wind the cable around brackets in the speaker case.

4. Lower front of projector by turning lock lever knob to the left, pressing down on front of projector, and turning lock lever to the right.

5. Attach speaker cover to the projector case and latch.

The lamp used in this projector and several other Graflex models is a 250-W TruFlector lamp. It has a built-in reflector that directs the light rays through the film without the need for a condensing lens system. The lamp, Code DLR, can be operated at several intensities. Lamp life is rated at 100 hours when it is operated at normal intensity. The light output at high intensity is equal to that from a 1200-W lamp, but estimated life at such intensity is only 10 hours.

The entire front panel of the lamphouse can be removed by pressing the button just below the take-up sprocket and drawing the panel away from the projector. When the lamp chimney is raised, the lamp is accessible for changing. A new lamp is readily positioned by means of a key slot in the base. The lamp is pressed down and is positioned with an audible click.

The exciter lamp, Code BRK, is removed by pressing it down and turning it counter-clockwise. The three holes in the base of the new lamp are fitted over the pins, and the lamp is then pressed down and turned clockwise.

The projector can be stopped on an individual frame with the lamp on.

The light output, however, is cut down to one-third by a safety shutter which drops down between the lamp and the film. This shutter absorbs the heat, which would otherwise burn through the film.

The amplifier in the projector has no fuse, but there is a circuit breaker which will open in the event of any electrical problem. The amplifier pilot light will also fail to light. The reset fuse button on the control panel can be pushed down to reactivate the amplifier circuit.

RCA Motion-Picture Projectors.   The Radio Corporation of America has produced sound motion-picture projectors that have been widely accepted. Current models reflect improvements in materials, output, and performance. The basic threading pattern (Figure 5.17) and types of controls are quite similar for all the models, although the placement of the controls may vary.

The RCA projector described below is typical. The RCA 400 Junior-Senior model has had some modifications, but an understanding of one unit (Figure 5.18) should lead to early mastery of all other RCA models and modifications.

Set up

1. Set the projector on a flat sturdy table with the front legs even with the front edge of the table.
2. Lift off the speaker cover; remove the reel arms from the cover and attach to the projector. Current models have the arms permanently attached and folded into the projector case.
3. Slip the reel arm belts over the pulleys on the arms.
4. Remove the speaker cable and unwind from the take-up reel. Set speaker cover in optimum position and plug in speaker cable at the base of projector. Place empty reel on take-up arm.
5. Remove the power cord from its storage space at the base of the projector and plug it into a wall outlet.

Adjust

1. Switch on amplifier.
2. Set OPERATE-REWIND lever in OPERATE position; the lever is located in front of the feed sprocket.
3. Set the SILENT-SOUND knob on SOUND.
4. Turn control switch from OFF to PROJECTOR to LAMP.
5. Direct the light onto the screen. Raise the front of the projector by turning the hand crank at the front of the projector clockwise.
6. Loosen lens lock screw; focus on the edges of the lighted area by turning the projection lens. Tighten the lens lock screw.
7. Rotate control switch to the OFF position.
8. Check the sound system by rotating volume control knob clockwise until a "hiss" is heard. Turn it back to zero.

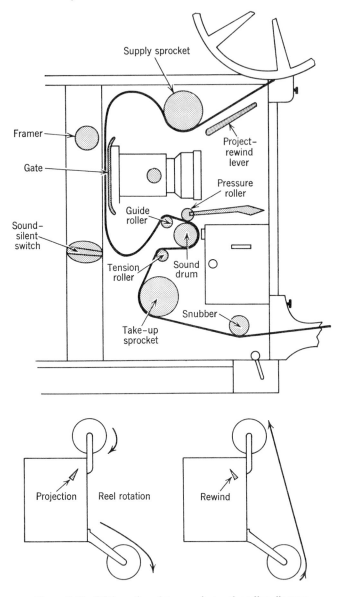

Figure 5.17   RCA motion picture projector threading diagram.

Thread
1. Place a reel of film on the feed arm spindle. Unwind about 5 ft. of film; film should unwind in a clockwise direction.
2. Open film gate by swinging back the projection lens system.

Figure 5.18   RCA motion picture projector. *Courtesy Radio Corporation of America.*

3. Follow the threading path imprinted on the face of the projector. Set the film under the feed sprocket by holding down the sprocket shoe. Make certain that the film perforations fit over the sprocket teeth.
4. Set the film in the film channel, allowing a loop above the channel even with top of feed sprocket. Close the film gate.
5. Allow a loop below the film channel. Lead the film over the guide roller and under the pressure roller. Pressure roller can be raised by pushing down the end of the arm that supports it.
6. Set the film around the sound drum, over the lower guide roller, and under the take-up sprocket. Be certain that the sprocket teeth fit into the film perforations before closing the sprocket shoe over the film.
7. Lead the film under the snubber roller and attach to take-up reel. Turn the reel clockwise to take up the slack in the film.

Operate
1. Turn the control switch to PROJECTOR, then to LAMP.
2. Bring up volume to optimum level at the same time as adjusting the focus of image on the screen. Set the tone control at the desired level.

3. Observe operation of projector to make certain that loops are maintained, film is winding properly, and focus is sharp.

4. To reshow a section of film, turn control switch to OFF and then to REVERSE and to LAMP. Turn down the volume during the reversal.

5. At the final action of a film, turn the control switch to PROJECTOR and turn down the volume. When all the film has been run through the projector, set the control switch at OFF.

Rewind

1. Attach the end of the film to the hub of the empty feed reel. Turn several turns counterclockwise.

2. Position operate-rewind lever at REWIND. Turn control switch to PROJECTOR.

3. After film is rewound, turn control switch to OFF.

Pack up

1. Lower the front of the projector by turning the crank in counter clockwise.

2. Unplug the speaker cable from the projector and speaker case. Wind the cable on the empty 400-ft. reel by setting the reel on the feed arm. Set the control switch at PROJECTOR and guide the cable onto the reel. Be certain that the speaker plug does not strike against the side of the projector.

3. Place the speaker cable in the speaker case. Remove the arms and attach these in the speaker case. On newer models the arms remain attached but fold into the projector.

4. Push the drive belts into the interior of the projector case. Unplug the power cord, coil it, and place it in its storage compartment.

5. Fit the speaker case cover over the projector. Latch it securely.

The projector has built-in lubrication designed to last for the life of the projector. The projection lamp can be changed by loosening the lamphouse screw. The entire lamphouse assembly is hinged and can be drawn outward for easy access to the lamp. The lamp ordinarily used has a 750-W rating, Code DDB; but a 1000-wat lamp, Code DFD, can also be used.

The exciter lamp, Code BGB, can be reached by loosening the set screw on the exciter lamphouse. The lamphousing is hinged and can be moved aside; the lamp base is also hinged and facilitates the task of changing the lamp.

Newer models of RCA projects are shown in Figure 5.19.

Victor Motion-Picture Projectors. The Victor Animatograph Corporation, Division of Kalart, produces many projectors; for classrooms, large rooms, and auditoriums; silent projectors, rear-screen projectors, and magnetic sound projectors. The model most widely used in the classroom and most typical is the Victor Model 70–15 (Figure 5.20).

(a)

(b)

Figure 5.19   RCA motion picture projectors. *Courtesy of Radio Corporation of America.*

Figure 5.20   Kalart/Victor 16 mm sound-motion picture projector. *Courtesy of Kalart/Victor.*

The Victor Model 70–15 has several interesting features. The feed reel is located at the rear of the projector, and the take-up reel is at the front. The same sprocket serves as a feed sprocket as well as a take-up sprocket. Another sprocket is used to draw the film through the sound head. Three loops are needed in the film path. If any of the loops are lost, a safety trip stops the projector (Figure 5.21).

A complete description of operating procedures is contained below:

Set up

1. Set the projector on a flat, sturdy surface facing the screen. Unclasp the top of the case and take out the reel arms and cords.

2. Unhinge the speaker case from the side of the projector and set it aside.

3. Insert the reel arms at top of the projector. First loosen reel arm lock screw, and after arms are inserted, tighten again. The feed arm with the larger pulley is set at the rear.

4. Three belts are used. Rear belt is used on rear reel with an open loop. The two front belts are turned with a half twist; one is placed on

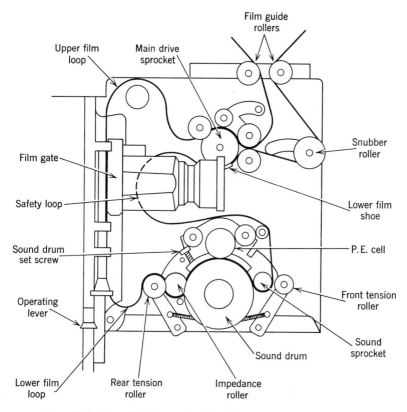

Figure 5.21   Threading diagram for Victor/Kalart sound motion picture projector.

the feed reel pulley and the other on the take-up reel pulley. More complete directions are located at the top of the projector.

5. Place the speaker at optimum location, attach the cable and plug it into the speaker jack on the control panel. Unwind and plug in the power cord.

Adjust

1. Turn on amplifier switch and exciter lamp switch on control panel.
2. Push down on MOTOR switch and LAMP switch.
3. Direct the lighted area on the screen. Projector can be raised by turning the knob at the front of the projector.
4. Adjust the focus on the screen by sharpening edges of projected area. Loosen the lock screw above the lens before turning the lens.
5. Check the sound system by turning the volume control knob clockwise until a "hiss" is heard. Then turn back the knob. Pull up MOTOR and LAMP switches.

Thread

1. Set the reel of film on the rear reel feed arm spindle. Attach the film to the front take-up reel. Turn reel clockwise several turns to secure attachment. Both reels should be locked on with the spindle catch.
2. Draw away and down on the rear tension roller and the front tension roller near the sound drum. Open the lens gate by drawing on the lens and swinging it away from the projector. Open the top and bottom sprocket shoes on the drive sprocket.
3. Draw enough film from the feed reel to reach to the base of the projector. Place the film over the sound drum, under the left stabilizer roller and over the rear tension roller which is moved back into position. On the right of the sound drum, the film is placed around the sound sprocket and the front tension roller is moved back in place.
4. Set the film leading to the take-up roller reel along the path indicated by the white line on the projector: behind the film guide roller, in front of the snubber roller, underneath the feed sprocket; close the bottom sprocket shoe when film is firmly set.
5. Take the film leading to the take-up reel and place it according to the white line that is printed on the side of the projector: a safety loop around the middle safety trip, under the drive sprocket (close the sprocket show when film is firmly set), between the two small rollers in front of the drive sprocket, in front of snubber roller, behind the front film guide roller, and to the take-up reel.
6. Set the film in the film channel and close film gate securely.
7. Drawing film from the supply reel, place film over the drive sprocket, between the black rollers, and in front of film guide roller. Lock film in place by lowering sprocket shoe.

Operate

1. Move operating lever upward; push down on MOTOR switch and LAMP switch.
2. Adjust fine focus by turning projection lens; also turn up volume control knob to optimum level of sound.
3. Observe operation of the projector and correct poor sound-picture synchronization, framing, tone, and volume.
4. Any difficulty in the film's passing through the projector will result in the tripping of a safety switch that automatically releases the operating lever. The difficulty is overcome by feeding in enough additional film to overcome the tension on the safety switch.
5. As the last frames of the film are being shown, the LAMP switch should be pushed up and the VOLUME turned down.
6. When all the film has been run through the projector, the MOTOR switch is moved up.

Rewind
1. Attach the film directly to the empty feel reel. Turn reel several turns counterclockwise.
2. Push SAFETY switch to get operating lever in down position. Make certain rear tension roller is in forward position.
3. Push down on MOTOR switch and push in REWIND LOCK RELEASE.
4. Hold down REWIND lever until film is completely rewound.

Pack up
1. Switch off the amplifier and exciter lamp.
2. Disconnect power cord and speaker cable.
3. Remove the arms and place them in lift-off top of projector. Place cable and cord in the lift-off top.
4. Hinge speaker case to side of the projector. Place top of projector in position and fasten securely.

It is possible to halt the projector for showing a still picture on the screen by tripping a safety switch and holding down on the still picture lever. Sometimes the shutter must be moved from the path of light. This can be done by turning the hand-operating control at the front of the projector.

The lamp used in the Victor Model 70–15 has a light output of 750 W, Code DDB. It is reached by removing the lamphouse cover and lamp vent assembly. For removal, the lamp is pressed down and turned counter-clockwise one-quarter turn.

To reach the exciter lamp, located just behind the sound drum, the chrome lock screw must be loosened. The black plastic cover and the drum can be removed, revealing the lamp. The exciter lamp (Code BVK) is removed by pressing in on it and turning it counterclockwise.

The Duolite Model ST-18 (Figure 5.22), although usable in the conventional manner, is specially adapted for audiences from one to 20 persons.

A rear-projection screen is built into the projector so that screen and projector are one self-contained unit. The image is projected through a 5/8-in. lens onto a mirror which directs the light onto the back of a translucent screen constructed into the side panel of the projector case. The screen measures 10 × 14 in.

The special value of a unit such as this one lies in the fact that it can be used under normal lighting conditions without loss of image clarity. It is for this reason that rear-projection systems are being studied with the thought of developing more applications for their use in the classroom. Another outgrowth of this study is the possibility of moving the projector from the middle of the classroom to the front of the room—where it can be more readily controlled by the teacher.

Normal projection

Elevation

Rear screen

Figure 5.22   Kalart/Victor Duolite Model ST-18.

This projector is capable of using either standard film or magazine-loaded film for continuous loop showing.

Care and Maintenance of Projector and Films

The audiovisual department of individual school systems can usually be relied upon to maintain the projectors and films. But it is well for the the classroom teacher to be aware of some of the rudiments of equipment and material care (Figure 5.23).

The lens surfaces and the gate aperture of the projector should be cleaned before and after every showing. For lens surfaces it is best to use a lintless cleaning material such as the special lens tissue which is readily available at camera shops. A liquid lens cleaner should be used to remove stubborn dirt. The gate-aperture area and the film channel should be cleaned with a brush. This tends to remove the dirt, grime, and lint that could wear and scratch the film. It also removes the dirt that would otherwise be projected as a fuzzy edge of the picture appearing on the screen.

Oiling and general lubrication are best left to the technicians in the audio-

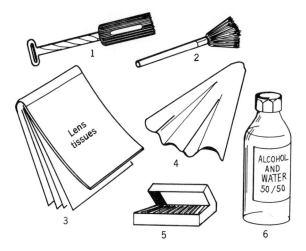

Figure 5.23 The projectionist should acquire the habit of keeping his equipment clean. All glass surfaces such as lenses, reflectors, and lamps should be free of dirt, dust, oil vapor deposits, and finger marks. Similarly, all surfaces that come in contact with film must be kept free of dirt, dust, and caked emulsion. The projectionist should have a cleaning kit including the following material: 1. A stiff bristle brush. 2. A soft amel's hair brush. 3. Lens tissue. 4. A clean, soft, lintless cloth. 5. Some toothpicks. 6. A small bottle of pure grain alcohol-and-water mixture (50/50 mixture).

visual department; too much oil is as bad, if not worse, than not enough oil—and directions for lubrication vary with the projector.

Replacement of items such as pulley belts, lamps, and fuses can be accomplished by the classroom teacher. New belts must match the old in length and in thickness. Lamps and fuses should always be of the same code designation as the original. Substitutions should be used only with the full assurance that they are safe. Serious damage could occur in a projector, for example, if a 1000-W lamp were substituted for a 750-W lamp merely because the two lamps "looked" the same.

Motion-picture film is expensive to produce. Yet, if properly cared for, it can be used for hundreds of showings. Careless handling and threading cause scratches in the emulsion, creases in the film, enlarged or torn sprocket holes, breaks in the film, perforations in the sound track or in the film, burned spots, and dirt and fingerprints on the film (Figure 5.24).

If a film breaks the ends should be trimmed, scraped, and cemented together, provided the teacher has the equipment and the competence to do the job. If not, the film ends should be overlapped and wound tightly until the film can wind itself without slipping; a marker should be placed in the reel indicating the break. *Never* use pins, staples, clips, or tape to hold broken film together.

DAMAGE	PROBABLE CAUSES
Scratches	1. Dirty rollers, dirty gate, dirty film channel. 2. Tightening film after it is wound (Cinching). 3. Letting loose film fall on floor. 4. Frozen rollers.
Creases	1. Stepping on film. 2. Pinching film in closing film can. 3. Loose film on floor.
Enlarged or torn sprocket holes	1. Too much tension on gate or take-up reel. 2. Jerking movement of take-up reel. 3. Shuttle worn or out of adjustment. 4. Worn sprockets. 5. Dry film. 6. Film worn out. 7. Loss of loop.
Breaks	1. Faulty film splice. 2. Sudden jerk on take-up. 3. Film improperly placed in film channel. 4. Loss of loop.

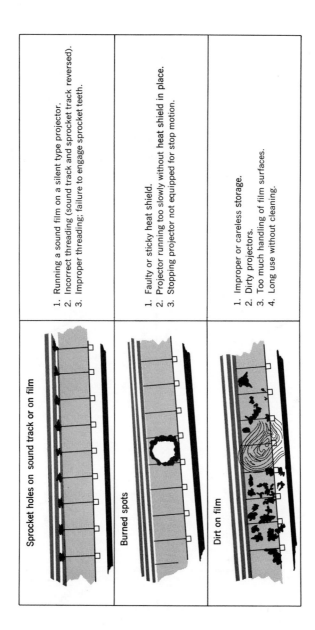

Sprocket holes on sound track or on film

1. Running a sound film on a silent type projector.
2. Incorrect threading (sound track and sprocket track reversed).
3. Improper threading; failure to engage sprocket teeth.

Burned spots

1. Faulty or sticky heat shield.
2. Projector running too slowly without heat shield in place.
3. Stopping projector not equipped for stop motion.

Dirt on film

1. Improper or careless storage.
2. Dirty projectors.
3. Too much handling of film surfaces.
4. Long use without cleaning.

Figure 5.24 Types of film damage.

Inexpensive splicers are available. They are designed so that the two broken ends of the film are separately clamped with the emulsion or dull side up (Figure 5.25). The ends are evenly trimmed by means of a cutter provided on the machine. A small area (1/10 in.) of the image surface of one film is then scraped away and wiped clean. Liquid film cement is applied to the cleared area. The end of the other film is immediately clamped down over the cement surface, and the two are fused together within 15 to 30 seconds.

Solving Problems in Motion-Picture Projection

Difficulties in the projection of motion-picture films can occur at any time. If the source of the trouble is quickly diagnosed, it can be corrected

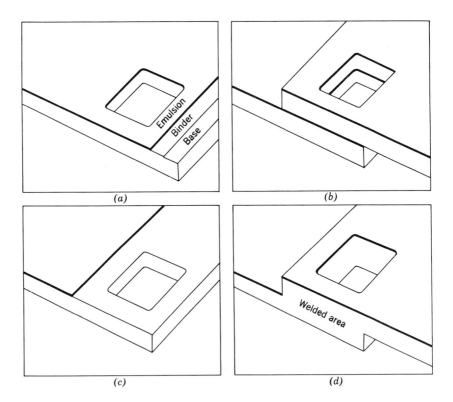

Figure 5.25   Operations involved in the splicing of motion picture film. (*a*) Position film emulsion side (dull side) up. (*b*) Trim ends of film and overlap one sprocket hole. (*c*) Scrape away emulsion from the end of one film. (*d*) Apply cement, press overlay film onto cement area. Allow enough time for films to fuse and dry.

with a minimum of interruption in the presentation (Figure 5.26). A few of the problems and their correction are listed below:

Probable Causes of Trouble	NO SOUND	IMPAIRED SOUND	NO PICTURE	POOR PICTURE	HUM OR OTHER NOISE	IRREGULAR MOTOR	PICTURE AND SOUND NOT SYNCHRONIZED	LOSS OF FILM LOOP
1. Low line voltage		×		×	×	×		
2. High line voltage					×	×		
3. Speaker disconnected or improperly connected	×	×			×			
4. Amplifier not on	×							
5. Amplifier tubes defective	×	×			×			
6. Exciter lamp defective	×	×			×			
7. Photoelectric cell defective	×	×			×			
8. Projector lamp burned out			×					
9. Projector lamp out of alignment				×				
10. Lens incorrectly focused				×				
11. Film incorrectly threaded	×	×		×	×		×	×
12. Volume control not on or defective	×	×			×			
13. Fuse burned out	×							
14. Projector cable broken or loose	×	×			×	×		
15. Defective motor belts		×		×				
16. Poor acoustics		×						
17. Dirty sound lens	×	×			×			
18. Dirty projection lens and reflectors				×				
19. Speed control at wrong position		×		×				
20. Film channels dirty	×	×		×				
21. Lack of or too much oil		×				×	×	
22. Motor governor brushes dirty or damaged		×				×	×	
23. Motor commutator dirty or damaged		×				×	×	
24. Poor contact in line cord	×	×	×	×		×		
25. Poor screen or extraneous light				×				
26. Defective or dirty film		×		×				×
27. Line polarity or plugs switched	×	×			×			
28. Film gate pressure shoe not seating properly		×		×				×
29. Faulty switch	×		×					

Figure 5.26   Trouble chart for motion picture projectors. This table identifies with an × the probable causes that should be investigated when the trouble symptoms appear. When the projectionist is not qualified to make the necessary repairs, an audiovisual coordinator should be consulted.

1. The motor of the projector does not run, even though the switch is turned on.
   Check to see that all plugs are secured in the outlets.
   Check the plugs for defective wiring.
   Check to see if power is being supplied by the outlet.
2. The lamp in the projector does not light, even though the switch is turned on.
   Be sure motor switch is on.
   See if lamp is properly inserted in socket. Check filament of lamp.
   If new lamp fails to light check wiring of socket and switch.
3. Film mechanism does not run, even though the motor is operating properly.
   If clutch mechanism is available, turn it clockwise to engage gears.
   Be sure controls are set for PROJECTION and not REWIND.
   Check drive belt on pulley; work reels by hand to make sure the belts are not binding.
4. Light from projector appears to be deficient.
   Clean the condenser and objective lens.
   Reposition lamp in socket, making sure that filament is parallel to screen.
   Check for foreign matter in aperture.
   Check the wattage of lamp being used.
   Projected image may be too large (Figure 5.27).
   If there is a lens door, make sure it is completely open.
5. Sound volume is too low to be heard clearly.
   Check to see that connections on speaker cord are secure.
   Clean the bulb on the exciter lamp. Try a new exciter lamp.
   Check tubes in the amplifier.
   Check to see if sound drum is turning properly.
   Adjust film if it is loose on the sound drum.
   Try film on another projector. The sound track may be poor.
6. Action or motion is jerky on the screen.
   The film may be new and stiff ("green"). Running the film through the projector a few times will correct the condition.
   Check the film channel for dirt, burrs, or other defects.
   Examine sprockets to see if they are engaged properly.
   Reset the loops in the film.
7. The entire picture is not in focus on the screen
   Clean and adjust lens.
   Be sure the film gate is closed securely.
8. Picture on the screen is upside down or reversed.
   Rewind the film if image is upside down.
   If reversed, turn the film over and rewind (silent film).

Chart of image sizes

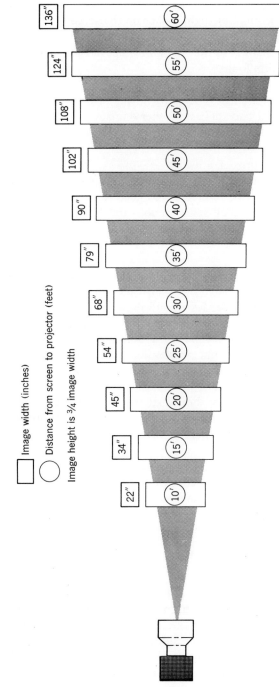

□ Image width (inches)

○ Distance from screen to projector (feet)

Image height is ¾ image width

Figure 5.27 Chart of image sizes with motion picture projectors using standard 2-in. lens. For good projection check the following points: 1. Adequacy of room facilities. 2. Screen type matched to seating plan. 3. Proper screen size and location. 4. Proper projector location and lens focal length. 5. Proper speaker location. 6. Room darkened to suit image brightness. *Courtesy of Eastman Kodak.*

155

9. There is objectionable light flicker on the screen.
   The shutter or intermittent claw may need to be repaired.
   Clean film channel so that the film is flat in the channel.
   Adjust the film loops.
   Check film for bad splices or other damage.
10. Loops in film are lost repeatedly during projection.
    Check film for bad splices or other damage.
    Check film gate to see that it closes properly.
    Check film channel to see that it is clean.
11. Take-up reel turns erratically.
    Make sure that reel is not rubbing against some obstruction.
    Pulley belts may be too loose and need replacement.
    Be certain that pulley belts are not rubbing against the projector or some obstruction.

Summary

The use of the classroom sound motion-picture film has grown tremendously as research has proven the instructional values inherent in the medium (Figure 5.28). The design and production of simple but efficient equipment has proved to be a further stimulus. The films have value, however, only if used by the teacher in a well-integrated instructional plan. Careful selection of films and previewing on the part of the teacher is a prerequisite. Important also is the preparation of students for the selection of significant information. The presentation should follow good projection techniques, and the teacher should strive to achieve a favourable room environment. Follow-up activities as motivating factors for further learning also play a most important part in the use of film projection as well as other media.

The classroom teacher is the focal point around which these learning activities take place. The knowledge of projection equipment and materials acquired by the teacher should increase the scope and effectiveness of learning and thereby contribute significantly to the successful presentation of audiovisual materials used in the classroom.

8-MM PROJECTION

The production and use of 8-mm motion-picture film has always been popular in the home. The 8-mm cameras are relatively inexpensive and the needed skills for using the camera can be acquired with little practice. High quality, low-cost films are resulting in finer pictures, while projection equipment is light-weight, compact, and easy to operate.

To all of these advantages, another has been added: it is now possible to have an iron oxide stripe coated along one edge of the film. Sound

Figure 5.28   The use of the classroom sound motion picture film has grown tremendously.

is recorded magnetically on this stripe and can be played back on the same 8-mm sound motion-picture equipment. This development was pioneered by the Calvin Company in 1952 and was further advanced by the Kodak Sound 8 Projector in 1960. Since that time, several companies have undertaken the development of new equipment.

The 8-mm silent film was used as early as 1870 by the French. Its acceptance in the schools was slow because the quality of the image was poor in comparison with that of the 16-mm film. Improved film and cameras now make possible projection films that can be enjoyed by small groups in the classroom. Without a great investment in time, equipment, or materials, teachers can film field trips, develop documentaries, or record the progress of students in the acquisition of certain skills.

Receiving a great deal of attention today is the single-concept film, sealed in a cartridge for continuous loop operation, and running from less than a minute to approximately 4 minutes. The teacher or students can produce these films in subject areas that are difficult to understand or visualize: the flow of blood through a circulatory system; movements of the amoeba and paramecium; fundamentals of volleyball; fundamentals of knitting, etc. The new Technicolor projector Model 800 (Figure 5.29) allows students or the teacher to position the film cartridge in the projector, turn on the switch, direct the light on any screen surface, focus, and then watch the film as many times as is necessary to acquire a skill or gain the information. The Model 900 is equipped also with a stop switch that allows the viewer to

Figure 5.29   The Technicolor Model 800 8mm motion picture projector. The projector is used with short single-concept films packaged in cartridge form. *Courtesy of Technicolor Corporation.*

study a single frame. A zoom lens permits the viewer to secure an enlarge-ment of a particular frame or segment of the movie without relocating the projector.

Compactness, light weight, and ease of operation commend this projector to students of all ages for group as well as individual viewing. The popular-ity will grow as the commercial producers increase the library of films avail-able to the classroom teachers.

Several problems still hinder the rapid growth and utilization of these films. One is the lack of standardization in frame size and film perforations; another is the reluctance of school administrators to promote this medium when there is such a heavy investment in 16-mm films and equipment. It is hoped that standardization will soon be achieved so that the 8-mm film and projector can take its place in the classroom with other audiovisual media.

Kodak's 8-mm Sound Projector.   Eastman Kodak has introduced in its Instamatic sound projector (Figure 5.30) a unit that utilizes Super 8 films—

Figure 5.30   Eastman Kodak 8mm sound projector. *Courtesy of Eastman Kodak.*

8-mm films with larger frame areas than those used on earlier films. The projector has a built-in speaker. Microphone and phono inputs allow for recording commentary or music on the magnetic recording strips.

The films can be recorded and shown at 18 or 24 frames per second. The lens has a focal length of 3/4 in. The lamp is DKR low-voltage one that directs a brilliant light onto the screen.

The projector can accommodate a 1200-ft reel for a 1-hour showing. manually to the take-up reel. Operating controls are similar to those of 16-mm. projectors.

Fairchild Mark IV. The Fairchild Camera and Instrument Company is The film is threaded automatically through the projector and is attached one of several producers of 8-mm automatic continuous sound projectors. The Mark IV, with its built-in rear-projection screen, is entirely self-contained (Figure 5.31). The sound system, speakers, lens system, projection mechanism, and screen are all enclosed in one cabinet that weighs 22 pounds. The screen area is $8\frac{1}{2} \times 11$ in.

The 8-mm magnetic-sound motion-picture film is completely enclosed in

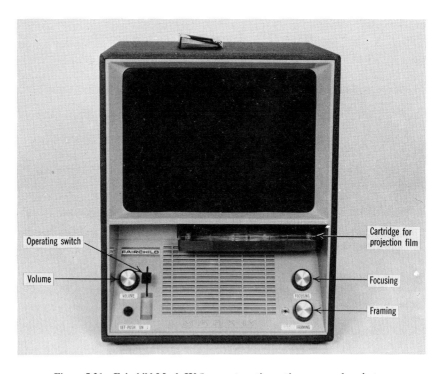

Figure 5.31   Fairchild Mark IV 8mm automatic continuous sound projector.

a plastic container. The cartridge has a maximum capacity of 400 ft of color film or 22 minutes of projection time. The ends of the film are joined together in a continuous loop, so that the film can be shown repeatedly without rethreading.

Operation of the projector involves pushing the cartridge into the front feed slot and lowering the control lever on the front panel; the image then appears on the screen. Control knobs on the front panel allow for framing and focusing the projected image. A volume control knob can be turned to adjust sound at the optimum level.

The lamp operates on a low wattage (50 W), but it directs as much light on the screen as do 500-W lamps of earlier design. The reflector is built in with the lamp and directs the light through the film gate so that a condensing lens is not needed.

Commercial films are currently being made available in cartridge form for use in the Fairchild Mark IV.

SELECTED REFERENCES

Alcorn, Marvin D., James Kinder, and Jim. R. Schunert, *Better Teaching in Secondary Schools* (2nd. ed.), New York: Holt, Rinehart & Winston, 1964.

Allen, William H. "How Effective Are Teaching Films?" *Teaching Tools*, **4**, 10–11, (Winter, 1956-1957).

Brown, James W., Richard B. Lewis, and Fred F. Harcleroad, *Audio-Visual Instruction Materials and Methods*, New York: McGraw-Hill, 1964, Chapter 8.

Cross, A. J. Foy and Irene F. Cypher. *Audio-Visual Education.* New York: Crowell, 1961. Chapters 3, 4 and 5.

Dale, Edgar, *Audio-Visual Methods in Teaching* (rev. ed.), New York: Holt, Rinehart & Winston, 1961, Chapter 15.

Dale, Edgar. "Using Films for a Purpose," *The News Letter* **21**, 1–4 (April, 1956).

Erickson, Carlton W. H. *Fundamentals of Teaching With Audiovisual Technology.* New York: Macmillan, 1965, Chapter 7.

Finn, James D., and Joan Rosengren. "8mm Sound Film," *Audiovisual Instruction* **7**, 90–93, (February, 1962).

Flory, John. "8-mm. and a New Era in Educational Film," *Audiovisual Instruction* **6**, 14–15, (January, 1961).

Forsdale, Louis, and Joan Rosengren Forsdale. "The New 8mm Format," *Audiovisual Instruction*, **11**, 39–41, (January, 1966).

Haas, Kenneth B., and Harry Q. Packer, *Preparation and Use of Audiovisual Aids*; (3rd. ed.) Englewood Cliffs, N. H. Prentice-Hall, 1955, Chapters 1 and 15.

Kinder, James S., *Audio-Visual Materials and Techniques* (2nd ed.) New York: American Book Company, 1959, Chapters 7, 8, and 9.

Mannino, Phillip, *ABC's of Audiovisual Equipment and the School Projectionist Manual.* (rev.) State College, Pa.: M. O. Publishers, 1959.

Miller, Elwood E. "Film Clip Project-Halfway Point," *Audiovisual Instruction*, **11**, 34–37. (January, 1966).

Miller, Neal E., and others. "Graphic Communication and the Crisis in Education." *Audio-Visual Communication Review*, 5, (Fall 1957).

Sands, Lester F., *Audio-Visual Procedure in Teaching*, New York: Ronald Press, 1956, Chapter 20.

Swarthout, Sherwin G., and R. Murray Thomas. *Integrated Teaching Materials*. New York: David McKay, 1963.

Wendt, Paul R. "What Research Says to the Teacher." *Audio-Visual Instruction.* Washington D. C.: NEA, 1957, No. 14.

Wittich, Walter Arno, and Charles Francis Schuller, *Audio-Visual Materials, Their Nature and Use* (2nd ed.). New York: Harper & Bros., 1962, Chapter 13.

INSTRUCTIONAL MATERIALS

"Choosing a Classroom Film," 16-mm film, 18-mm., sound, b & w or color, McGraw-Hill, 1963.

"Film Tactics," 16-mm film, 23 min., sound b & w, U.S. Navy, 1945.

"How to Use Classroom Films," 16-mm film, 15 min., sound, b & w or color, McGraw-Hill, 1963.

"How to Use a Teaching Film," 35-mm filmstrip, 38 frames, color. Basic Films, 1957.

"New Tools for Learning," 16-mm film, 20 min., sound, b & w, Encyclopaedia Britannica, 1951.

"A Teacher Utilizes a Motion Picture Film," 35-mm filmstrip, 30 frames, b & w, Extension Division, University of Oklahoma, 1949.

"The Unique Contribution." 16-mm film, 36 min., sound, b & w or color, Encyclopaedia Britannica, 1960.

6

RECORD PLAYERS

In any consideration of audiovisual equipment primary attention is usually given to projection devices: overhead projectors, motion-picture projectors, slide projectors, and opaque projectors. On the other hand, sound plays a vital role in the instruction that can be offered by the classroom teacher, and therefore it should not be overlooked.

The section on sound in Chapter 3 explained some of the technical aspects associated with "audio." The characteristics of sound—frequency, intensity, and quality—are especially important in the design of playback equipment. It is the role of such equipment to play back the sound with the highest possible fidelity. Manufacturers of records and record players have accomplished this to the apparent satisfaction of many school administrators and classroom teachers. It is estimated that there are over 400,000 record players in our classrooms and over 3.5 million disk-recordings being used.[1]

The popularity of record players can be attributed to the wide range of materials that are available and are applicable to classroom activity. On the elementary level the equipment is used to tell stories with appropriate sound effects. It can be used with appropriate visuals to create memorable learning experiences, such as might be the case with a recording of "Peter and the Wolf"; it provides background music for youngsters using rhythm instruments and devices or for rhythmic activities and exercises (Figure 6.1); it brings into the classroom sounds of many natural events and happenings.

The work of singers, actors, poets, and musicians can be presented to the members of the class at the flick of a switch (Figure 6.2). The words of famous statesmen and important personages can be heard through the records of "The Cavalcade of United States Presidents," "I Can Hear It Now," "You Are There," and various other types of dramatization. Records provide teachers with the means for group or individual study in areas such as the humanities, English literature, and modern languages.

[1] "Audiovisual Equipment and Materials in U.S. Public Schools", *op. cit.*, p. 6.

Figure 6.1   Record players can be used to provide background music for rythmic activities and physical fitness exercises. *Courtesy of Newcomb Audio Products Co.*

Recorded sound has come a long way since the invention of the first practical recording device by Thomas Edison in 1877. His tinfoil cylinder was followed by the wax cylinder, to the development of which Alexander Graham Bell devoted a great deal of his time. The design of the current record-disk is attributed to Emile Berliner.. The materials used in recordings have varied and have been the subject of lengthy experimentation to determine a base that would be durable yet offer good fidelity. Plastics of several varieties are now being used, but not before metals, waxes, shellac, and wood were tested.

The instructional value of records in the classroom has been the subject of much research and experimentation. The results indicate that, as a supplemental aid, phonograph records both improve understanding of difficult concepts and serve to improve retention of learned materials. As Rulon established in one of his studies, however, records hold no special value for motivating students to further study.[2]

[2] Rulon, Philip J., "The Effect of Phonographic Recordings Upon Attitude", *Harvard Education Review*, **14**, 20–37, (1944).

Figure 6.2   Record players can be used to tell stories with appropriate sound effects.

Students do like to listen to records as an adjunct to regular instruction, but the records that are used in class should be carefully selected so as to achieve the teaching objectives. The four-step plan for audiovisual utilization should be put into effect when one considers the place of records in the instructional program. The selection process is an especially difficult one in view of the many recordings that are now being commercially produced. A good teaching record is one that is interesting; its material must be presented in a lucid, lively style. It should develop a limited number of points, illustrate them with concrete examples, and provide a good summarization. (Records used primarily for "enrichment" purposes would not necessarily follow the same pattern of utilization.)

TECHNICAL ASPECTS OF PHONOGRAPH RECORDS

For the most part, new developments and improvements of playback equipment followed the breakthroughs and radical changes in the makeup of phonograph records. Changes in depth of grooves, spacing of grooves, composition of surface coatings—all of these factors contributed to improvements in the phonograph design. It would be well then to review briefly the development of the phonograph disk or record as it exists at the present time.

The first recordings were made on cylinders; however, by 1900, much of the recording was being done on flat disks made of bakelite with a shellac finish or coating. Recordings for approximately the next 50 years were made on this type of disk, which measured 10 or 12 in. in diameter. The grooves cut into the surface of the disk conformed to the nature of the sound that was being recorded (Figure 6.3). The groove is modulated in a lateral direction rather than vertical, which means that the needle moves from side to side during playback. Low notes produce the most perceptible

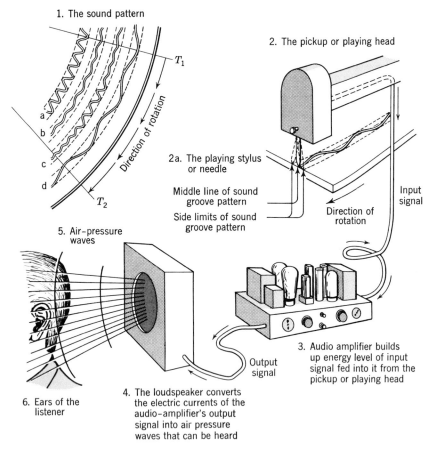

Figure 6.3   The reproduction of sound by means of the phonograph record. *U.S. Office of Education.*

fluctuations whereas the higher notes produce a movement that is hardly discernible. These fluctuating curves or grooves follow a rigid pattern. They begin on the outside edge of the disk and follow a circular path toward the center core. The depth of the groove is 0.002 in., and the width of the groove path is 0.004 in.—or approximately 120 lines per inch. The sound on these records is recorded with the disk revolving 78 times per minute. Thus the playback speed is referred to as 78 rpm (revolutions per minute).

The 78's had several distinct drawbacks. For one thing, the playing time was limited to three minutes for the 10-in. record and five minutes for the 12-in. record. The records were fragile, and breakage was quite frequent. The grooves gathered dust and dirt, a fact that resulted in a high level of noise and distortion in the playback.

Various mechanical devices were devised to stack records and change them automatically to extend the playback period without attending to the changing of the records. One change was introduced in the 1930's: a record conforming to the 15 minute time segment for use on radio was developed. It was called the *transcription*. The mechanics of the recording were the same in all but one respect—the speed was reduced from 78 rpm to $33\frac{1}{3}$ rpm. The size of the record was increased to a maximum diameter of 16 in.

By 1948, after many years of experimentation, Columbia Records was sufficiently impressed with its new record's capability of overcoming the disadvantages of the old 78. It introduced the LP. The LP (longplaying record) was designed to accommodate up to 25 minutes of recording on one side of a 12-in. disk. This was done by reducing the size and depth of the groove and more than doubling the number of grooves per inch. The speed was reduced to $33\frac{1}{3}$ rpm. The disk was made from a highly flexible but tough vinylite material. The quality of sound on this unbreakable disk was far superior to that of the older records.

These changes in the record, however, required multiple changes in playback equipment—particularly in the speed of the turntable and the diameter of the needle. Much of the equipment today is provided with controls that allow the turntable to rotate at various speeds and allow either a standard needle or a microgroove needle to be moved into position.

In 1949 RCA introduced its answer to the problems associated with the use of the old 78's. This was a relatively inexpensive wafer-thin disk, 7 in. in diameter, that played at a speed of 45 rpm. This design allowed for individual selection of recorded material. With few modifications, standard changers could be used; and with this size record the changers operated smoothly, quietly, and rapidly. Because of their lack of bulk, large numbers of these records could be stored or transported conveniently. The groove and the needle used were the same as for the LP or $33\frac{1}{3}$ rpm record.

The latest record disk to be developed is one that operates at a turntable speed of 16 rpm. It looks like the 45 and uses the same needle, but it has a playing time of 30 minutes. The records were originally made as talking books. As the fidelity and playback quality have improved, there are more such recordings being made of instrumental and vocal groups.

Figure 6.4 presents a comparison of characteristics of disk-recordings.

	Standard	Tran-scription	Long Play	45	16
Speed in RPM	78	33	33	45	16
Grooves per inch	110	110	250	250	400
Maximum diameter	12 in.	16 in.	12 in.	7 in.	7 in.
Maximum flying time per side	5 min.	15 min.	25 min.	8 min.	30 min.
Needle tip radius[a]	0.003 in. (standard)	0.003 in. (standard)	0.001 in. (microgroove)	0.001 in. (microgroove)	0.001 in. (microgroove)
Force on needle[b]	$\frac{1}{4}$ oz.	$\frac{1}{4}$ oz.	$\frac{1}{4}$ oz.	$\frac{1}{4}$ oz.	$\frac{1}{4}$ oz.
Center hole diameter (approx.)	$\frac{1}{4}$ in.	$\frac{1}{4}$ in.	$\frac{1}{4}$ in.	$1\frac{1}{2}$ in.	$1\frac{1}{2}$ in.

[a] Universal needles have an 0.002 in. tip and are used in inexpensive equipment.
[b] This is often erroneously called needle pressure.

Figure 6.4   Characteristics of disk-recordings.[3]

Care should be exercised in the handling and storage of recordings (Figure 6.5). The plastic materials used reduce the danger of breakage, but chipping and scratching of the surfaces will affect the quality of the recorded sound. Recordings should be handled by grasping the edges. Oils from the hands will attract dirt and dust to the grooves of the records. The recordings should not be exposed to excessive temperatures, for this will cause a warping effect. It is impossible to achieve acceptable playback results from an uneven surface.

When stored, the records should be placed in protective jackets. They should be positioned in vertical or horizontal racks. Haphazard arrangements of records could result in warpage.

Record surfaces can be cleaned by lightly wiping them with a chemically treated cloth. These cloths attract the dirt that is attached to the record surface through static electricity. In an emergency, it is possible to use a slightly moistened, soft, lintless cloth.

[3] Wyman, Raymond, *op. cit.*, p. 89.

Hold edges

Keep dust and heat away

Figure 6.5   Careful handling and storage will maintain the quality and extend the life of the record. Sidney C. Eboch, *Operating Audiovisual Equipment***, Chandler Publishing Co.**

BASIC DESIGN OF THE RECORD PLAYER

The record player or phonograph has two basic systems: the sound system, which consists of the pickup (tone arm), the amplifier, and the speaker; and the motion system, which involves the motor and the turntable. Record players may vary in design, depending on the manufacturer, but the basic controls are similar (Figure 6.6 and 6.7).

Electrical power is fed into the motor and amplifier by means of a switch. Sometimes a single switch controls both; in some cases the switch is combined with other controls. The speed or turntable control may also regulate the power to the motor. Sometimes the amplifier switch is made a part of the volume control.

The volume-control knob determines the amount and the intensity of the sound that is being reproduced.

Most record players have a tone control that allows for the adjustment of the bass and treble frequencies that are being reproduced. This may be a single knob control with treble and bass at opposite ends of the scale or separate knob controls may be designed for individual adjustment of the bass and treble characteristics.

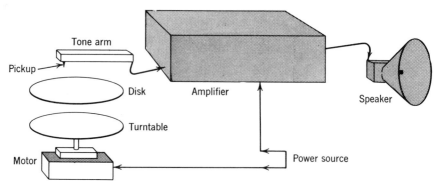

Figure 6.6   The appearance of record players may vary, but the basic designs are similar. Sidney C. Eboch, *Operating Audiovisual Equipment*, **Chandler Publishing Co.**

The speed of the turntable is determined by a selector switch or lever located near the outer rim of the turntable. Most units are geared to operate at four speeds: 78, 45, 33⅓, and 16 rpm. Most units have a neutral point at which the selector switch should be set when the turntable is not in operation. This disengages the drive mechanism from any contact with the turntable. It also reduces the uneven wear on the drive mechanism that could cause erratic rotation of the turntables.

An added speed control is available on some models. The variable-speed control permits finer adjustment of tempos and rhythms within the specific speed categories (Figure 6.8). For cases in which the quality of the reproduced sound is dependent on the precise adjustment of the turntable speed, a stroboscopic device can be attached. This determines the true speed of the turntable. An inexpensive cardboard disk placed on the turntable serves the same function (Figure 6.9). This device, known as a "strobe," has a series of concentric circles of dots. Each circle or band represents a different speed. When the turntable is operating at a particular speed, the dots in the band measuring that speed should appear to be motionless.

The pickup or needle is located at the end of the tone arm—the bar that swings out over the turntable. Record players that have multiple speed selections also have provision for two needles. One is used for the standard 78 and the other for microgroove records. The needle is positioned by turning a lever at the end of the tone arm. Markings on the lever indicate which needle is set. Sometimes, coding is used, such as color—red for microgroove and white for standard; symbols—large arrow for standard and small arrow for microgroove; or abbreviations—M (microgroove), F (fine), LP (long-playing records); or 33⅓ rpm, N (normal), S (standard), and 78 (for the turntable speed).

A uniform needle pressure of about ¼ ounce is necessary for the needle

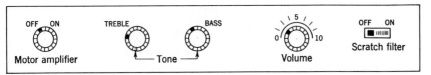

Figure 6.7   Typical controls for the record player. Sidney C. Eboch. *Operating Audiovisual Equipment.* **Chandler Publishing Co.**

to track properly without jumping or damaging the grooves (Figure 6.10). This pressure can be adjusted by setting a tension spring underneath the tone arm, near the supporting post.

STEREOPHONIC RECORDINGS AND PLAYBACK EQUIPMENT

There are few applications for the use of stereophonic sound in the classroom that would justify the purchase of such playback equipment. Its principal advantage lies in the broader dimension that it gives to the playing of music, especially of the concert-hall variety. The introduction of special effects through stereophonic sound may also play a part in some classroom presentations.

"Murgatroyd! Quit using that record player as a merry-go-round!"

Figure 6.8   *Courtesy of Graflex, Inc.*

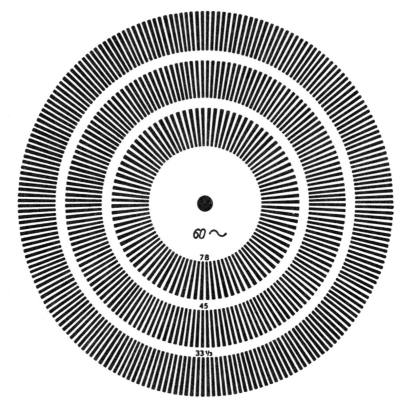

Figure 6.9 A cardboard disk, or "strobe," can be used to detect any variations from a set turntable speed.

Stereophonic record players utilize a single motion system, or motor and turntable, but a dual sound system (Figure 6.11). The dual sound patterns are created by cutting a separate pattern on either wall of the groove in the record. A single needle picks up the signals from both tracks and feeds them into the cartridge, which separates the signals. The signals are then fed into separate amplifiers and then into separate speakers. By separating the speakers, the effect of dimension and depth in sound is heightened.

WORKING WITH THE RECORD PLAYER

There are few teachers or prospective teachers who have not had some experience in the operation of a record player. Yet it will help to observe some basic rules concerning the use of the equipment.

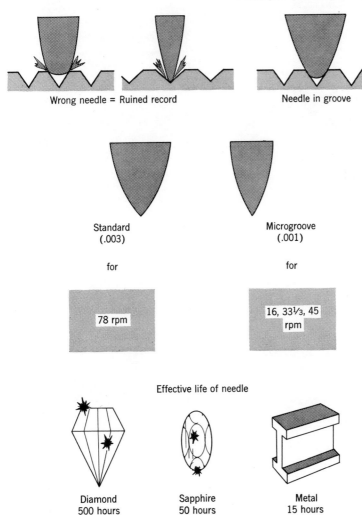

Wrong needle = Ruined record

Needle in groove

Standard
(.003)

Microgroove
(.001)

for

for

78 rpm

16, 33⅓, 45
rpm

Effective life of needle

Diamond
500 hours

Sapphire
50 hours

Metal
15 hours

Figure 6.10   Correct selection of the needle will ensure quality reproduction of sound with a minimum of wear of the record. Sidney C. Eboch, *Operating Audiovisual Equipment,* **Chandler Publishing Co.**

1. Place the record player on the surface that is flat and stable. Any variations may cause distortion in the sound or cause the needle to jump over grooves.
2. Select the correct speed to conform with the recorded speed of the phonograph disk. Overlooking this detail may result in some humor, but it will certainly contribute nothing to the learning situation.
3. Be sure the correct needle is flipped into position in the tone

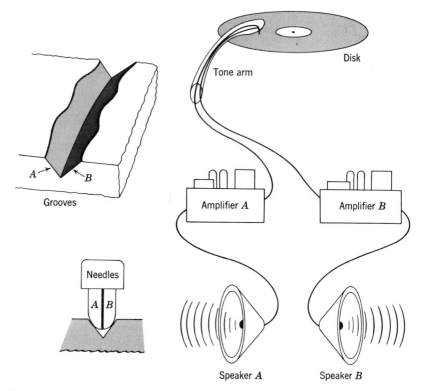

Figure 6.11   In stereophonic recording the two tracks of sound are on a single record, but the sound is fed into a dual amplifying system. Sidney C. Eboch, *Operating Audiovisual Equipment,* **Chandler Publishing Co.**

arm. A microgroove needle on a 78 record will produce a thin, raspy sound. A 78 needle will generally ruin a microgroove record with one playing.

4. Place the pickup arm gently on the record. This will lesson the chance of damage to the record and to the needle. Some of the more expensive turntables have safety devices that will absorb the shock of the needle being accidentally dropped on the record.

5. Safeguard the grooves in the record. Do not press down on the tone arm while it is on a record; do not drag the tone arm and the needle across the grooves of a record.

6. Fasten securely any screws or clasps that may be attached to the tone arm. Failure to do this may result in distortion of the sound.

7. Fasten the tone arm securely to the arm rest when the record player is being packed up. This will prevent damage to the needle when the machine is being transported.

BASIC FEATURES OF SELECTED RECORD PLAYERS

There are many models of record players produced among the hundreds of thousands currently in service in our school systems. To list and describe all of them would serve little purpose. The models briefly considered below are typical of those in normal use in the elementary and secondary classrooms, as well as in college classrooms.

Audiotronics.   The Audiotronics Corporation produces several models, two of which are described here (Figure 6.12). The Model 300-E (Figure 6.12 *a*) is a low-priced unit that contains all the basic features of a record player in a single compact case. Its amplifier delivers 10 watts through a 10-in. dual oval cone speaker. This delivers adequate sound for a normal-size classroom. A standard phono jack is provided for single or multiple headset use. The speaker is automatically silenced when the jack is used.

The phono motor is geared to the four speeds. A "pop-up" 45-rpm adapter that will not interfere with other records is a feature of the turntable. A plastic post pilot lamp is visible from any part of the room when the set is turned on. The post also prevents the pickup arm from being placed on the wrong side of the record.

The ON–OFF switch, which controls both the amplifier and the motor, is connected to the tone-control knob. A second knob controls the volume. The instruction panel is conveniently mounted on the motorboard. The weight of the unit is 13 pounds.

Another model combines added power and added features with a corresponding increase in wieght—23lb. The machine produces 20 watts of sound. The sound is directed through a 12-in. speaker located in the cover of the case. This speaker can be positioned away from the record player to improve audibility.

The four-speed turntable has a separate ON-OFF switch. The drive mechanism retracts to a neutral position automatically when the power is turned off. It plays all records from 7 to $17\frac{1}{4}$ in.

Input jacks have been provided for a microphone and tape recorder and radio, with separate controls for each. A built-in illuminated strobe and variable speed control knob allows for precise adjustment of the recorded speed

Califone.   The Rheem Califone Corporation offers a wide range of models. The Califone Model 1440 is a self-contained player (Figure 6.13). The turntable has a direct center drive, and measures 10 in. in diameter.

The tone arm can be securely anchored when not in use. A floating deck minimizes the effect of any movement or jar while the unit is in operation. The amplifier produces an output of 7 watts; it is equipped with an 8-in. oval speaker; and uses an extended-range ceramic cartridge with a needle that is easily changed.

(a)

(b)

Figure 6.12 **Audiotronics record players.** *Courtesy of the Audiotronics Corp.*

176

(a)

Speed changer

Safety stop

Tone–arm rest

Tone

Power   Volume

(b)

Figure 6.13 Rheem Califone record player. *Courtesy of Rheem Califone Corp.*

An output jack is provided for an external speaker, amplifier, or headphones. The total weight is 17 lb.

The pickup arm is automatically secured when it is at rest. It can be locked into place when the unit is being transported. Push-button controls allow the needle to be lifted or lowered with a touch of the needle pressure button. Construction tends to minimize the effects of floor vibrations or warped records.

The Rheem Californe AV Series 1815 contains several added features. A pause control allows the teacher to stop the record at any point, and then instantly resume the playback without difficulty. A variable speed for rhythm control with stroboscope is built into the unit.

The speaker is a 12-in. dual cone unit in a detachable cover. It can be moved away from the turntable for optimum listening. Input jacks are provided for microphones and other sources of sound so that this record player can also serve as a public address system. Its amplifier is rated at 12 watts, which provides adequate power for a large classroom or small auditorium.

Newcomb.   The Newcomb Audio Products Company is a major producer of record players (Figure 6.14). The Newcomb Model R-124 can be operated at the four standard speeds. Contained in the unit is a 9-in. oval dual cone speaker which is powered by a 10-W amplifier.

It utilizes a plug-in ceramic cartridge with dual sapphire needles. Spring-suspension feet help to absorb any vibrations that might otherwise cause the needle to jump the grooves. A separate output jack is provided for an external speaker, headphones, or headphone-listening center. A jeweled pilot light indicates when the amplifier and motor are in operation. The total weight is 20 lb.

The Newcomb Model R-164V is a medium-power, portable combination transcription player/public address system that will play any size record up to $17\frac{1}{4}$ in. in diameter. The R-164V has a 12-in. round dual-cone, high-fidelity loudspeaker with a 25-ft. cord. The speaker enclosure forms the lid of the case. It has a jeweled pilot light and lighted operating panel; it utilizes a plug-in ceramic "power point" cartridge with dual sapphire needles.

The unit has a microphone input jack with separate control for adjusting the volume of the microphone. A separate volume control is used for the phono sound; it has individual bass and treble control knobs. The output jack can be connected to the speaker, to headphones, or to a headphone-listening system.

The R-164V has a long tone arm of cast metal, a protective drop pad, a hideway power cord, four-speed settings, a tempo control which varies speed as much as 20%, a pickup stop post, a pickup lock screw, and a separate motor power switch that automatically retracts the idler. Total weight is 25 lb.

SELECTED REFERENCES

Marvin, James S. Kinder, and Jim R. Schunert. *Better Teaching in Secondary* ools (rev. ed.). New York: Holt, Rinehart Winston, 1964. Chapter 9.

n, Rhea, and Iris Comfort. *How to Teach Better Listening.* Washington D.C.: NEA,

List of Phonograph Records, Brooklyn, N.Y.: Record Division, Children's ding Service (annual).

Cardalog," edited by Max U. Bildersee, Albany, N.Y.

of Audiovisual Materials. Chicago: Educational Screen and Audiovisual Guide.

G. Robert. "How Useful Are Lessons on Listening?" *Elementary School Journal,* 146–151 (December, 1961).

A. J. Foy, and Irene F. Cypher, *Audio-Visual Education.* New York: Crowell, . Chapters 12 and 13.

n, Raymond L. *Audiovisual Machines,* Lubbock, Texas: Texas Tech Press, 1964. pter 9.

Sidney C. *Operating Audiovisual Equipment.* San Francisco: Chandler, 1960. Chapter

sic: A Selection of Folk Songs, Ballads, Dances, Instrumental Pieces, and Folk Tales he *United States and Latin America: Catalog of Phonograph Records.* U.S. Library Congress, Music Division, Recording Laboratory, Reference Department (revised m time to time).

James S. *Audio-Visual Materials and Techniques* (2nd ed.). New York: American k, 1959, Chapters 10 and 11.

Charles F. "Person to Person Teaching," *Saturday Review,* **47** 50–51 and 60 (July 1964.

Record Catalog. New York: Harrison Catalogs (revised annually).

Sue E. "The Effect of Training in Listening on Specific Purposes," *Journal of cational Research* **54** 276–277 (March, 1961).

Raymond. *Audiovisual Devices and Techniques.* Amherst: University of Massachu- s, 1960. Chapter 5.

(a)

(b)

Figure 6.14 Newcomb record players: (*a*) **Model R-124;** (*b*) **Model R-164V.** *Courtesy of Newcomb Audio Products Co.*

RCA.   The Radio Corporation of America produces a record player
called The Scholastic Portable (Figure 6.15). The record player is simply
designed, compact and self-contained, lightweight (12 lb), and easy to
operate. It has a lift-off lid, a permanently fastened, pop-up 45 spindle,
and a four-speed selector with neutral position to disengage the idler
mechanism. The power output is 3 watts, and the machine has a $5\frac{1}{4}$-in.
speaker in cushioned baffle. The unit is equipped with a locking tone-arm
carrying guard; the pickup consists of a ceramic "flop-over" cartridge and
two sapphire needles.

The RCA Scholastic has individual volume and tone controls. The power
switch is connected to the volume control knob.

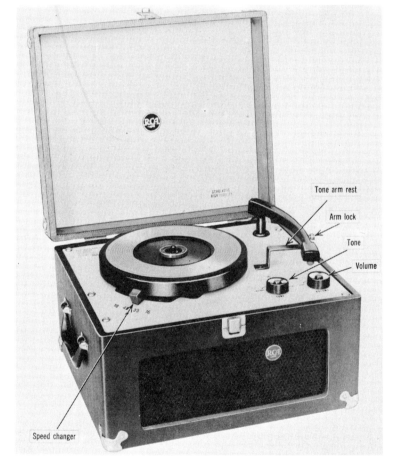

Figure 6.15   RCA record player, the Scholastic Portable. *Courtesy of the Radio Corporation
of America.*

LISTENING SYSTEMS

Record players have proven to be valuable
instruction. The record player has also been
small groups in the classroom without disrupt
might be going on. This is accomplished throu
listening systems and headphones (for example,
from the phonograph can be directed through
plugging the headphones into the speaker ou
phones are to be used, the headphones are plug
box that may have as many as eight plugs. Th
turn connected to the speaker output jack of th
The major suppliers of record players also ma
systems. The personalized audio system can be u
in situations wherein listening by one group is
activities going on in the room at the same ti
can be used with any other medium utilizing sou
sound filmstrips, radio, television, and tape reco

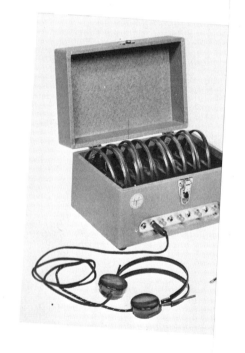

Figure 6.16   Audiotronics listening system. *Courtesy of*

7

TAPE RECORDERS

In its survey of a few years ago the United States Department of Health, Education and Welfare determined that there were 89,000 tape recorders in use in the public school classrooms and that an estimated 40,000 were about to be purchased. These figures represent a high rate of utilization for a device that did not make its appearance in the classroom until well after the end of World War II.

Briefly, the tape recorder consists of three parts: the pickup, microphone, or other sound input; the amplifier; and the reproducer or magnetic head (Figure 7.1). The recording process is relatively simple. Sounds to be recorded are directed at the microphone or fed into the tape recorder through other inputs; the mechanical vibrations are changed into electrical vibrations; these vibrations are then intensified by the amplifier, which, in turn, activates a magnet. When the tape is pulled past the magnet at a constant rate of speed, a varied sound pattern is established on the iron-oxide-coated tape. The motion system allows the tape to be rewound.

When the equipment is turned to the PLAY position (Figure 7.2), the tape that contains the mechanical vibrations passes a second magnetic head, which picks up the signals and transforms them into electrical vibrations. The vibrations are amplified and activate the loudspeaker.

RESEARCH ON EFFECTIVENESS IN THE CLASSROOM

The wide popularity of tape recorders in the classroom has prompted many studies to determine the effectiveness of this medium as an instructional aid. Gibson, in reporting on a study conducted by the National Association of Secondary School Principals, reported that tape recorders could be used with a high degree of success in teaching spelling to high-

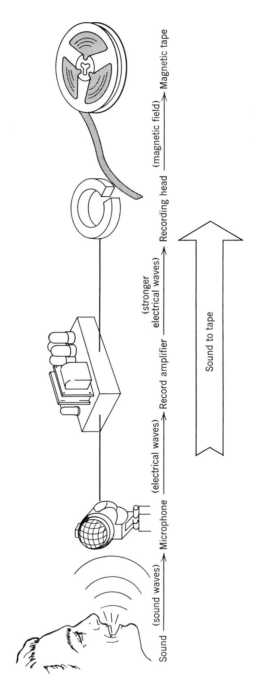

Sound (sound waves) Microphone (electrical waves) Record amplifier (stronger electrical waves) Recording head (magnetic field) Magnetic tape

Sound to tape

Figure 7.1 Tape recording requires the use of the pickup, the amplifier, and the recording head.

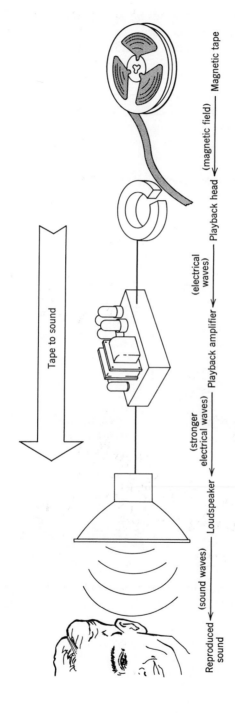

Figure 7.2 Tape playback requires the use of the playback head, the amplifier, and the loudspeaker.

ability groups.[1] Popham reported no significant difference in learning between groups taught by tape recorders as contrasted with those who were given identical "live" presentations. Most of the studies stress "the no significant difference" aspect when live presentations are contrasted with taped.[2]

The determinations of these studies have prompted increased use of recorded presentations in the classroom. Such recordings are either locally produced by the classroom teacher or can be easily obtained through such agencies as the National Tape Repository at the University of Colorado.

APPLICATIONS OF THE TAPE RECORDER

The value of the magnetic tape recorder lies in the many applications for its use other than as a substitute for a live presentation. A few of the many uses of the tape recorder are listed below:

Figure 7.3   The tape recorder can be used to record samples of individual student performance for purposes of self-evaluation.

[1] R. E. Gibson, "Final Report on the Westside High School Teaching by Tape Project," *Bulletin of the National Association of Secondary School Principals*, **44**, 52–62 (January, 1960).

[2] W. James Popham, "Tape Recorded Lectures In College Classrooms," *Audiovisual Communication Review*, **9**, 109–118 (March–April, 1961).

I. Implementing classroom instruction.

    A. Recording samples of individual student performance for purposes of self-evaluation (Figure 7.3) aimed at:

        1. Helping students overcome poor speech habits such as faulty pronunciation, poor choice of words, grammatical errors, speaking too rapidly or too slowly, "bunching" words, and poor inflections or accents.

        2. Helping students correct actual speech defects such as nasal resonance, slurring of syllables, giving incorrect vowel values, lisping, giving too much force to sibilants, and stammering.

        3. Training students to express ideas clearly, concisely, logically, and forcefully (Figure 7.4).

Figure 7.4   Use of the tape recorder in the classroom helps train students to express ideas clearly, concisely, logically, and forcefully.

4. Teaching singing and the playing of musical instruments.
5. Helping the students acquire the techniques of effective dramatization and interest-compelled narration.
6. Helping students develop conversational facility in a foreign language.

B. Making recorded examples of expert performance in such fields as public speaking, logical argumentation, dramatic expression, vocal and instrumental music, and the like, for playing back to students as examples of the respective degrees of achievement they should strive to attain in these fields (Figure 7.5).

C. Recording class-group discussions or, perhaps, entire class sessions for such uses as:

1. Evaluation by the class group itself.
2. Analysis by the instructor (either alone or in conference

Figure 7.5   Students ponder question in music theory posed by tape recorder. *Courtesy of Ford Foundation.*

with his supervisor), in order to evaluate his instructional techniques.

    3. Use by supervisors to illustrate especially effective instructional techniques for the benefit of beginning teachers.

    4. Analysis by faculty committees or by curriculum study groups to discover whether or not desired objectives are being accomplished with an optimum expenditure of time and effort.

    5. Playback to bring absentees up-to-date on the work of the class.

    6. Playback to class group or to individual students for purpose of review.

II.   Making educational program recordings for class-group listening.

    A. Recording interviews by students or by faculty members with local civic leaders, visiting specialists, "celebrities," for subsequent playback to class groups.

    B. Making off-the-air recordings of educationally useful radio broadcasts for subsequent listening (when most convenient, and as often as needed) by class groups, to meet such instructional needs as:

    1. Giving students access to new, up-to-the-minute content materials not readily available from conventional sources.

    2. Giving students access to otherwise unobtainable appreciational materials.

    3. Giving students access to a wide variety of significant and divergent viewpoints on public issues by spokesmen for recognized social and economic groups and organizations.

    4. Enabling students to hear worthwhile radio programs that would otherwise be missed because of class-schedule conflicts.

    C. Making edited rerecordings to serve specific teaching applications, such as making up a composite recorded program of the kind where the announcer or narrator (1) states or develops a central theme or point of emphasis, (2) re-records excerpts from previously recorded programs that illustrate specific points, (3) ties these together with appropriate narrative or expository continuity, and (4) concludes by summarizing the points established and suggesting the direction which continuing listener inquiry might profitably take.

    D. Making recordings of educational programs produced within the local school or school system expressly for use for class-group listening.

    E. Making rerecorded copies of educationally useful programs in the local program-recording library for use by the several schools in the school system.

III.   Recording in connection with dramatics and radio workshop activities

A. Making voice test and audition recordings for purposes of classifying students according to "character-type" potentialities.

B. Recording samples of individual student achievement for such purposes as (1) analysis of accuracy of character interpretation and portrayal, (2) development of effective microphone speaking techniques, and (3) deciding on the most effective microphone "perspective" and filter effects.

C. Recording short and simple student dramatizations of favorite scenes from literature or drama aimed at developing appreciations.

D. Recording natural sounds and simulated effects, "echo" or "filtered-microphone" effects, musical interludes and bridges, and interview continuities for use in connection with radio workshop dramatizations.

E. Recording short drama sequences for checking effectiveness of recorded effects and for determining their proper timing.

F. Recording the finished production of the student-produced play for use, in transcription form, over a local broadcast station, or for other school program production workshops.

IV.   Recording services to school administration and management.

A. Secretarial and stenographic applications, such as:
    1. Dictation recording and transcribing.
    2. Conference recording and transcribing.
    3. Telephone conversation "confirmation" recording and transcribing.
    4. Recording and transcribing office interviews and meetings.

B. Making recordings of programs and announcements distributed over the school's central sound system for purposes of record, or for analyzing sound-system use.

C. Recording oral make-up work of the pupil so that the teacher can play it back at his convenience.

D. Producing sound commentary by pupils or teachers for filmstrips, slides, motion pictures.[3]

The listing of ideas for possible uses of the tape recorder in the classroom seems to be an endless proposition as more teachers "discover" this tool.

[3] *Suggestions for Organizing and Administering A Tape Recording Library*, Chicago; Jack C. Coffey Co., Inc; pp. 7–11; and *The Tape Recorder In The Elementary Classroom*, St. Paul, Minn.: Minnesota Mining and Manufacturing Co., 1955.

THE TAPE RECORDER'S MECHANICAL SYSTEM

The tape recorder is normally composed of a tape deck or transport, the necessary electronic circuitry for amplification, and a speaker or speakers (Figure 7.6). All tape recording or reproducing begins with the tape moving past the tapehead (recording head) (Figure 7.7). The tape, a thin ribbon of plastic coated with tiny flecks of iron oxide, passes the recording head, (Figure 7.8) which is emitting magnetic waves conforming to the sound vibrations that are being fed into the tape recorder. The tape is then magnetized in patterns that correspond precisely to the original sound. This magnetic pattern recorded on the tape is permanent until it is magnetically erased or reinscribed. When the recorded tape is played back the process is simply reversed. The magnetic patterns on the tape induce an electric current as it passes the pickup head. The electrical vibrations are amplified, fed through the loudspeakers, and are heard as sound waves.

A drive motor supplies the power to the two spindles on which the tape reels are placed. The motor, the amplifier, and the speakers are usually contained in a single case when tape recorders are designed for classroom use.

The importance of the motor in the tape recorder is reflected by the many controls that are associated with it (Figure 7.9). The motor switch turns power into the motor. It may be a separate switch or it can be con-

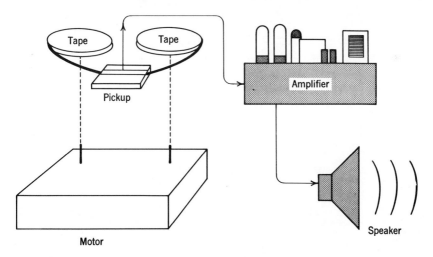

Figure 7.6 The basic components of a tape recorder consist of the transport mechanism, electronics circuitry, and the loud-speakers. Sidney C. Eboch, *Operating Audiovisual Equipment*, **Chandler Press. Publishing Co.**

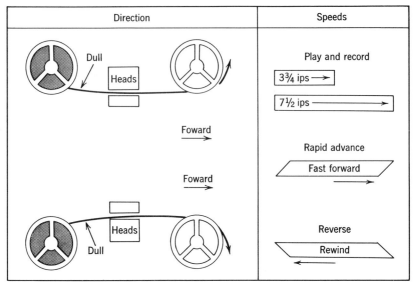

Figure 7.7 The dull side of the recording tape always faces the recording heads. The several tape speeds built into a recorder are designed to meet specific needs of the operator. Sidney C. Eboch, *op. cit.*, p. 60.

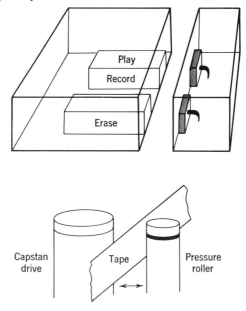

Figure 7.8 The tape is drawn past the play–record head through the action of the pressure roller against the capstan drive. Sidney C. Eboch, *Operating Audiovisual Equipment*, **Chandler Publishing Co.**

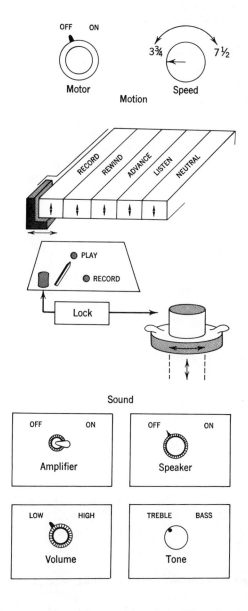

Figure 7.9 Not all of these controls would be located on any one recorder, but they serve to illustrate the variations that are possible. Raymond L. Davidson. *Audiovisual Machines,* Texas Technological Press.

nected with the speed selector, the amplifier switch, or the volume or tone control knobs. When it is connected with another control, the initial movement of the control turns on the motor; further movement activates the second control.

It is possible to have the motor on without any movement being imparted to the tape by using a neutral control. This disengages the drive mechanism; on many units this is accomplished by means of the STOP button. A FAST FORWARD control allows the tape to be moved rapidly without any recording or playback of sound. A REWIND control permits the rapid return of recorded tape to the unwind reel for playback purposes.

The speed selector controls the rate of movement of the tape during recording or playback. The speed is measured in inches per second (ips); standard speeds are $7\frac{1}{2}$ and $3\frac{3}{4}$ ips. Slower speeds are available and provide economy in the use of tape. Faster speeds, however, result in higher fidelity in the recording. With most tape recorders, speeds should not be changed while the tape is in motion.

The RECORD control advances the tape, at the selected speed, past the recording head where the tape is magnetized with the sound fed into the unit. A record safety lock device must also be operated at the same time as the RECORD control. This prevents the accidental recording of sound. In most recorders a demagnetizer or erase head is activated and removes all previously recorded signals as the tape moves toward the record head. The safety lock device performs a valuable function in preventing the accidental erasure of recorded tapes.

The PLAY control moves the tape forward at the selected speed. It is this control that permits the operator to listen to what was previously recorded on the tape. The playback speed should always be set at the speed of recording.

The sound controls are similar to those on other types of audiovisual equipment. The amplifier switch controls the power to the amplifier. It may be separate, or it may be connected with other controls. The VOLUME control regulates the intensity of sound during recording and also during playback. The TONE control permits the adjustment of pitch in the sound that is played back. A speaker switch, also called a monitor switch, enables a person to hear the sound that is being recorded. Its use requires careful positioning of the microphone to minimize the condition called "feedback."

A most important control is the recording-level monitor. This removes the guesswork out of whether the recorded signal is too strong or too weak. If too strong, the recorded sound will be distorted and rasping to the ears; if too weak, the recorded sound may be too faint to be heard by all in the classroom.

Monitors (Figure 7.10) are of three general types: magic eye, neon bulb, and meter. The magic eye utilizes a fan-shaped light to indicate recording level; if the sides of the fan do not move, the signal is too weak; if the sides of the fan overlap, the signal is too strong. The neon bulb has a a filament structure that reacts to the strength of the signal.

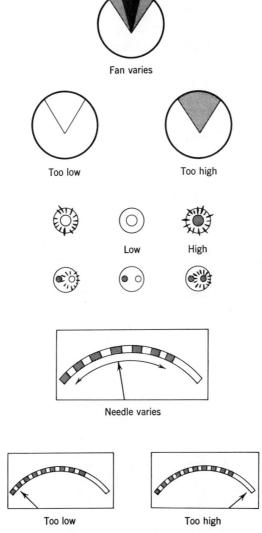

Figure 7.10 **Monitors or record-level controls take the guesswork out of recording. They indicate whether the signal-recorded is too weak or too strong. Sidney C. Eboch,** *Operating Audiovisual Equipment,* **Chandler Publishing Co.**

A steady illumination indicates heavy signal strength; no illumination indicates a weak signal. An intermittent flashing signal is desirable with this control.

The meter has a moving needle that fluctuates with the strength of the signal. The desirable position for the needle is usually marked on the face of the meter.

The need for locating a certain point in a reel of tape is resolved by use of a simple counter (Figure 7.11). In most tape recorders the meter has a range of from 0 to 999 and is activated at any time that the tape is moved in the recorder. It should be set at 0 for the start of any tape.

SOUND INPUTS FOR THE TAPE RECORDER

Sound is introduced into the tape recorder in two basic ways: by microphone and through the use of wire connectors with other audio playback equipment.

Most classroom recorders are equipped with crystal or ceramic microphones. Although adequate for recording speech, these microphones are limited in range and fidelity and therefore are not suited for recording music. For higher-quality recordings the dynamic microphone is recommended. It is rugged and its frequency response range is wide and uniform.

Microphones vary also in size, shape, and pickup direction. Microphones designed to pick up sound from one direction only are ideal for those situations where extraneous sounds might interfere with the quality of a recording, and are well-suited for recording the voice of one person. A bidirectional microphone picks up sound in an arc from either side of the microphone. It is preferable for picking up the voices of two or more speakers who may be facing each other with the microphone between them. An omnidirectional microphone is capable of picking up sound in a complete circle around the microphone. It is best-suited for use with a large group or for random pickup of voices in the classroom. Most recorders are equipped with omnidirectional microphones.

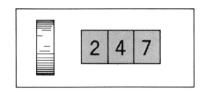

Figure 7.11   The counter allows the contents of a tape to be indexed for ease of playback
Sidney C. Eboch, *Operating Audiovisual Equipment*, Chandler Publishing Co.

One interesting characteristic of microphones is the lack of selectivity in the pickup of sounds. The jangling of bracelets, the tapping of a pencil, the scraping of a chair—all these sounds are recorded when a microphone is used. The human ear tends to disregard or ignore these other sounds, but the microphone does not.

Effective use of the microphone requires careful placement of the microphone (Figure 7.12) and care in the adjustment of the volume. A microphone stand is a must. It provides more variety in placement and eliminates the possibility of picking up vibrations and other extraneous noises from tables and sounding boards. One should avoid holding the microphone in the hand, and should keep it at least 3 ft. away from walls to avoid reverberating noises and echoes. One should also avoid placing the microphone on the same table with the recorder or on a piano or radio. Once the recording has started, the microphone should not be touched, for the slightest disturbance will cause noise on the tape. The microphone should be kept away from "hum" fields such as amplifiers, fluorescent lamps, and transformers. The microphone should not be placed in line with any "live" external speaker. This will produce an extremely loud shriek known as feedback.

For the normal speaking voice, the microphone should be placed between 12 and 24 in. away from the speaker and should point directly at him. Children should stand close to the microphone, and those with louder voices should be farther back.

If a speaker has excessive sibilance or over-accentuates letters such as "p" or "t", the microphone should be turned at an angle so that

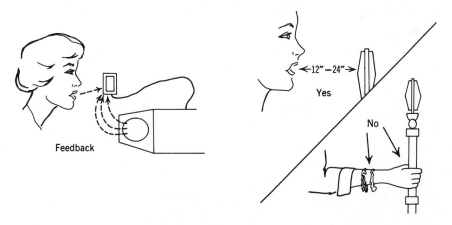

Figure 7.12   Placement of the microphone is important in order to insure that only the desired sounds are being picked up by the microphone and to minimize the conditions leading to feedback. Sidney C. Eboch, *Operating Audiovisual Equipment*, Chandler Publishing Co.

the speaker is talking across the front. The same technique prevents distortion during shouted passages in a dramatic reading, or any other extremely loud sound.

The microphone should be level with the person's mouth. The degree of loudness with which the speaker talks depends upon the effect desired, because voice characteristics change with effort. Too low a voice volume should be avoided because the low frequencies may blur; too high a voice volume should be avoided because it will cause distortion.

Off-the-air recording by means of the microphone can be supplemented by another technique—direct input into the tape recorder (by means of a wire connector) of sound from the radio, record player (Figure 7.13), television set, or another tape recorder. The closed circuit between the originating sound and the recorder eliminates the accidental pickup of

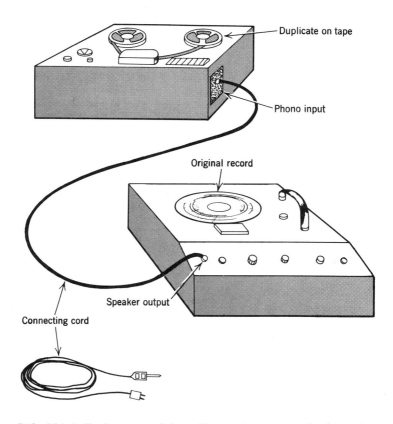

Figure 7.13   Disk duplication on tape. It is possible to make a tape recording from a phonograph record or disk. John E. Morlan. *Preparation of Inexpensive Teaching Materials,* Chandler Publishing Co.

any room noises. It is possible to carry on normal activities in the same room where such a recording is being made. The wire and connectors are inexpensive. If not supplied with the tape recorder, they can be purchased from a local audiovisual dealer and used with little instruction. Most audio equipment now has output jacks for plugging in tape recorders. Such devices allow for the simultaneous recording of a live voice and "canned" music (Figure 7.14).

It is important that the volume level in the originating audio equipment be compatible with the adjustment of the volume control on the tape recorder. Unless they are carefully matched, distorted or weak sounds may be the result on the tape.

The Y-cord is one type of input connector that can be used. A telephone plug for insertion into the tape recorder jack is on one end, and two alligator clips for attachment to loudspeaker leads are on the other end.

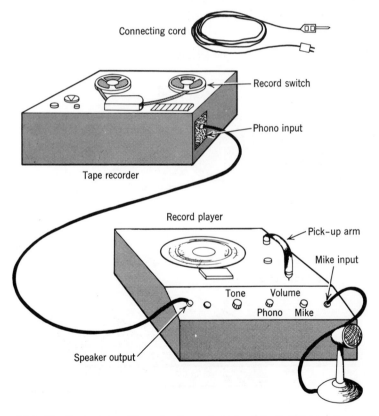

Figure 7.14 **Simultaneous recording of voice and music. John E. Morlan,** *Preparation of Inexpensive Teaching Materials*, **Chandler Publishing Co.**

This cord can be used for picking up sound directly from the loudspeaker—in which the case the plug is inserted into the output jack of the recorder. The same wire can be used as a connector to an auxiliary speaker during playback. The telephone plug in that case would be set into the output plug of the tape recorder.

A wire with telephone plugs on either end is used to connect two tape recorders. One plug is placed in the speaker output jack of the tape recorder originating the sound; the other plug is placed in the record jack of the sound recorder (Figure 7.15). The sound as it is being recorded can be listened to by turning on the speaker or monitor switch of the second tape recorder.

ACCESSORY CONTROLS AND DEVICES

As the popularity of the tape recorder has increased so also have the various accessory items that increase the flexibility of the medium; for example, a remote-control switch now allows the user to stop the tape

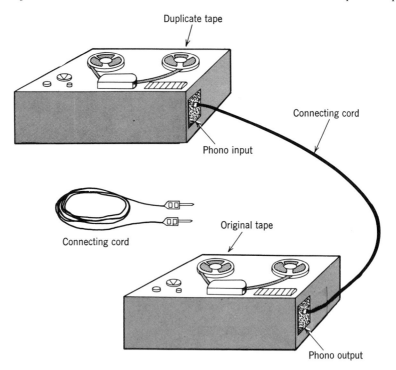

Figure 7.15   It is possible to make a tape recording from another tape. John E. Morlan, *Preparation of Inexpensive Teaching Materials*, **Chandler Publishing Co.**

recorder during the record or playback setting without affecting the setting of any of the controls. The control may be either a foot switch or a hand-held push-button control.

Synchronizing devices for matching taped sound with the automatic changing of slides or advancing of filmstrips is an area that is receiving much attention. Several of these devices and attachments have been described in earlier chapters.

Tape recording is being developed for many specialized uses both in and out of the classroom, and these uses are having an effect on the design of the units. There are now tape recorders that are completely transistorized and battery-operated, which means that they are miniaturized and can be set up anywhere for recording purposes. There are units mounted in tables with wheels in which the sound is directed through earphones instead of through loudspeakers. Such a mobile instructional center can be used by small groups of youngsters in a corner of a classroom while activities involving other youngsters are going on in the room.

Tape recorders are being built into individual learning centers for individualized study. More attention will be given to this and other tape applications in the section dealing with the language laboratory. Our attention in the next few pages will be directed toward the use and operation of regular classroom-type tape recorders.

GENERAL INSTRUCTIONS FOR OPERATING TAPE RECORDERS

Despite the number of controls and attachments for the tape recorder, the unit itself is relatively easy to set up and operate. Instructions for specific models are clearly printed inside the cover or on the tape deck itself. The instructions given below are those that can be applied to the use of any tape recorder (see Figure 7.16). Additional information will be given in the description of typical models of tape recorders.

Set up
   1. Set the tape recorder in a horizontal manner on a flat, sturdy surface. Few classroom recorders will operate well in a vertical position.
   2. Unwind the power cord; plug one end into the recorder (if unattached) and the other into an electrical outlet.
   3. Familiarize yourself with location of various controls for STOP, PAST FORWARD, REWIND, PLAY, and RECORD. Remember that the recording control safety lock must be activated at the same time as the RECORD switch.

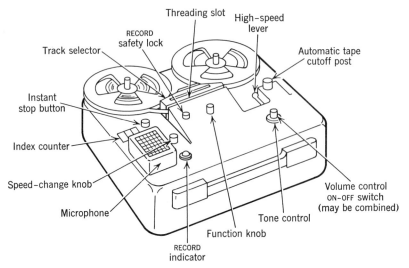

Track selector

RECORD safety lock

Threading slot

High-speed lever

Automatic tape cutoff post

Instant stop button

Index counter

Speed-change knob

Microphone

RECORD indicator

Function knob

Tone control

Volume control ON-OFF switch (may be combined)

Figure 7.16 Drawing of a typical tape recorder indicating the number of controls and their relative positions.

4. Note the locations of the various input and output jacks: external amplifier jack, external speaker jack, inputs for the microphone, for phono or for tape recorders. Observe the type of recording level indicator, the counter, and the threading path for the tape. Turn the monitor to OFF and plug in the microphone.

5. Try out various controls to be sure they are functioning. Turn on PLAY switch and note if take-up spindle is turning. If not, there may be a cut-off switch in the threading path that is activated when no tape is passing through the recorder.

6. Turn the RECORD controls on; speak into the microphone; vary the volume level, and note the effect on the record level indicator.

7. Turn off the recorder before starting the threading operation.

Thread

1. Position an empty reel on the take-up spindle and a full reel of tape on the other spindle. The tape should be wound on the full reel with the dull side (iron-oxide coating) toward the inside.

2. Place the tape in the recording slot and around any guides that may be in the threading path. Attach the end of the tape to the hub of the take-up reel and rotate the reel several turns. Both reels should turn in a counter-clock-wise direction.

Operate

1. If recording, turn on RECORD switch at the same time as releasing the RECORD SAFETY LOCK device. Turn the tone control to TREBLE.

Watch the record level indicator while speaking into the microphone and while bringing up the volume level. Better recordings are made by speaking in a strong voice and turning down the volume control. Any previously recorded material on the tape will be erased when the recorder is set on RECORD.

2. If playing, turn the volume down; turn on the PLAY control; bring the volume up to a desirable level; adjust the tone control to produce the most pleasing sound.

Pack up

1. Return all the tape to the original supply reel by switching the REWIND control. Do not leave any loose ends of tape in the winding; make sure that all breaks are repaired by splicing.
2. Remove both the supply and the take-up reels from the spindles.
3. Unplug the microphone and put it away in its proper place.
4. Unplug the power cord, wind it and place it in the case.

THE RECORDING TAPE

The recording tape is $\frac{1}{4}$ in. in width and is made of various plastic materials. One side is coated with a magnetic iron-oxide, which gives it a dull appearance. Most recorders on the market are twin- or dual-track machines. This means that only one-half the width of the tape is receiving the recording or is being played back. After a length of tape is run through the recorder, the reels can be swapped and the tape run through the machine again for additional recording or playback. In a 1200-ft. reel of tape there is space for 2400 ft. of recording when the tape is used with a dual-track recorder (Figure 7.17).

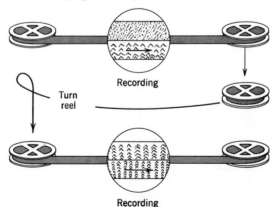

Figure 7.17   Dual-track tape recorders record sound on one-half the width of the tape. The reel can then be turned over and a recording made on the second half width. Sidney C. Eboch, *Operating Audiovisual Equipment,* Chandler Publishing Co.

Cellulose-acetate plastic bases are available in tapes of 1.0 and 1.5 mil thicknesses (thousandths of an inch). A standard 7-in. reel of tape (1.5 mil) provides 32 minutes of dual track recording time (one way) at $7\frac{1}{2}$ ips. The 1.0-mil plastic base tape is both economical and practical for recordings where high strength is not required, and it provides one-and-one-half times the recording time of 1.5-mil tape. A new tape produced by DuPont, called Mylar, has unusual strength and may result in even thinner bases—with corresponding economies.

The lengths of tapes that are commercially available vary. For classroom use the reels most commonly used are 3, 5, or 7 in. in diameter. These lengths provide the flexibility that may be needed in home and classroom recording.

Recording and playing times of tapes are dependent on four factors: (a) reel size, (b) thickness of the tape, (c) recording speed, and (d) the number of tracks used in recording. Mention was made that most classroom tape recorders are dual-track machines. Newly developed stereophonic sound tape recorders will utilize the entire width, with each channel being recorded on half the width of the tape. With improvements in recording heads, there are now four-track recorders being produced. This, of course, increases the flexibility of the tape recorder for conventional recording, stereophonic recording, and special-effects recording. Our concern here, however, is primarily with dual-track recorders.

Figure 7.18 indicates the relationships between the various factors affecting the playing time of the tape. In making the choice of recording speed, one should keep in mind that the slower speed provides economy in the utilization of tape but that the faster speed provides improved sound quality.

With proper care tapes can be used indefinitely. Tests conducted with tapes played thousands of times indicated little impairment to the quality of recording or playback. Tapes can be damaged by exposing them to high temperatures or to magnetic fields such as those in electric motors or in loudspeakers.

Tape Length (Feet)	Single Track		Dual Track	
	$3\frac{3}{4}$ ips	$7\frac{1}{2}$ ips	$3\frac{3}{4}$ ips	$7\frac{1}{2}$ ips
150	$7\frac{1}{2}$ minutes	$3\frac{3}{4}$ minutes	15 minutes	$7\frac{1}{2}$ minutes
300	15 minutes	$7\frac{1}{2}$ minutes	30 minutes	15 minutes
600	39 minutes	15 minutes	60 minutes	30 minutes
1200	60 minutes	30 minutes	120 minutes	60 minutes

Figure 7.18 The approximate playing time in minutes for various lengths of tape at various speeds.

A good tape rarely breaks, and when it does the break is usually a clean one that can be mended without any special cutting. Simply align the torn edges precisely against each other and cover them firmly with splicing tape. A break of this type can be easily mended on the tape recorder without removing tape reels from their spindles. Lay the tape ends flat on the surface of the recorder in order to press the splicing tape firmly in place, and carefully trim the excess splicing tape from both edges.

In free-hand splicing for editing or other purposes a pair of sharp scissors or a new razor blade can be used (Figure 7.19). The procedure is as follows:

1. Place the ends of the tape together, overlapping slightly, with the glossy side facing up.

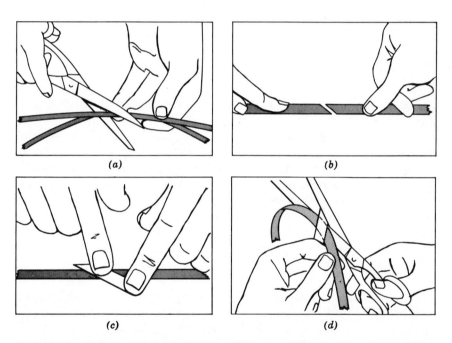

(a)   (b)

(c)   (d)

Figure 7.19 Editing may be accomplished by finding the portions to be corrected and then speaking the corrected version into the microphone. When large portions are to be deleted, cutting out and splicing is the best method. Scissors or knife used in splicing must not be magnetized because this might erase the recording on either side of the splice. (a) Overlap the ends to be spliced. Cut both tapes at the same time at 60° angle. Ends will line up perfectly. (This eliminates detection of splice on recording.) (b) Align both ends of tape, uncoated side up (shiny on plastic tape, grey on paper.) (c) Cover aligned ends with splicing tape, evenly and securely. (d) Trim off excess splicing tape. (Cut into the recording tape backing very slightly as illustrated by dotted lines. This eliminates possibility of a sticky splice.)

2. Cut both pieces of tape at once, using a diagonal cut, which can vary from 45° to 60°. For tighter editing a 90° cut can be made.
3. Put both ends of the tape, with the glossy side facing up, on a hard, even surface. Align both ends of the tape and apply $\frac{3}{4}$ to 1 in. of splicing tape, pressing it down firmly. Remember that splicing tape always goes on the glossy side of recording tape and never on the dull magnetic side of the tape.
4. Trim away the excess splicing tape. If a sticky edge of the splicing tape is left, it can cause binding when the tape is run through a recorder, or it may catch on another part of the tape and slow the recording speed, or cause an unwanted break.

A number of mechanical tape-splicing devices are available that give greater precision in cutting and aligning than is generally accomplished by the hand method.

DESCRIPTIONS OF SELECTED TAPE RECORDERS

The features of several typical tape recorders are described below. The models selected are those designed primarily for classroom use.

Audiotronics. The Audiotronics Corporation has produced several models of tape recorders. Its Model 100M (Figure 7.20) is a dual-track, dual-speed unit that features all of its controls, switches, and jacks on the top of the recorder, making it easy to operate. Operating instructions are also marked on the tape deck. Threading is facilitated by placing the tape in front of the recording head and pulling it back under the shield of the recording head. The tension provided by the take-up reel keeps the tape against the recording head; there are no pressure pads.

The amplifier produces 10 W of power and directs it into 6 × 9 in. dual-cone speakers; there is an auxiliary output jack for external speaker or earphones. There is also storage space in the case for reels, microphone, and the power cord. Radio and mike inputs can be used simultaneously for mixing of recordings. A monitor channel allows for listening either through earphones or through the speaker while recording. The machine can also be used as a portable public address system. The total weight is 22 lb.

Bell & Howell. Bell & Howell, Inc., has developed several models of tape recorder. One portable model is a two-speed dual-track recorder (Figure 7.21). Push-button controls simplify the settings for RECORD, PLAY, REWIND, FORWARD, and STOP. The PLAY and RECORD buttons have a safety interlock to prevent accidental erasures.

A 5 watt amplifier powers two $5\frac{1}{4}$-in. speakers. Additional speakers can be

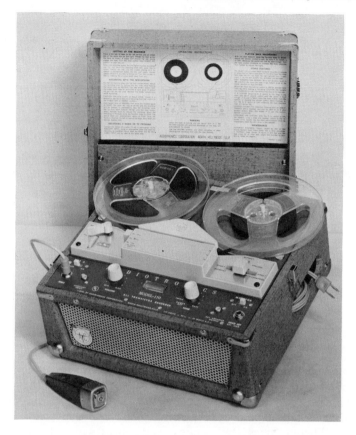

Figure 7.20   **Audiotronics tape recorder.** *Courtesy of the Audiotronics Corp.*

tied-in or earphones can be connected to the speaker output jack. A single combined control starts the recorder and varies volume for either RECORD or PLAY. A special PAUSE CONTROL permits instantaneous starting and stopping of the tape. There are two input jacks: one for the microphone, the other for the radio or phonograph. The 8-ft power cord is permanently attached. Total weight is 38 lb.

RCA.   The Radio Corporation of America offers the "Scholastic" tape recorder (Figure 7.22). This unit is a dual-track recorder that operates at three speeds: $7\frac{1}{2}$, $3\frac{3}{4}$, and $1\frac{7}{8}$ ips. It utilizes three motors to handle the transport of the tape at various control settings. Push buttons are used for START, FAST FORWARD, REWIND, and PAUSE controls. A push-button control for STOP has been provided in the triple-width model.

The threading is easily accomplished by dropping the tape into the

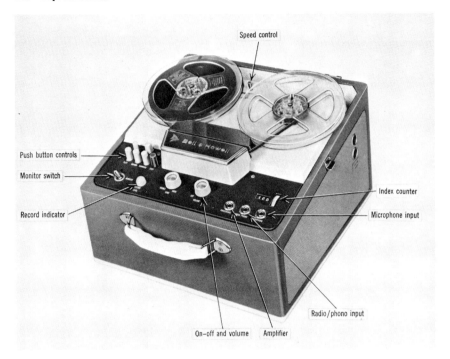

Speed control

Push button controls

Monitor switch

Record indicator

Index counter

Microphone input

Radio/phono input

On–off and volume   Amplifier

Figure 7.21   Bell & Howell portable tape recorder. *Courtesy of Bell & Howell. Inc.*

recording slot and around a safety switch. The recorder automatically shuts off if the tape breaks or runs out.

The amplifier provides 10 W of power and utilizes two speakers, a 5 × 7-in. woofer and a 3-in. tweeter. The detachable lid can be closed with the 7-in. reels in place. Total weight is 33 lb.

Revere-Wollensak. Revere-Wollensak, a division of the 3M Company, produces several models of tape recorder (Figure 7.23). Model T-1500 is a dual-track, two-speed machine. The tape is simply dropped into the recording slot and attached to the hub of the takeup reel to accomplish the threading.

Push buttons are used for the STOP, RECORD, and PLAY controls. A lever, when moved to the left, controls the REWIND and, when moved to the right, controls the FAST FORWARD. The RECORD SAFETY LOCK device is also used as a pause control. Markings on the tone control facilitate settings at various levels of pitch. The recorder can be used as a public address system. Power output from the amplifier is 10 watts; a single $5\frac{1}{4}$-in. speaker is used. Total weight is 20 pounds.

The Revere M2 tape recorder contains some distinctive features. It

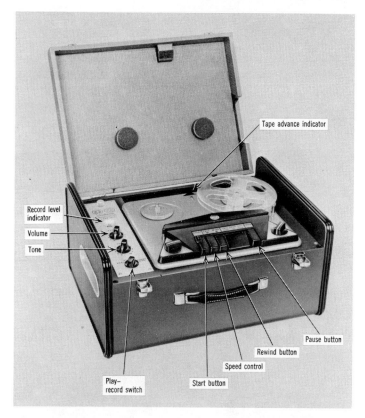

Figure 7.22   RCA Scholastic tape recorder. *Courtesy of Radio Corp of America.*

records and plays back stereo sound and it utilizes tape cartridges that are self-threading and self-rewinding.

The completely enclosed $3\frac{3}{4}$-in. square plastic cartridge contains up to 450 ft. of tape, providing up to 48 minutes of stereo or 96 minutes of monaural recording. As many as 20 tape cartridges can be loaded into the recorder at one time for playback. To operate, the PLAY key is pushed down; it takes almost 15 hours to run through an entire loading of stereo tapes.

The Revere M2 has two sound channels employing 9-watt amplifiers and 5 × 3 speakers. Jacks are provided for external speakers and earphones; double microphone and radio-phono inputs permit the stereo recording. Recording speed is $1\frac{7}{8}$ ips. Volume and tone controls as well as record-level indicators are provided for each channel. Push-buttons control the settings for PLAY, RECORD, and STOP.

Figure 7.23   3M Company tape recorders. The Revere M2 (a) records and plays back stereo sound on tape cartridge. *Courtesy of Revere-Wollensak, division of 3M Company.*

Rheem Califone. The Rheem Califone Model 3080 (Figure 7.24) is a dual-track, three-speed machine. It has a power output of 7 watts and uses a speaker measuring 8 × 4-in. Input jacks and output jacks as well as the controls are all located on the top deck of the tape recorder. The VU-METER facilitates setting the proper record level through observation of the needle position on the dial. Two controls must be activated simultaneously for RECORD, which minimizes the danger of accidental erasures of tape. The tape is easily threaded by dropping it into the recording slot and attaching the end of the tape to the hub of the take-up reel. Total weight is 23 pounds.

Norelco. The North American Philips Company, Inc., offers several tape recorders. Its "Continental" (Figure 7.25) is a three-speed, four-track stereo playback/mono record and playback machine. It uses a magic-eye, record-level indicator; it has a program indicator to designate

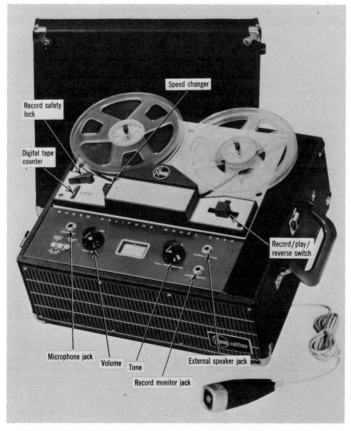

Figure 7.24 Rheem Califone classroom tape recorder. *Courtesy of Rheem California Corp.*

Figure 7.25   **Norelco Continental tape recorder**. *Courtesy of North American Philips Co.*

the track that is being utilized. Push-buttons are used for the following controls: PLAY, RECORD, FAST FORWARD, STOP, and the various tape speeds. A special feature is a "sound-on-sound" button for recording over previously recorded sound without erasing the original; it also has mixing facilities for recording any two sources of sound simultaneously.

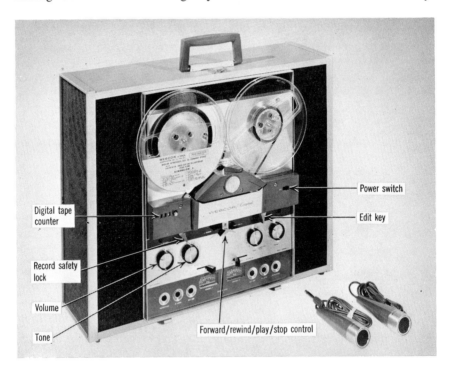

Figure 7.26   Webcor Coronet tape recorder. *Courtesy of Webcor, Inc.*

The tape is easily threaded by placing it into the recording slot and attaching the end of the tape to the hub of the take-up reel. The machine automatically stops when the end of the tape passes through. Total weight is 30 lb.

Webcor.   Webcor, Inc., is a producer of many models of classroom and professional tape recorders. The Webcor Coronet (Figure 7.26) is a stereo tape recorder. Its "Synchrotrack" feature enables a person to record one track, play it back, and, while listening, record a second track.

The unit can operate at three speeds; it has four speakers. Its "Magic Brain" automatically aligns RECORD, PLAYBACK, and ERASURE tracks. It is designed for two- and four-track stereo operation. Individual controls and VU-METERS are provided for each channel.

ELECTRONIC-LEARNING CLASSROOMS

Improvements in the quality of tapes and tape recorders during the past 10 years have led to much experimentation involving classroom use of this medium. Much of the early work was done in the instruction in modern languages; but the areas of application have widened considerably in recent years (Figure 7.27).

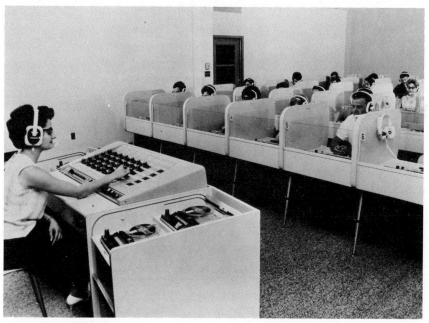

Figure 7.27   A classroom equipped with electronic equipment can provide individual instruction for each person or for several groups of persons.

The use of microphones, tape recorders, tape playback decks, head-phones, mobile carts, record players, and booths have allowed for great flexibility in the arranging of instructional groups. A classroom equipped with such electronic equipment could provide individual instruction for each person or for several groups of persons, or it could provide for the class as a whole. The arrangement of these elements into various learning centers will be explained below in greater detail.

The electronic classroom has several advantages:

1. The teacher is able to supply the student with live or recorded material on an individual basis. The student is able to respond to this information on an individual rather than on a group basis.
2. A recorded lesson can be used over and over again with identical output. When a teacher is called upon in drill situations to repeat exercises, some variation is bound to occur that will affect learning.
3. Listening is facilitated. Individual volume controls adjust the loudness for each student. Earphones block out all extraneous noises and permit the student to concentrate on the recorded lesson.
4. Students can be exposed to the knowledge and skills of many teachers—not just one, as in a regular classroom situation.
5. The work of students can be evaluated through analysis of the recorded material as well as through "paper and pencil" techniques.
6. Under certain programs, students can work individually at their own rate of learning.
7. The teacher can monitor the progress of individual students without disturbing other students.[4]

The potential flexibility of electronic circuitry does not confine the use of learning centers to individual classrooms. Learning stations can be set up in libraries, in corridors, or at the rear of regular classrooms. Inexpensive study booths, or carrels, can be set up to provide privacy and freedom from distractions. In instances in which the use of this equipment is programmed in a certain course of study, however, it is convenient to set aside classrooms and equip them as learning laboratories.

The widespread use of electronic equipment for the teaching of modern foreign languages has promoted the use of the term "language laboratory"; however, the facility can be adapted to any situation in which audio skills are necessary and drill and repetition are part of the learning task. The types of installations can be classified according to these categories: listen-respond; listen respond (audio-active); and listen-respond-record.

The "listen-respond" installation is the simplest. It consists of

[4]David M. Crossman, *The Electronic Classroom: A Guide for Planning*, Albany: State Education Department, New York, 1964, pp. 5–7.

headphones through which students are able to listen to the audio material; they then respond in a directed manner. This system can be made highly mobile and can be set up in various locations, especially when used on the elementary level.

An improvement on this system came about with the installation of a microphone and amplifier at each station, to which the headphones were connected. This enabled the student to respond in an active way and allowed him to hear not only the recorded program material but his own voice as well. This "listen-respond (audio-active)" mode is particularly well-suited to the teaching of foreign languages.

The addition of a tape recorder to a student station creates a different learning situation. The student is able to record his response to a drill exercise and listen to it in comparison to the original program material. Such an arrangement doubles the cost of each station, and there is still some doubt that this added expense is justified by any marked increase in learning.[5]

The equipment that is to be used in electronic classroom installations varies with the complexity of the setup.

The basic components (Figure 7.28) include the following:

I.   Teachers console (the main control center from which all programs are distributed and controlled)
A.   Program sources—material can be distributed through any of the following components contained in the console:
  1. Two tape playback decks; when equipped, they can also be used to record student responses.
  2. One record player.
  3. One microphone, connected so as to allow communication with all stations or individual stations.
  4. One motion picture audio source—channel sound into individual headphones while watching the movie.
  5. One spare jack—for possible use with radio, or TV.
B.   Monitor unit—permits the teacher to listen to the activity of any student without the student's awareness; also permits two-way communication with the student without disturbing the class.
C.   Additional control functions
  1. Electrically controlled student position locking system.
  2. Room light controls.
  3. Remote control circuit for operation of projection equipment.

[5] John B. Carroll, "Research on Teaching Foreign Languages", in *Handbook of Research on Teaching* (American Educational Research Association, New York: Rand McNally, 1963, pp. 1080–1082.

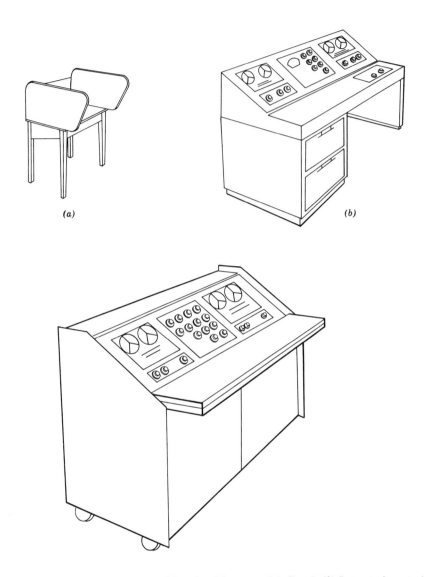

(a)   (b)

Figure 7.28   Typical components of learning laboratory. (a) Carrel. (b) Instructor's control
console. (c) Boom-type (microphone attached) headsets are available for both instructor and
student positions. All dynamic, with a noise-cancelling microphone, this headset employs a
durable tamper-proof cord. The nonboom headset is used with installations employing a desk-
mounted microphone. (d) Module. For use with portable equipment, the module provides
protection and storage for five student positions with self-contained amplifiers and boom-type
headsets. At the end of class, headsets and cords are quickly packed without wrapping, thereby
eliminating the handling of dusty cords. *Courtesy of Instructomatic, Inc.*

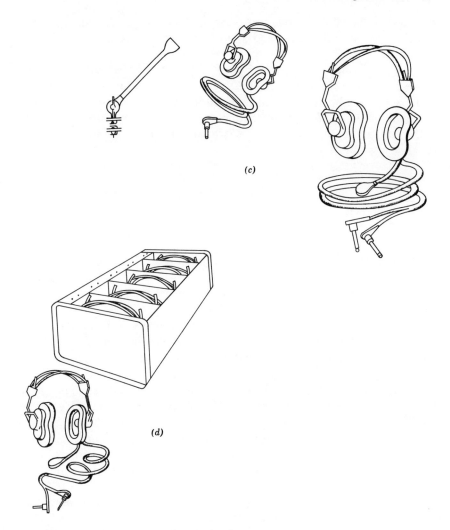

(c)

(d)

Figure 7.28 (*continued*)

II.   Headphones and microphones for student stations (in some installations, recorders are also included)

III.   Booths—early construction involved the use of panels that completely isolated the student from the class and the instructor—in the interest of privacy and reducing distractions. Newer equipment reduces the need for such paneling. Fully cushioned earphones keep out all sound; microphones are sensitive only to sound in the immediate environs.

IV.   Individual study carrels (areas where students can "make up" work; a facility for students who need additional work; an area where students can do advanced work)

A.   Some units are equipped with slide and filmstrip viewers, 8-mm single-concept projectors, as well as record and tape players.

B.   Units are being designed that will allow a student to dial for visual and audio material and have it channeled directly to receivers in the carrel.

C.   Still in the future: library information retrieval systems permitting rapid access to printed information.[6]

SELECTED COMPONENTS FOR ELECTRONIC–LEARNING CLASSROOMS

Ten years ago there were two manufacturers producing components for use in electronic-learning centers; today there are 27. The models and the types of equipment being offered vary widely (Figure 7.29). Therefore it is not our purpose to catalog all of this equipment but rather to offer a few examples and illustrations.

American Seating produces a series of components for fixed or portable installations. The three audio teaching systems—listen-respond, listen-respond active, and listen-respond record—can be accommodated in a single electronics laboratory in whatever proportions may be desired.

The Chancellor Electronic Learning Center puts complete control of all teaching functions at the instructor's fingertips. The model contains controls for student programs, student intercom monitors, and student recorder controls. Program sources can be live, tape recorded, or disc recorded. The console can conduct up to eight programs simultaneously. Lighted push-button controls indicate the extent of utilization of equipment in the student booth.

American Seating student booths (Figure 7.30) are of flexible construction. Dividing panels can either be permanently erected, omitted, or hinged for greater flexibility. The complete range of components allows the student to hear the lesson and his own response through his headset; to control channel volume and microphone volume separately; to fully intercommunicate with the instructor's control console; to call the instructor by signal light; to hear and talk to other students under the instructor's selective control; to record the master lesson

[6]David Crossman, op. cit., pp. 22–34; James W. Brown, "Student Response Systems," Audiovisual Instruction, 8:214–219 (April, 1963); Andre Humbert, "Tape Development and the Language Laboratory," In 1965 Educational Communications Convocations Proceedings, Albany: State Education Department, New York, 1965, pp. 82–86.

and his own response on a dual-track booth recorder; to play back the master lesson and his own response for comparison; to rerecord his own response as often as desired; and to work independently of the console.

Among the several models offered by Webster Electric is its Mobile Tape Teaching Laboratory (Figure 7.31). The Model WTLM provides, in one compact mobile unit, facilities for converting any classroom into a complete teaching laboratory.

As many as 13 microphone headsets may be plugged directly into the console or into extension cords from the console. Twenty-four (listen-only) student positions may be added by plugging headset extension cords into the outlets of the console. Program material is distributed to all 36 students simultaneously. Any individual audio-active student position or any group of positions may be selected for monitoring and recording. Recorded responses, together with the original program and the instructor's comments, may be replayed for the benefit of other students.

With this model, seating arrangements are completely flexible. Optional extension cords permit seating both audio-active and audio-passive students within a 16-ft. radius of the laboratory.

The Radio Corporation of America produces several series of components. The RCA EDC-101 Learning Laboratory (Figure 7.32) is an electronic system that serves as an aid in teaching a variety of subjects. The chief functions provided by this system include multiple lesson distribution, simultaneous recitation by all the students in the class, and individual instruction for each student through monitoring, intercommunication and announcement facilities. The EDC-101 can accommodate up to 64 student positions, each of which may be equipped with a recorder. The system is available as either a fixed or a mobile installation and is completely transistorized.

MAGNETIC TAPE SPECIALIZED EQUIPMENT

Many ingenious applications for the use of magnetic tape are being developed at the present time. These devices require the production of specialized playback equipment. A few of the items are described below to indicate the direction that these new developments are taking.

Audio-Sell Tape Cartridge Repeater. Audio-Sell, Inc., produces several units involving specialized applications. The Tape Cartridge Repeater (Figure 7.33) utilizes a recorded tape loaded into a *Fidelipac* cartridge. The tape is connected in the cartridge in a continuous loop.

The easily loaded cartridge contains up to 20 minutes of taped information. It is activated by pressing a button on the speaker, which can be positioned away from the playback unit. The unit is completely

Figure 7.29   There are many different kinds of learning laboratory currently in use.

Figure 7.29 (*continued*)

transistorized to ensure highest quality and instant start-up of the message with no warm-up time required for the amplifier. The loop cartridge rewinds the tape automatically and sets itself to repeat for the next presentation. The cartridge can be keyed to stop itself for button-activation.

This equipment is useful for giving audio descriptions for exhibits in museums, auditoriums, or the classrooms. It also provides low-cost instructional tape playback for language laboratories.

Audio-Sell Pulsematic. The Audio-Sell Pulsematic is a tape cartridge sound unit that allows the slide or filmstrip projector to advance automatic-

Figure 7.30 Student listen-respond booths. *Courtesy of American Seating.*

ally through an inaudible signal recorded on the tape. To operate this machine the cartridge is easily snapped into the unit, the Pulsematic adapter cord is plugged into the projector, and the START switch is turned on.

The Pulsematic uses dual track sound tape—one track for the narration, the other for the inaudible 3000-cycle signal. Recording can be accomplished on any standard stereo tape recorder. The Pulsematic is fully transistorized for instant starting without warmup.

The unit is equipped with its own speaker and it also has output jacks for external speakers.

Cousino Syncro-Repeater. The Cousino Electronics Corporation offers many models of specialized tape-recording equipment. The Syncro-Repeater (Figure 7.34) is especially suitable for synchronized audiovisual projection when coupled with most push-button remote-controlled slide and filmstrip projectors. The unit is compact, completely transistorized, and has all audio record and playback facilities, including trip-tone recording and playback. The tone may be optionally used for end-of-cycle shut off in place of standard metal foil tabs.

The Syncro-Repeater uses a continuous-loop cartridge tape (Figure

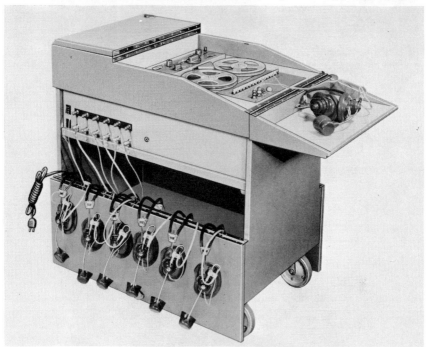

Figure 7.31   Webster Electric Mobile Tape Teaching Laboratory. *Courtesy of Webster Electric Corp.*

7.35). Variable playing times are available up to 40 minutes at $3\frac{3}{4}$ in. per second.

The standard features include "on demand" start with push-button, built-in amplifier and speaker, and external speaker jack. The power outlet can be turned on or off with message to light up or animate displays. A slide switch allows for optional continuous and repetitive replay of tapes or automatic shut-off when the metal foil tab is located on the tape.

Cousino Audio Vendor. The Cousino Audio Vendor is a continuous-loop cartridge tape (packed in a dustproof plastic case) that will fit most standard

Figure 7.32   EDC-101 Learning Laboratory, teacher's console. *Courtesy of Radio Corporation of America.*

Figure 7.33   Audio-Sell, Inc. Tape Cartridge Repeater. *Courtesy of Audio-Sell, Inc.*

Figure 7.34   Cousino Synchro-Repeater. *Courtesy of the Cousino Electronics Corp.*

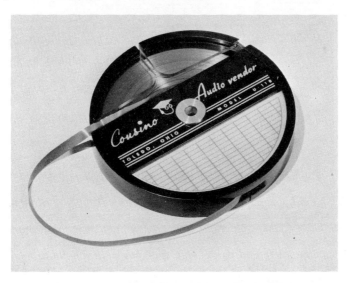

Figure 7.35   Cousino continuous-loop cartridge tape.

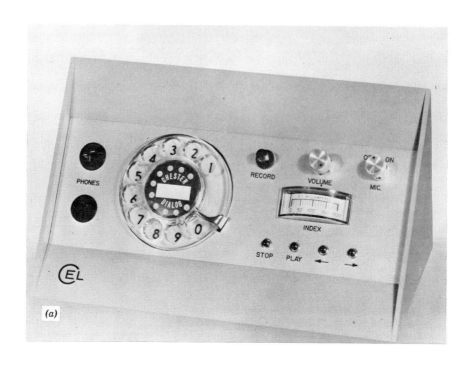

Figure 7.36   By dialing a number (a), a student can listen in the privacy of his own booth to any one of many taped programs stored in a remote library (b). The technician is making an adjustment on one of the four-track, three-motor tape decks developed by Chester Electronic Laboratories for their Dialog Learning Laboratory system. Each tape deck is equipped with an electronic eye to rewind immediately upon completion of the lesson material called for by the dial and switching system. (c) Dialing positions in the laboratory and at other points in the building will operate through the control panel.

tape recorders (Figure 7.35). Audio Vendors are available in playing times of from 3 to 60 minutes at $3\frac{3}{4}$ ips.

The Audio Vendor is designed to repeat recorded material automatically. It is especially useful in teaching foreign languages, dramatics, dancing, voice, and correction of speech impediments. No adapter or special equipment is necessary to put the device to immediate use.

Chester Dialog. Chester Electronic Laboratories uses magnetic tape in a unique information retrieval system. The Chester Dialog concept provides a means for storing and then making instantly available large numbers of prerecorded taped programs from a remote tape library. Simply by dialing the proper number, any student activates the remotely located tape machine and listens to any program in the library (Figure 7.36)—thereby

(c)

Figure 7.36 (*continued*)

allowing each student to select the material most appropriate to his learning needs.

Owing to the remotely-located equipment, the student position is entirely free of conventional tape equipment except for a combination earphone-microphone and telephone dial. At the same time the teacher is relieved of preoccupation with tapes and equipment and fulfilling the role of tape librarian and technician; thus he is able to concentrate on monitoring and tutoring students.

Only one copy of each program is required because any number of students can listen to the same program at the same time. In addition, the programs in the library can vary in length from 1 to 30 minutes, and many different lessons and courses can be offered simultaneously.

The following are some of the different types of programs that may be incorporated into a system of this type:

1. Languages (with or without full recording for the student).
2. Reproduction of lectures automatically recorded by remote control from the lecture area.
3. Required music.
4. Speech therapy.
5. Business-education information such as dictation exercises.

The entire system consists of a student booth, or study carrel, a teacher's console, and a remote library. The study carrels may be located in any area in the school, with no restrictions on distance from the program source.

The teacher's console contains individual switches to enable undetected monitoring of student positions and also student lights to indicate the activity of each student. The instructor may also intercommunicate with any or all students.

In addition to the taped programs available from the remote library the console has nine additional program sources. Any four of these, at any one time, can be directed by the teacher to any one, or all, of the student positions for classroom-type instruction. The switching and electronic equipment comprising the remote library utilize transistorized plug-in construction and standard telephone-system components. This design, combined with the remote location (away from possible tampering by students), ensures maximum trouble-free operation.

SELECTED REFERENCES

Bastion, J. Wallace. "Use of Color Slides and Magnetic Tape in Teaching Spanish." *Audiovisual Guide*, **20** 18–20 (March, 1954).

Brentano, Sister Mary Theresa. "Tape: Multiplier of Teacher's Time and Personality," *Audiovisual Instruction*, 7, 368–371 (June, 1962).

Brown, James W., and James W. Thornton, Jr. *New Media in Higher Education*. Association for Higher Education and Department of Audiovisual Instruction, NEA, 1963.

Cookson, F. B. "Tutoring by Tape," *Music Teachers National Association Proceedings*, 1950, pp. 121–126.

Dale, Edgar. *Audio-Visual Methods of Teaching* (rev. ed). New York: Holt, Rinehart & Winston, 1961, pp. 290–302.

Davidson, Raymond W. *Audiovisual Machines*. Lubbock, Texas: Texas Tech Press, 1964. Chapter 10.

Eboch, Sidney C. *Operating Audio-Visual Equipment*. San Francisco: Chandler 1960. Chapter 4.

Gibson, Romain. "Can Tapes Teach?" *Educational Screen and Audiovisual Guide*, **37** 180–181 (April, 1958).

Grassell, E. Milton. "Tailor-Made Tapes Really Click," *Instructor*, **66** 30–34 (January, 1957).

Haas, Kenneth B., and Harry Q. Packer. *Preparation and Use of Audio-Visual Aids* (3rd ed.) Englewood Cliffs, N.J.: Prentice-Hall, 1955. Chapter 13.

Hayes, Alfred S. *Language Laboratory Facilities: Technical Guide for the Selection, Purchase, Use, and Maintenance*. Washington, D.C.: U.S. Office of Education, 1963.

Hensell, Kenneth. "Dialing for Education," *California Education*, **1** 28–30 (October, 1963).

Hoogs, Marilyn J., and James H. Cole. "Adventures in Aural Imagery," *Audiovisual Instruction*, 3 48–49 (February, 1958).

Johnson, Marjory C., and Catherine C. Seerley, "Foreign Language Laboratories in Schools and Colleges." Washington, D.C., Bulletin No. 3, 1959.

Kinder, James S., *Audio-Visual Materials and Techniques* (2nd ed.), New York: American Book Company, 1959. Chapter 10.

LeBel, C. J. *Fundamentals of Magnetic Recording*. New York: Audio-Devices, 1951.

LeBel, C. J. *How to Make Good Tape Recordings*. New York: Audio-Devices, Inc., 1956.

Luce, Arnold E. "Tapes for Teaching," Instructional Materials for Elementary Schools. Thirty-Fifth Yearbook of the Department of Elementary School Principals. Washington, D.C.: NEA, 1956. pp. 225–230.

Mathieu, Gustave. "Language Laboratories," *Review of Educational Research*, **32**, 168–178 (April, 1962).

Mellenbrush, Julia. *The Tape Recorder in the Classroom*, Austin: Visual Instruction Bureau, U. of Texas, 1959.

National Audio Tape Catalog. Washington, D.C.: NEA, 1967.

Sands, Lester B., *Audio-Visual Procedures in Teaching*, New York: Ronald Press, 1956. Chapter 25.

Tape Recorder in the Elementary Classroom, A Handbook of Tested Uses. St. Paul: Minnesota Mining & Mfg. Co.

Tape Recording in the Classroom, Handbook for Teachers and Administrators. St. Paul: Minnesota Mining & Mfg. Co.

Teaching and Training With Tape Recorders (booklet). Chicago, Ill.: Bell and Howell Co.

Wittich, Walter Arno, and Charles Francis Schuller, *Audio-Visual Materials, Their Nature and Use* (2nd ed.). New York: Harper, 1957. Chapters 10, 11.

INSTRUCTIONAL MATERIALS

First The Ear, tape, 30 min., Minnesota Mining & Mfg. Co., 1960.

Language Laboratory in Action, 16-mm film, 14 min., sound, color, Electronic Teaching Laboratories, 1961.

Letter for An American School Boy, 16-mm film, 27 min., sound, b & w, United World, 1954.

Next Voice You Hear, 16-mm film, 13 min., sound, color, Electronic Teaching Laboratories, 1961.

The Tape Recorder, 16-mm film, 6 min., sound, b & w, Iowa State University, 1960.

Tape Recording for Instruction, 16-mm film, 15 min., sound b & w, Indiana University, 1956.

8

BROADCAST SOUND
SYSTEMS

CLASSROOM RADIO

Radio has long held out promise of being of invaluable assistance to the teacher in the classroom because it is a means of presenting worthwhile learning experiences simultaneously to large numbers of students (Figure 8.1). In remote areas it is particularly helpful in competently covering subject matter that might otherwise not be offered at all. Its importance is growing, despite the popularity of other media of communication. The number of FM radio stations in the United States is well over one thousand. FM broadcasting is the type most often used for educational broadcasts because the quality of the sound is superior, and because the radio signal is not subject to the interference of atmospheric and electrical conditions.

Many stations are being built in the larger school systems and on the campuses of colleges and universities. Students gain in several ways— through the reception of the programmed material and through the planning and producing of the programs themselves.

Radio has suffered from a few handicaps in the classroom. For one thing, it is difficult to schedule programs that will be acceptable to the majority of students in the programming area. Teachers and students find it hard to go back or to skip ahead in scheduled studies in order to use programs out of phase with the school's curriculum. Tape recorders have helped to alleviate this problem, however. Pertinent material can be recorded and played back at the optimum time in the course presentation.

Another problem is the inability of students and teachers to prepare themselves adequately for off-the-air broadcasts. In some cases manuals are available, but they are too often lost or misplaced. Again, the tape

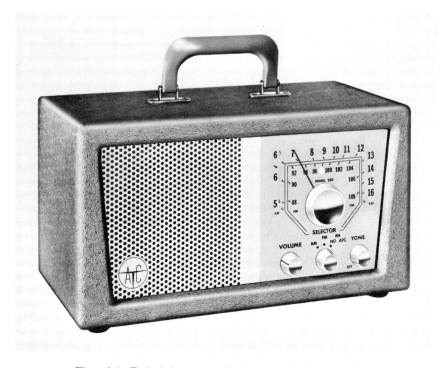

Figure 8.1   Typical classroom radio. *Courtesy of Audiotronics, Inc.*

recorder offers some assistance in allowing the teacher to preview, audition, and edit program material before it is presented to the students.

A criticism of radio teaching is that it is too often one-way communication; the students have little opportunity to participate in the instructional activity other than in a passive way. This problem is being overcome by having telephonic hookups between the classrooms and the local studio. In other cases a direct correspondence is set up between the program teacher and the students. This constant "feedback" of information aids the studio teacher in the organization and presentation of his material.

A recent survey indicated that there were over 110,000 radio receivers in our public schools, and approximately 40,000 additional sets were being purchased. Research concerned with the use of radio in education indicates that this emphasis on radio is well-placed. Radio compares favorably with conventional teaching methods in experimental studies, and is well liked by the students. Alvin Barr, in his research,[1] found little difference in the effectiveness of instruction in classes in which radio

[1] Alvin S. Barr, et al., "Radio In The Classroom," Madison, Wisconsin: University of Wisconsin Press, 1942.

was used extensively as compared to classes where conventional methods were used. In an experiment dealing with instruction in elementary science, however, it was found that radio did produce better results than did conventional methods.[2]

On the other hand, several experiments have demonstrated no significant gains from the use of radio. Reid was able to establish that radio did not necessarily stimulate outside reading; Cook did not find that radio listeners acquired more information than did those who did not listen.[3]

Radio is no different from any other audiovisual medium insofar as its planned use is concerned. Effective utilization can be accomplished by following the four-step plan described in Chapter 2. When its full potential has thus been explored, radio has been found to be beneficial as an instructional tool for music, science, safety education, social studies, and current events.[4] It provides enrichment, increased appreciation, understanding of new techniques and skills, and makes students aware of new ideas and opinions in the community and in the world. Not all radio materials are applicable to a particular subject area. Thus it would be well to keep in mind the slogans developed in the Los Angeles school system governing the use of radio:

Choose programs wisely.
Evaluate thoughtfully.
Listen widely.
Develop standards for judging programs.[5]

CENTRAL SOUND SYSTEM

The central sound system located in a school building or complex of school buildings is a composite of various audio sources so organized that they can be channeled to any room or groups of rooms as desired. Connected to the system are audio sources such as radio, tape recorders, record players, and microphones for announcements and other forms of local programming. The key to the system is the control panel, usually

[2] J. Robert Miles, "Radio and Elementary Science Teaching," *Journal of Applied Psychology*, **24**, 714–720 (1940).

[3] Dean C. Cook, and Cemzek, C. L., "The Effectiveness of Teaching by Radio," *Journal of Educational Research*, **33**, 105–109 (1939).

[4] Haugh, Oscar M., "Relative Effectiveness of Reading and Listening to Radio Drama as Ways of Imparting Information and Shifting Attitudes" *Journal of Education Research*, **45**, 489–498 (March, 1952).

[5] James S. Kinder, *Using Audiovisual Materials in Education*, New York: American Book Company, 1965, p. 85.

located in the administration office. The control panel—with its keys, switches, microphone, amplifiers, and other audio equipment—is the distribution point for all program material.

The central sound system (Figure 8.2) is proving useful as an administrative tool. It helps in the location of key personnel; announcements can be made with assurance that everyone will be reached; fire and disaster drills can be easily controlled. In the classroom the central sound system is useful because any program can be directed to it by the teacher merely by calling the office. No other equipment has to be moved or operated.

The system (Figure 8.3) is often built in or near a small studio to enable students to utilize it for closed-circuit radio broadcasting. Varied activities can be originated in the studio and beamed back to the classroom or classrooms. These activities could include: political speeches, news reports, weather announcements, dramatic presentations, readings, and so forth.

There are some disadvantages to the system, however: breakdown are sometimes frequent and need to be corrected; equipment quickly becomes obsolete and needs to be updated; improperly trained announcers can ruin the effectiveness of a broadcast; poor timing of announcements and programs will not gain many friends for the central sound system.

An effective system requires adequate equipment, a plan for the optimum

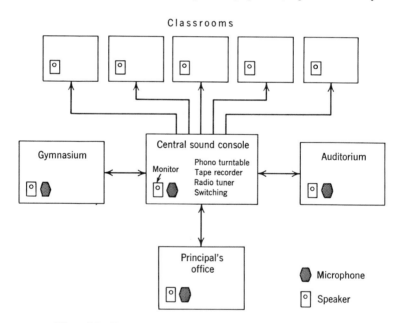

Figure 8.2 **The central sound system should serve the entire school.**

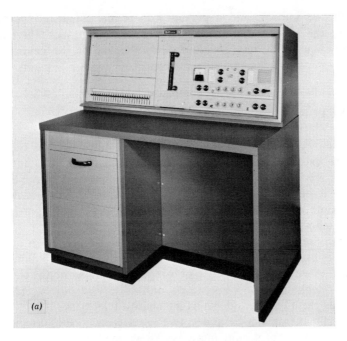

(a)

(b)

Figure 8.3 Typical central sound systems. *Courtesy of DuKane. Inc.*

235

use of the equipment, and a person who is interested and capable of overseeing the execution of the plan. Any weakening of these three factors could produce conditions unfavorable to the use of the central sound system.

TELELECTURE

Any classroom equipped with a telephone output jack is capable of using a recent audio innovation called the telelecture. The equipment consists of a telephone, an amplifier, and a microphone. The amplification is such that both sides of the telephone conversation can be heard in the classroom or small auditorium. The system even allows participation by the members of the class.

The purpose of the classroom phone, or telelecture, is to allow the students to use a wide range of resources without having to leave the classroom or without the expense of bringing lecturers into the classroom. With this technique any specialist, public servant, or world-famous person is as close to the students as the nearest telephone.

Many refinements can be added to the telelecture, such as the use of slides, filmstrips, or motion pictures. These materials must necessarily be sent in advance and set up. Their showing can be accomplished according to a prepared script, or according to the verbal directions of the lecturer.

The telelecture is being received with a great deal of interest and approval on college campuses and in various school systems. It offers another means of distributing the special talent of a teacher or resource person to a larger group of students without great expense to the school system and without what students are apt to consider the undesirable features of a "canned" presentation.

SUGGESTED REFERENCES

Broderick, Gertrude C. "Whither Radio?" *Journal of The American Association of University Women,* **50** 83–85. (January, 1947).

Brown, James W., Richard Lewis, and Fred F. Harcleroad. *Audio-Visual instruction Materials and Methods.* New York: McGraw-Hill, 1959. Chapter 9.

Dale, Edgar. *Audio-Visual Methods of Teaching* (rev.ed.). New York: Holt, Rinehart & Winston, 1961. pp. 278–283.

Kinder, James S., *Audio-Visual Materials and Techniques,* (2nd ed.). New York: American Book Co., 1959. Chapters 11, 16, 17; pp. 507–509, 511–512.

Kingson, Walter K., and Rome Cowgill. *Drama Acting and Production* (rev. ed.; handbook). New York: Holt, Rinehart & Winston, 1952.

Levenson, William B., and Edward Stasheff. *Teaching Radio and Television*. New York: Holt, Rinehart & Winston, 1952.

McKnown, Harry C., and Alvin B. Roberts. *Audio-Visual Aids to Instruction* (2nd ed.). New York: McGraw-Hill, 1949. Chapter 13.

National Broadcasting Company. *How Schools Can Use Radio*. New York: Radio Corporation of America, 1939.

Neol, Francis, and others. *Using Radio in the Classroom*. Sacramento, California: State Department of Education, 1953.

Sands, Lester B., *Audio-Visual Procedures in Teaching*. New York: Ronald Press, 1956.

School Sound Systems. Washington, D.C.: U.S. Office of Education and Radio Manufacturers Association, Joint Committee on Standards for School Audio Equipment, Radio Section, Radio Mfg. Association, 1946.

Schramm, Wilbur Lang, *Mass Communication*, Urbana, Ill.: University Press, 1947.

Sterner, Alice P., *A Course of Study in Radio and Television Appreciation*. Maplewood, New Jersey: Audiovisual Guide, 1950.

U.S. Office of Education and the Radio Manufacturers Association. *Classroom Radio Receivers—Basic Specifications*. Washington, D.C.: U.S. Office of Education, 1948.

Wheaton, Elizabeth Lee. "How to Put on a Radio Show," *The Grade Teacher*. 73, 11 (November, 1954).

Willis, Edgar E. *Foundations in Broadcasting*. New York: Oxford University Press, 1951.

Wittich, Walter Arno, and Charles Francis Schuller. *Audio-Visual Materials. Their Nature and Use* (2nd ed.). New York: Harper, 1953.

Woelfel, Norman, and Tyler, I. Keith. *Radio and School*. Yonkers, N.Y.: World Book Co., 1945.

9

EDUCATIONAL TELEVISION

Television has played an increasingly important role in our lives since its general introduction to the American public after World War II. In 1946 there were six television stations servicing a total of 8000 receivers. Today there are almost 600 stations catering to the demands of almost 50 million television receivers. Surveys indicate that adolescents and adults spend an average of $2\frac{1}{2}$ hours per day viewing television during the week, and this figure is even higher for weekends. It has also been demonstrated that television is playing an important role in shaping attitudes, creating interests, presenting factual information, and offering unprecedented opportunities for new and wonderful learning experiences through the coverage of national elections, rockets, space travel, genetics, and other similar sophisticated topics.

School officials and teachers are recognizing the tremendous impact that television can have as an instructional medium in the classroom (Figures 9.1 and 9.2). In 1952 the Federal Communications Commission reserved nearly 300 television channels for education. In 1953 KHUT (University of Houston) went on the air as the first exclusively educational television station. Since that time over 160 other stations have been licensed and are operating with programming that can be classified as cultural and educational.

Illustration from Robert E. de Kieffer and Lee W. Cochran. *Manual of Audiovisual Techniques.* Englewood Cliffs: Prentice-Hall, Inc. 1962, p. 205.

Figure 9.1 Fourth graders watch intently as the Spanish teacher begins the morning lesson in the Palo Alto, California, school system.

The remarkable impact of television on education is evident in a report of the United States Office of Education. Of 320 school systems planning to build new schools in 1961, 13% reported plans for including closed-circuit systems (one that would allow program origination as well as reception). Of the secondary schools, the total was 26%. If provisions for receiving broadcast television were included, the estimate is that over half the nation's schools have some television facilities. It is interesting to observe that whereas it usually takes 15 years for 3% of the school systems to adopt a new practice, educational television has made the grade in five years.

RESEARCH ON EFFECTIVENESS OF ETV

Among all the other new educational media, it is television that seems to show the greatest educational potential. It is also probably the most tested and researched medium, since thousands of experimental studies have been conducted in this field. Overwhelming evidence indicates that

Figure 9.2 A seventh-grade teacher presents a lesson that is being recorded on a videotape recorder for later playback to students. *Courtesy of Ampex Corp.*

the use of television in the classroom is generally more effective than use of conventional classroom techniques and that instruction can be provided to large groups without lessened instructional quality.

Several conclusions drawn from various studies[1] involving the use of television are noted:

1. Pupil achievement can improve significantly when television is consistently used as a teaching aid. This is true regardless of age, grade, subject, or pupils' range of ability—even after the novelty effect has worn off.
2. Television accelerates the teacher's professional growth. Classroom teachers learn by observing the techniques of the television instructor.

[1]Shibler, Herman L., "What Research Says About ETV," *Midwest Program on Airborne Television Instruction News*, **2**, (September, 1963); *Washington County Closed Circuit Television Report*, Hagerstown, Maryland, 1962; "The Ford Foundation and The Fund For The Advancement of Education," *Teaching by Television*, New York: The Ford Foundation, 1961; *And TV, Too!* (Washington, D.C.: Department of Audiovisual Instruction and Department of Classroom Teachers, NEA, 1961.

3. Television makes it possible to upgrade the curriculum and enrich the educational program more easily and economically than before. New courses can be introduced and special services offered to the classroom—talks by scientists, poets, government leaders.

4. Television is especially useful as an instructional aid to add new learning experiences to the school program. It does not "replace" the teacher or "substitute" techniques and procedures which would eliminate regular classroom learning activities and personal teacher-pupil relationships. Its effectiveness is dependent directly on the way it is used by the classroom teacher.

5. The operational costs of television usually can be met without increasing the normal school budget. Savings to pay for television can be effected through redeployment of teaching equipment, changed organization within schools, and altered scheduling of personnel.

6. The problem of finding and retaining top quality teachers is eased. Teachers make their skills more widely available through television. The challenge of teaching on television gives many good teachers an added reason for remaining in the profession.

7. Television changes the role of the classroom teacher and makes him— along with the studio teacher—part of a *teaching team*.

8. Television brings greater equality of opportunity for all pupils. In an underprivileged area or in the most cultured district children participate in the same lessons and special events through television.

9. School television facilities can serve the public in a variety of ways— for adult education, community projects, and the dissemination of many kinds of information. The schools can serve as centers for interested adults.

FITTING TV INTO THE INSTRUCTIONAL PROGRAM

The extent to which television should be used in the classroom is a topic that is in itself undergoing a great deal of study. However, most people agree that its use should be limited if television is considered as a medium of communication and not as a new method of teaching. Another factor limiting its use in the classroom is the tremendous preparation time involved for each program. There is also increasing acceptance of the fact that television is not a self-contained educational entity but draws its significance only in the particular educational context in which it is employed. The television lesson should generally be followed as soon as possible by a session with the classroom teacher.

The length of a television lesson has also been subject to question. The fact that the attention span of a first grader is shorter than that of a high school pupil has bearing on the question. So also does the fact that pupils at the same grade level can profit by a longer television lesson in a subject such as art than in others, such as conversational French, wherein more concentration is required. In the television research project conducted in Washington County, Maryland, elementary pupils spent 7 to 13% of their classroom time watching television. The lessons ranged in length from 13 to 25 minutes and were followed by work in the subject with the classroom teacher. Junior-high-school students spent about one-third of their classroom time watching television lessons and high-school students less than 10%. Although the project proved to be an endorsement for television, there was no indication that the percentages noted above reflected the optimum television viewing times.

Considering television as a medium of communication means that TV's effective use would be dependent upon the four-step plan for the utilization of audiovisual materials and equipment: teacher preparation, student preparation, presentation, and follow-up activities.

Teachers' guides and student notes are prepared for most programs being directed at the classrooms. The teacher is able to familiarize himself with the material to be presented. Through his efforts the students should be highly motivated and well-disposed toward receiving the information that is being telecast.

The television presentation could take any one of several forms. It could be used to:

Present viewpoints
Create interests
Provide the latest information
Dramatize aspects of the lesson
Direct attention
Pace learning activities
Utilize special talents
Enlarge objects
Present ideas visually
Bring immediate community and world events into the classroom
Provide in-service education for teachers.

Depending on the nature of the presentation, the classroom teacher would prescribe any one of the following pupil activities during the telecast:

Listening
Observing

Taking notes
Following directions
Organizing information
Raising questions
Weighing alternatives
Withholding judgment
Noting need for more information
Reaching tentative conclusions.

After the telecast is over the classroom teacher can use the time to accomplish any one or several of the following:

Express ideas
Discuss alternatives
Clarify misunderstandings
Develop group plans
Arrive at decisions
Guide pupil growth
Make practical applications
Provide opportunity for individual and group projects
Demonstrate and experiment
Test pupil achievement
Evaluate pupil learning.

The activities of the pupils after the telecast should be related directly to the material presented. Such activities might include:

Asking and answering questions
Discussing
Practicing
Performing experiments
Investigating (individual and group)
Reading
Working on projects
Making applications
Creating
Evaluating.[2]

Television is a conveyor of ideas, not a creator. It transmits instantly the spoken or the written word, the picture, the sights and sounds, and the action of events as they take place. It enables the viewer to hear as well as to see what occurs. A lesson does not automatically become better, more forceful, or more challenging because it is telecast. School personnel

[2]Washington County, *op. cit.*, p. 78.

do the planning and teaching; what is taught and how it is taught depend on their cooperative efforts. Careful planning and continuous evaluation are necessary because the value of television is directly related to the way the medium is used.

KINDS OF EDUCATIONAL TELEVISION

Television can be subjected to many different kinds of classifications. The distinctions to be drawn here will be as simple as possible. First of all, television can be divided into two main categories—broadcast television or "off-air reception" (Figure 9.3), and closed-circuit tele-

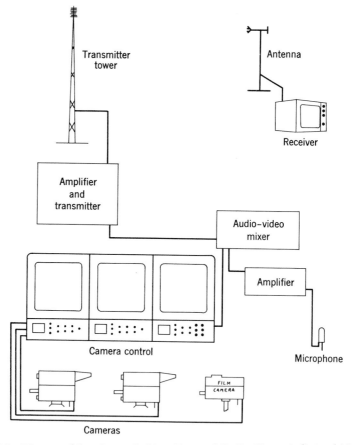

Figure 9.3 Diagram of broadcast television. Raymond L. Davidson, *Audiovisual Machines,* **Texas Technological Press.**

Figure 9.4 Line to classroom or auditorium TV receiver or receivers. *Robert de Kieffer and Lear W. Cochran op. cit., p. 207.*

vision or "cable" television. In broadcast open-circuit television the signal is sent out from a transmitter and covers an area from 45 to 70 miles, depending on the terrain. If the terrain is rough or mountainous, the distance will be shortened; if it is level, the signal will travel a considerable distance. Broadcast-television signals tend to travel in a straight line from the transmitter tower to the antenna where the signal is received. Anything that intervenes will interfere with the reception of that signal.

Closed-circuit television broadcasting, on the other hand, is the transmission of pictures and sounds to a limited network (Figure 9.4) connected by cable or a microwave system (Figure 9.5). This network may consist of one school, a whole school district, or several districts. It could consist

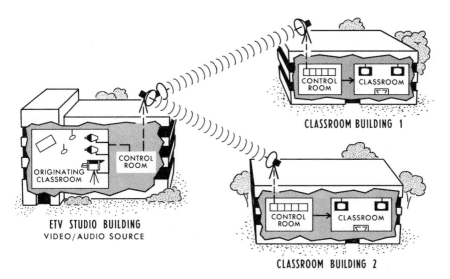

Figure 9.5 ETV microwave relay link, interbuilding diagram.

of a camera and receivers set up in one room for purposes of enlarging objects. The telecast cannot be received by other sets outside the selected network and the signal does not have to meet FCC commercial broadcast regulations.

Another way of categorizing television is by a consideration of the types of programming that are available for classroom use. These range from the nationwide courses broadcast over commercial and educational stations to the single-classroom systems where one specific lesson is being broadcast for one specific group.

Several courses in physics, chemistry, mathematics, and economics have been offered for college credit on a national basis over the NBC television network. The programs were well received even though offered early in the morning. The programs presently being offered on the national networks are primarily for enrichment purposes; few of them are aired during school hours for actual use in the classroom.

MPATI. The Midwest Program of Airborne Television Instruction (MPATI) came into being in 1960 as a means of broadcasting instructional television programs directly into the classrooms in a multistate area. The lessons are recorded on magnetic tape (videotape) and are then played back and broadcast from an airplane that circles a single location in Northern Indiana (Figure 9.6). The broadcast can be picked up in a radius of 200 miles by 17,000 school districts and colleges enrolling approximately 7 million students. The telecasts are designed to be an integral part of a specific curriculum. Study guides distributed by MPATI enable the classroom teachers to effect this integration.

Statewide CCTV—South Carolina. State-wide closed-circuit television systems such as the one in South Carolina overcome the expense and hazards of off-air transmission. This system provides several programs at the same time on different channels for the various grade levels and subject areas. Evaluative tests indicate that ETV has brought to many of the schools a higher level of instruction than would have been possible without television. Students in rural areas are now receiving the benefits of instruction previously available only in the more affluent urban areas.

State-wide and regional open-air broadcasting for education are growing rapidly, leading toward the integration of independent ETV stations into ETV networks. WGBH in Boston originates many of the programs that are directed into the classroom. At the same time it shares its programs with other stations in the Eastern Educational Television Network.

Television can be set up according to school districts, either as closed-circuit broadcasting or open-air broadcasting. The Anaheim, California, project and the Hagerstown Project (Maryland) both utilized closed-

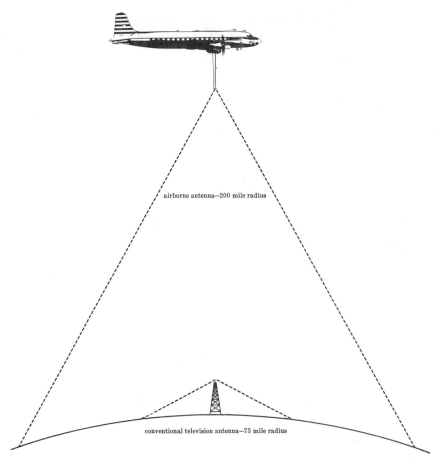

airborne antenna—200 mile radius

conventional television antenna—75 mile radius

Figure 9.6 Transmitting television signals from an airplane, the distinguishing feature of the Midwest Program of Airborne Television Instruction. *Ford Foundation.*

circuit television for beaming the programs into the classrooms. These successful projects were characterized by extensive planning and careful orientation between the television and classroom teachers to ensure the proper level of content. The Des Moines project, because of the large rural area involved, utilized off-air broadcasting for its ETV station. The community broadcasting of cultural and. educational programs increased further the interest in adult education activities in the area. The program is considered to be highly successful.

Within a single school system the individual schools can share their teaching staffs (Figure 9.7) and individual talents through the use of

Figure 9.7   Teachers make their skills more widely available through television.

closed circuit television. Master-antenna systems allow for the most effective pickup of off-air transmission. These signals can then be transmitted over the closed circuit.

The use of a single camera by classroom teachers is becoming increasingly common. The camera is mounted over a demonstration table and is connected to one or several television receivers that may be scattered about the room. With the use of this system it is possible for the students to observe experiments, to follow demonstrations, study pictures, and examine small objects with greater facility than was ever possible previously.

THE CLASSROOM TEACHER AND TELEVISION

The techniques of television broadcasting are not easily explained or master. But the increased importance of television to the classroom teacher does call for a brief description of the kinds, types, and purposes of the major pieces of broadcast equipment.

The classroom teachers' major contact will be with those individuals who plan or select the programs that are to be broadcast. As a subject specialist, the teacher has highly-valued opinions as to what part of the course content should be televised. His knowledge of the equipment and its capabilities will enable him to evaluate the potential of television for communicating various aspects of the lessons.

Operating the television receiver in the classroom may be the extent of the teacher's equipment utilization. But even here careful consideration should be given to several factors. The minimum-size television screen for a classroom should be 24 in. For best results no one should be seated beyond the distance of 12 times the width of the picture tube. The base of the picture area should be above the eye level to allow all students in the classroom an unobstructed view of the television picture (Figure 9.8 and 9.9). The television receiver can be mounted from the ceiling, supported by wall brackets, mounted on a pedestal, or set on a mobile platform for ease of movement from room to room. Most installations now are more of the permanent type.

The controls for the operation of the classroom receiver are similar to those for the regular home receiver. The set should be turned on, with the volume low, some minutes before the start of the scheduled program in order to achieve optimum clarity of picture. Lighting should be given some consideration, and subdued where possible. The top of the television receiver should be tilted forward, or a shade constructed on the front of the picture tube in order to minimize the glare and reflection from the overhead light.

TELEVISION EQUIPMENT

Because it is doubtful that many teachers would feel the need for a thorough analysis of the broadcast equipment used in commercial television, much of this section is concerned with equipment used on the local level in school systems with closed-circuit television facilities. In broadcast television the cameras convert the picture into electronic impulses at the same time as the sound is converted into impulses by the microphone. Both of these impulses are fed into a mixer after first being amplified separately. From the mixer the signal is sent to a transmitter, where the impulses are radiated from the antenna as invisible electromagnetic waves. The home antenna or the master antenna in the school system picks up the radiated TV signal and directs it into the receiver. In the receiver the signal is amplified, separated into sound and video impulses, and sent into the loudspeaker and the picture tube.

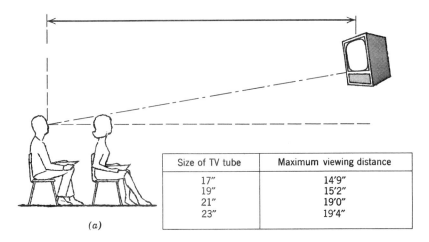

(a)

Size of TV tube	Maximum viewing distance
17"	14'9"
19"	15'2"
21"	19'0"
23"	19'4"

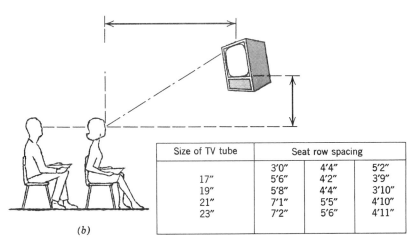

(b)

Size of TV tube	Seat row spacing		
	3'0"	4'4"	5'2"
17"	5'6"	4'2"	3'9"
19"	5'8"	4'4"	3'10"
21"	7'1"	5'5"	4'10"
23"	7'2"	5'6"	4'11"

Figure 9.8 Classroom capacity and viewing angles. (a) **Maximum viewing distance;** (b) **minimum viewing distance (30° is maximum vertical viewing angle).** *Courtesy of Educational Facilities Laboratory.*

Closed-circuit television systems are most widely used in school systems. They can receive off-air broadcasts through elaborate and highly efficient master antenna systems; more important, they permit the local origination of programs. Distribution of the programs is rigidly controlled by joining all receivers to a cable which carries the television signal. Programs originating on a closed-circuit system cannot be picked up off the air. The receiver must be connected to a cable in the system in order to share in the programming of that system.

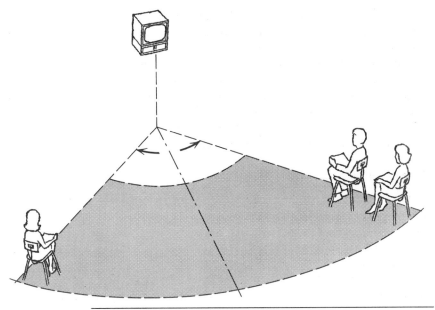

Furniture and spacing between			
chair 3'0"	tablet armchair 3'0"	 4'4"	desk and chair 5'2"
Size of TV tube	Number of viewers		
17"	32–34	21	20–23	16–18
19"	36–38	22	20–26	20–21
21"	52–54	31	31–36	24–29
23"	54–56	31	36–38	24–29

Figure 9.9   Horizontal viewing angle. A line of vision not more than 45° from the axis is the maximum angle recommended for viewing most material. (If certain televised material requires an absolute minimum of distortion, the angle may be reduced to 40° or even 30°.) *Courtesy of Educational Facilities Laboratory.*

The Television Camera

Basic to any television installation where programming is to be originated as well as received is the camera itself. Of the several types of TV camera available (Figure 9.10 and 9.11), the Vidicon camera is most practical for the majority of closed circuit installations. It is compact, rugged, requires a minimum amount of maintenance, and can be operated by anyone capable of tuning a TV receiver. It does, however, require somewhat more illumination than do other cameras.

Most cameras are equipped with viewfinders that are actually miniature TV monitors. These viewfinders indicate to the cameraman the nature of the picture that is being taken by the camera. For studio use, cameras are usually mounted on tripods with pan and tilt heads that permit the camera to be turned in any direction with fingertip control. When the camera must move in or back from the subject, a dolly with smoothly rotating and lockable wheels is a standard piece of equipment. The cameras are often equipped with a lens turret that allows flexibility in the positioning of the camera and the angle of the coverage (Figure 9.12).

Video Control Equipment

The signal that is generated by the camera can be sent directly to a television receiver in simple closed-circuit systems. In more complex operations, when several cameras are to be used and the program is to be relayed to several different locations, specialized control equipment is necessary.

The studio control console (Figure 9.13) is the heart of the studio operation; it contains every provision for controlling the signals from the cameras and the sound sources. From the console, the director can see each picture being transmitted from each camera, balance them for brightness and contrast, switch from one to the other, or fade out from one to another. One section of the console contains remote controls for operating projection equipment. Facilities are also provided for communicating with the cameramen through their headphones and with the studio in general through a loud-speaker. One monitor or viewer is provided for each camera, as well as a monitor for the signal going out over the distribution system.

Projection Equipment

The television camera is hardly limited to the transmission of live images. It can be used with auxiliary equipment to transmit filmed, printed, and recorded material of virtually every description. The integration of all these materials with live programming is perhaps of greatest significance.

Projection equipment can be used to direct the image onto a screen from which the TV camera then picks up the image, or the projected image can be directed into the lens of the TV camera. A film chain (Figure 9.14) comprises a television camera and one or more projectors mounted in a fixed-position assembly that maintains the necessary optical relationship. An optical device, the multiplexer, is used for smooth and instantaneous switching from one projector to another, such as from motion pictures to slides.

A professional-type film chain/multiplexer assembly, including a 16-mm

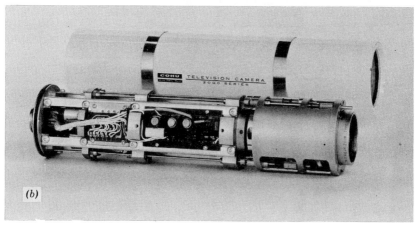

Figure 9.10 Television cameras for school use.

motion-picture projector, 35-mm slide projector, and mounting assembly would cost approximately $3500, not including the television camera itself.

Practical and economical alternatives are available, however, using the rear-projection screen techniques. On one application, the camera itself is mounted on a swivel for use with a pair of projectors. Apart from its initial savings, this method permits other uses to be made of all the equipment.

A school with a master distribution system and a film projection center can overcome some of the inherent problems met in the conventional method of showing films in classrooms. No time is lost in bringing the projector to the classroom or the class to the projector. Nor is there any

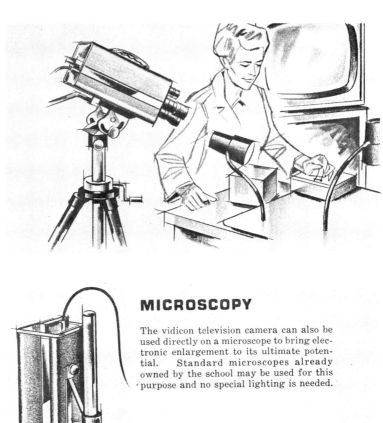

MICROSCOPY

The vidicon television camera can also be used directly on a microscope to bring electronic enlargement to its ultimate potential. Standard microscopes already owned by the school may be used for this purpose and no special lighting is needed.

Figure 9.11 *Courtesy of Sylvania Corp.*

ELECTRONIC ENLARGEMENT

Closed circuit television lends itself readily to a wide variety of uses simply as an electronic enlarger for the benefit of students within the same classroom as the teacher. The teacher needs little training in television beyond a short introduction to the equipment, and few preparations beyond those made previously.

The equipment for this purpose consists of a camera on a convenient stand or tripod, a monitor for the teacher's guidance and whatever receivers are needed to serve the students. (In a small class, a single receiver can serve both functions simultaneously.) Installation involves no more than connecting the camera to the receiver(s) and plugging the power cord of each into an AC outlet.

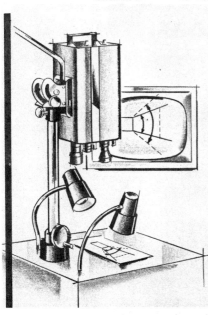

OVERHEAD TV

Another technique using the equipment already described is "overhead" television, similar in principle to the overhead projector. For this purpose, the camera is mounted on a close-up stand and used to "project" any opaque (flat or three-dimensional) object onto the television screen. Nothing has to be specially photographed, drawn, or reproduced on film.

Since the materials are resting on a horizontal surface, the teacher can move them about as he pleases, write on them, drop prepared overlays and otherwise take as much advantage of his "stage" as he chooses.

Of course, the size of the over-all televised image is limited by the size of the receiver's tube, but by lowering and raising the camera (or by using a zoom lens, preferably), any portion of the original material can be selected to fill the entire screen in close-up.

With such an opportunity thus afforded to make convenient and effortless use of visual aids, a teacher is more likely to incorporate more of them in his lecture than ever before.

Figure 9.11 (*continued*)

Figure 9.12 Television cameras are being designed to fit specialized broadcast situations.

256

change in the classroom atmosphere. The room stays lighted and the students can take notes without any difficulty.

Videotape Recording

The advent of the low-cost, portable videotape recorder may well have an effect on educational television comparable to the changes videotape has long since made in commercial broadcasting. Until 1963 videotape recorders cost approximately $50,000 and were warranted only in major state-wide or university installations. Now, however, any school with a master distribution system can look forward to the use of the growing libraries of specially taped lectures and courses. Even more significant, schools which would want to originate their own closed-circuit pro-

Figure 9.13   The studio console is the heart of the TV operation.

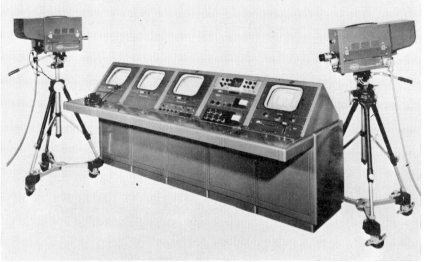

Figure 9.13 (*continued*)

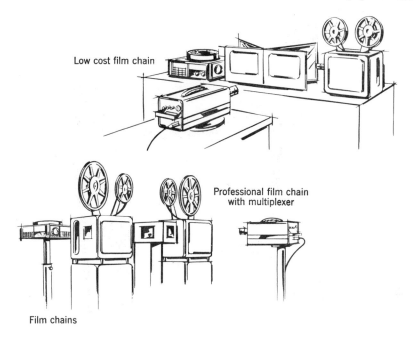

Low cost film chain

Professional film chain
with multiplexer

Film chains

Figure 9.14 Projected images can be directed into the lens of the TV camera. *Courtesy of Sylvania Corp.*

gramming can justify the original production costs by recording on tape (Figure 9.15) for repeated showings at any convenient hour.

The procedure for operating the videotape recorder is essentially the same as that employed with the audiotape recorder. Using a standard Vidicon camera and sound system, a complete program can be taped and played back instantly on any standard monitor. Tapes can be reused repeatedly, preserved indefinitely, and easily erased and edited to be kept up-to-date. Technical quality is equal to that of live broadcasting. One model using 1-in. wide tape offers about $1\frac{1}{2}$ hours of playing time per reel. Another model, designed for use with 2-in. tape, plays up to 5 hours per reel.

Of all the educational media used in the classroom, television has aroused the most controversy, has been the most thoroughly evaluated, and holds the greatest potential as an instructional tool. According to a Ford Foundation report: where television is most effectively used, it is *team teaching*. Television teaching is not a one-man operation. There are many people involved, all of whom have a contribution to make; and if anyone does not deliver his contribution, the whole operation suffers and

Figure 9.15   The Ampex Videotrainer is a self-contained, mobile, videotape recording system. It combines a videotape recorder with a television camera, television receiver, and all related equipment necessary for the production and display of videotape programs.

the teaching is usually ineffective. The members of the team include the studio teacher, the classroom teachers, the producer, the supervisor or consultant of the subject area, and the administrator. In situations in which TV programs have been most successful, these people have met together, planned together, and worked together.

SELECTED REFERENCES

Bowen, Charles G., and Raymond Wyman. "New Vistas of CCTV" *Audiovisual Instruction*, **11**, 188–189 (March, 1966).

Brown, James W., Richard B. Lewis, and Fred F. Harcleroad. *Audio-Visual Instruction Materials and Methods*. New York: McGraw-Hill, 1959. Chapter 10.

Cassirer, J. R. *Television Teaching Today*. Paris, France: United Nations Educational, Scientific, and Cultural Organization, 1960.

Costello, Lawrence F., and George N. Gordon. *Teach with Television*. New York: Hastings, 1961.

Dale, Edgar. *Audio-Visual Methods in Teaching* (rev. ed.) New York: Holt, Rinehart & Winston, 1961. Chapter 14.

DeCecco, John P. *Human Learning in the School.* New York: Holt, Rinehart & Winston, 1963. Chapters 3 and 6.

Design for ETV: Planning for Schools with Television. New York: The Educational Facilities Laboratories, Inc., 1960.

Diamond, Robert M. (ed.) *A Guide to Instructional Television.* New York: McGraw-Hill, 1964.

Educational Television: The Next Ten Years. Stanford: Institute for Communication Research, 1962.

Erickson, Carleton W. H. *Fundamentals of Teaching With Audiovisual Technology.* New York: Macmillan, 1965. Chapter 5.

Frazier, A., and J. E. Wigren (eds.). *Interaction in Learning: Implications for Television,* NEA, 1960.

Haas, Kenneth B., and Harry Q. Packer. *Preparation and Use of Audio-Visual Aids* (3rd ed.). Englewood Cliffs, N. J.: Prentice-Hall, 1955. Chapter 14.

Hall, Roger. *Taking Hold of Television.* New York: National Publicity Council, 1954.

Hilliard, Robert L. "New Directions in Educational Broadcasting," *Audiovisual Instruction,* **11,** 13–15 (January, 1966).

Instructional Television Materials: A Guide to Films, Kinescopes, and Videotapes Available For Television Use. Cambridge, Mass.: Northeastern Regional Instructional Television Library, 1964 and annually.

JCET Educational Television Factsheet. Washington, D.C.: Joint Council on Educational Television (published monthly).

Kinder, James S., *Audio-Visual Materials and Techniques* (2nd ed.). New York: American Book Co., 1959. Chapter 12.

Kumata, Hideya. *An Inventory of Instructional Television Research* (rev. ed.). Ann Arbor, Michigan: Educational Television and Radio Center.

Michel, Sister M. "Marywood's Mobile TV Unit," *Audiovisual Instruction,* **11,** 27–30 (January, 1966).

Morse, Arthur D. *Schools of Tomorrow— Today.* Garden City: Doubleday, 1960.

Radio and Television Bibliography. (Bulletin 1956, No. 2.) Washington, D.C.: Department of Health, Education, and Welfare, Office of Education, 1956.

Schramm, Wilbur, Jack Lyle, and Edwin B. Parker. *Television in the Lives of Our Children.* Stanford, California: Stanford, 1961.

Stascheff, Edward, and Rudy Bretz. *The Television Program* (rev. ed.). New York: Hill and Wang, 1962.

"Teacher Education," *Audiovisual Instruction,* **10,** No. 7, (September, 1965).

Teaching by Television. New York: Ford Foundation, Office of Reports, 1959.

"Television in Education." (Bulletin No. 21.) Washington, D.C.: U.S. Department of Health, Education, and Welfare, Office of Education, 1957.

Television in Instruction, an Appraisal. Washington, D.C.: Department of Audio-Visual Instruction, NEA, 1958.

INSTRUCTIONAL MATERIALS

"On the Air," 16-mm. film, 30 min., sound, b & w, Michigan State University, 1956.

"The Second Classroom," 16-mm. film, 30 min., sound, b & w, NEA, 1961.

"Teaching by Television," 33-mm, filmstrip, 48 frames, silent, color, Basic Skills, 1957.

"Television in Education," 16-mm. film., 30 min., sound, Bell Telephone Co.

"Television in Your Community," 16-mm. film, 11 min., sound, b & w or color, Coronet, 1956.

10

PROGRAMMED INSTRUCTION

In the past few years a great deal of attention and research has been devoted to programmed instruction. Misnomers and misinformation have tended to cling to this new instructional approach. Teaching machines, programmed learning, autoinstructional devices (with the implication of the effect on the teacher's position)—these, and many more, are terms that tend to be confused in any discussion or evaluation of programmed instruction.

The basic principles surrounding the theory of programmed instruction are simply stated:

1. Learning proceeds most easily if it is acquired in small steps. Even the most difficult concept can be learned if broken down to its elemental components, and these components individually learned in a logical order.
2. Active participation is more effective than passive reception. A person learns better if he must do something that helps embed what he has learned each step along the way.
3. Rewards strengthen or "reinforce" learning, and the greater the reward the stronger the reinforcement. In programmed learning, a student knows at once that he has learned something correctly.
4. Learning is best when a student proceeds at his own pace. In programmed learning, the lesson proceeds only when the student has completed a step and understood it.[1]

Much of today's interest in programmed learning is the result of the work and teaching of Professor B. F. Skinner of Harvard University. His work with teaching machines has led to a proliferation of devices being offered by various industrial concerns. Nearly 200 private companies are now producing or planning to produce teaching machines and/or programmed books for schools located throughout the United States.

[1]Wilbur Schramm, *Programmed Instruction: Today and Tomorrow* The Fund for the Advancement of Education, New York, 1962.

Skinner's teaching device was not the first. As long ago as the 1920's, Sidney L. Pressey at Ohio State University developed a machine that could test and teach. Its principle, too, was reward. To the student who completed an exercise correctly, it presented a piece of candy. Pressey declared that an industrial revolution in education was on the way. But the idea did not catch on until 30 years later, well after Skinner's work had been published. It was a time when the nation was deeply anxious about its educational system. Were children learning fast enough? Where would we find enough teachers? How could technical training be speeded? Machines and programmed texts loomed as a possible answer, and they soon were offered to the public in ever-increasing numbers.

The figures for the number of schools actively using programmed instruction is difficult to obtain. A study undertaken by the Center for Programmed Instruction for the United States Office of Education indicated a steady growth in the use of such materials. An interesting aspect of this study was the information that the emphasis was on programmed textbooks rather than on mchinery or "hardware." Less than 20% of the schools reporting use of programmed materials showed any inclination to use hardware.[2]

The proponents of programmed learning have cited many factors as contributing to the popularity of this method of instruction:

1. Programmed learning techniques take the drudgery out of teaching. Teacher reacts to new situations in a creative manner rather than in a routine way.
2. Students enjoy assuming the responsibility for their learning (Figure 10.1). It allows all pupils to participate actively at all times.
3. Students have, in effect, individual teachers; the feedback from these "teachers" provides high incentive for learning.
4. More content is covered in a given time and learning is more lasting than through conventional methods.
5. Learning step-by-step facilitates the mastery of skills and ideas.
6. The machines do not dictate the educational programs. Books or teachers will not be eliminated. Work of teachers will be redirected to more meaningful activities.

The results of the survey indicate the continued growth of programmed instruction in the classrooms at all levels.

[2]Center for Programmed Instruction, Inc., *The Use of Programmed Instruction in the United States Schools*, U.S. Office of Education, 1963.

Figure 10.1 Pupils are urged not to vie with each other to see who can complete more steps of the program at each session. They are told that learning rates differ and that slow learners are not necessarily less able or less intelligent than those who learn more rapidly. *Photo by Hella Hamid.*

TYPES OF PROGRAMS

The several types of programs that have been developed thus far can be grouped under the main headings of linear programming and adaptive programming.

Linear Programming

Linear programming involves the step-by-step presentation of material in a fixed, logical, sequential order. Steps are so small and the cues and "prompts" so many that correct answers are expected to the questions and are generally obtained. Reinforcement is immediate because the correct answer is available for comparison before moving on to the next bit of information or frame. The program is sef-contained from beginning to end; it does not depend on aid from any other sources. The goal of the program is to reduce the cues to as few in number as possible, yet to ensure the respondent the opportunity of answering the questions of filling in the blanks correctly.

Linear programming stemmed from the early work of Skinner. Skinner's plan called for the student to recall information and demonstrate his competence by filling in the blanks in statements before moving on to new information.

Many of the programmed textbooks being published currently are based on this approach. And so are the programs being used in the less expensive teaching machines. Figure 10.2 illustrates linear programming. Note the small steps or *bits* of information; the organization of the frame—the statement, the blanks, the space for writing in the response, the correct answer; and the use of cues or prompts.[3]

Adaptive Programming

Adaptive programming, also called *branching*, was developed by Norman Crowder and allows for the individual differences in the students' interest and background. Variations are introduced in the fixed sequence of step-by-step bits of information. If a wrong response is made to an item the program may direct the student to branch out from the main sequence in order to pick up the information that he may be lacking. Similarly, if a student demonstrates through his answers to certain items that he is familiar with the material being presented, the program may move him ahead more rapidly by allowing him to omit certain sections.[4]

Adaptive programming of material is available in textbook form, known as scrambled texts, or in machines, which in some cases are highly complex mechanisms. The machines use filmstrips or microfilms, and the tasks or questions appear in individual frames. The film can be manipulated through the machine at a high rate of speed in order to reach the various frames called for by the branching system.

In any analysis of programmed instruction it should be emphasized that the machinery or the hardware or the binding have no effect on the worth or value of the system. The value lies in the organization and construction of the program itself (Figure 10.3). It is in this area that programmed instruction has its greatest weakness: there have been too few good programs. Too much emphasis in the past has been placed on selling the hardware and extolling the merits of a particular machine as opposed to

[3]Evans, James L., *Principles of Programmed Learning*, TMI-Grolier, New York, 1962.

[4]Crowder, Norman A., "Automatic Tutoring by Intrinsic Programming," in A. A. Lumsdaine, and Robert Glaser, *Teaching Machines and Programmed Learning*, Dept. O A-V Instruction, NEA, 1959, pp. 286–298.

1	Learning should be fun.
	However, in the early stages of learning a subject,
	students often make many errors.
	Most people (do/do not) like to make errors.

do not

| 2 | When a student makes many errors in learning, he often decides that he does not like the subject. |
| | He would be more correct to decide that he does not like to make _____. |

errors

3	For a long time, educators, psychologists, and people in general thought it was impossible to
	learn without making a large number of *errors*.
	In fact, they even had a name for this kind of learning. They called it "trial-and-_____" learning.

error

4	Recent developments in the psychology of learning have cast serious doubts as to the necessity of
	"trial-and-error" learning. If the learning material is carefully prepared, or PROGRAMED, in
	a special way, the student can master the subject while making very few errors. The material you
	are reading right now has been prepared, or _____ in this special way.

programed

5	The basic idea of programed learning is that the most efficient, pleasant, and permanent
	learning takes place when the student proceeds through a programed course by a large number of small,
	easy-to-take steps.
	If each step the student takes is small, he (is/is not) likely to make errors.

is not

1

Figure 10.2   An example of linear programming. *Courtesy of Teaching Machines, Inc.*

266

6	A *programed course* is made up of many small, easy-to-take steps.
	A student can proceed from knowing very little about a subject to mastery of the subject by going
	through a _____ _____.
	If the programed course is carefully prepared, he should make (many/few) errors along the way.

programed course   few

7	Programed learning has many features which are different from conventional methods of learning.
	You have already learned one of these principles.
	This principle is that a student learns best if he proceeds by small _____.

steps

8	The features of programed learning are applications of *learning principles* discovered in
	psychological laboratories.
	You have learned the first of these principles.
	You can guess that we call it the Principle of Small _____.

Steps

9	The principles on which programed learning is based were discovered in
	(psychological/astrological) laboratories.
	The first of these principles is the Principle of Small Steps.

psychological

10	The first Principle of Programed Learning is
	The Principle of _____ _____.

Small Steps

2   Printed in U.S.A.

Figure 10.2 (*continued*)

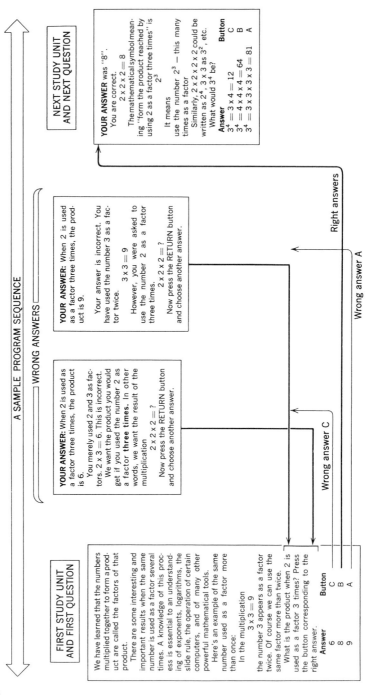

Figure 10.3   A sample of adaptive or branching programming.

another. Today subject specialists, using the principles of learning and carefully testing and evaluating their work, are producing programs of significant worth to the classroom teacher. In 1961 there was a total of 121 programs for use in schools at all levels. Today that number has increased five times, and the expectation is that the growth will continue.

Various research studies have indicated that when the objectives of a program were clearly set and programmed instruction is designed to achieve those objectives, students were able to gain as much, and sometimes more, from programmed instruction as they could from conventional methods of instruction. Without careful study of the needs of the curriculum and the quality of the programs, however, adoption of programmed instruction will not guarantee success; more often it will result in failure of the new approach.

Teachers and administrators contemplating the use of programmed materials should check these criteria:

1. Is the content adequate for the principles being taught?
2. It is well programmed: are the steps small enough?
3. Have the students been exposed to programmed material before, and, if so, what has been their reaction?
4. What has been the composition of the tested groupings; will it be necessary to use programs for some students and not for others in the same class?

Programmed materials stand a chance of having a high degree of success in the classroom if the above-noted criteria have been carefully checked and evaluated.

TYPES OF TEACHING MACHINES

If there is any area that has been exploited recently by equipment manufacturers, it has been the area of teaching machines. Equipment of all varieties and different price ranges are available (Figure 10.4). Some classification can be attempted along the following lines, as suggested by David Cram:

"There are *constructed response* machines in which the student writes his answer on a tape and compares it with the correct answer, which is exposed only when the student's answer is covered with a plastic window (so he can't change it when he sees the correct answer). A variation on this allows the student, after he has written his response, to uncover a clue (at the same time covering his response with a window). At this point he may write a second response if he wishes to amend the first one.

Figure 10.4 Examples of teaching machines. (a) *Courtesy Programmed Teaching Aids, Inc.;* (b) *Courtesy of Groflex, Inc.;* (c) *Courtesy U.S. Industries, Inc.;* (d) *Courtesy Grolier Educational Corp.*

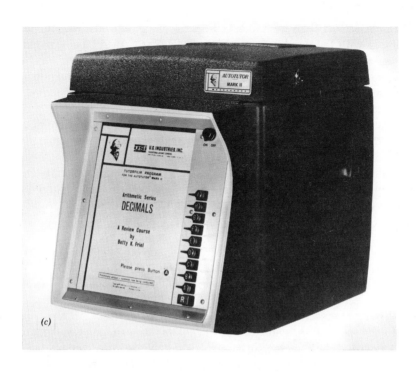

(c)

(d)

Figure 10.4 (*continued*)

The answer may then be unmasked (at the same time covering the second response with the window), and both answers may then be compared with the correct answer.

"There are *drill devices* in which each item comes back again and again; but when the student answers an item correctly a predetermined number of times, it drops out and does not reappear.

"There are *constructed response* machines in which the student does not write the response but rather constructs his answer mechanically by moving sliders.

"There are *multiple choice linear devices* which require the student to push buttons, punch holes in paper with a stylus, pull tabs, or type his answer on a keyboard, all of which immediately provide some knowledge of results (i.e., right or wrong).

"There is a *machine for branching programs* which presents the program on a microfilm viewer. The alternatives are selected by a choice of push-buttons.

"Finally, there is the *computer-oriented*, or self-organizing, program for developing motor skills.

"What will these machines provide?

"First, they all provide an environment in which the learner is, to a greater or lesser degree, in control. He decides when 'time is up' on a given item; he decides when he wants to know the correct answer. The knowledge that his mistakes will be recorded makes the control meaningful and motivates him to attend to the problem. From the teachers' point of view, the recording of responses permits evaluating both the effectiveness of the program and the performance of the individual student. Based on this record, the teacher may provide guidance or assistance as needed.

"Second, because the machine is to a greater or lesser degree responsive to the student, it provides an environment in which outside distractions are less noticeable. The student whose mind wanders during a lecture may miss an important point; a machine will not proceed unless the student is ready. The more attractive the learning situation, the more readily will students apply themselves to it. Motivational devices such as visible counters and timers, lights, and even buzzers are available on some machines.

"Third, although the initial cost of a branching machine is high, the program is stored on microfilm and thus is less costly and requires for less storage space than the equivalent program in scrambled book form.

"Fourth, machines may add a dimension of interaction that could not be achieved in any other way. The self-organizing program represents a constant and highly sensitive interaction between student and machine in the learning of motor skills; designs are feasible that would allow similar treatment of verbal subject matter. A computer with an undistractable brain ready instantly to call forth any information in its memory bank could, on the basis of student response to test items, redirect the student to any number of alternative paths, depending on the background and even the temperament of the student. Because a computer could time responses and compare them with all other responses, it could allow the student to compete with his own past performance, with his aspirations, or with other students. The machine could decide, on the basis of the time taken for each response, whether the student needs simpler steps or harder steps. It could, by constant testing, prevent the student from stumbling through the program without really paying attention. These designs are still speculative, however, and will require considerable research and improvement in programming techniques and skills before they can be realized."[5]

Grolier Educational Corporation.   The Grolier Educational Corporation is a leading producer of programmed materials and machines. Its programmed textbooks utilize the organization of programmed information with the form of the textbook. Text material is presented in a logical, fixed sequence. Students are required to participate actively by making responses to the questions either by writing them into the blanks provided or on separate sheets of paper. A simple sliding mask is used to simulate the machine function.

Grolier provides inexpensive machines in the use of which greater motivation and control of programmed material is desired. The Min/Max Teaching Machine is supplied with programs printed on $8\frac{1}{2}\times11$-in. sheets. A control knob allows the movement of each item or frame past an opening covered with plastic. A student responds to the queston by writing in a blank provided in another aperture. When the knob is turned, the answer is moved under a protective sheet of plastic at the same time that the correct answer is revealed. This prevents the student from changing his response when the correct answer is shown. Machines are available without the answer aperture, in which case the student responses are written on a separate sheet of paper.

The controls are so constructed that the sheet cannot be reversed. As each sheet of the program passes the aperture, it is directed to the bottom of the stack of sheets. The machine can be locked to prevent students from tampering with the order of the sheets.

The Ferster Tutor.   Programmed Teaching Aids, Inc., produces the Ferster Tutor, a book-size, inexpensive, self-instructional device that uses program tapes that are also produced by the company. When the

[5]David Cram, *Explaining "Teaching Machines" and Programming,* San Francisco: Fearon, 1961, pp. 77–78.

program tape is installed in the Tutor, the instructional material is viewed through the clear plastic window. The question appears on the left. The correct answer, printed on the program tape, is blocked from the student's view. The student writes his response on the answer tape through the cutout on the right side of the window. When the roller is turned, the student's response moves up under the plastic window where it cannot be altered or changed. At the same time, the correct answer appears in the center of the window. In this way the student can check his own answer immediately.

When the program tape is completed it can be reused by installing a new answer tape in place of the used one. Thus the program tapes can be used repeatedly.

The AutoTutor Mark II. United States Industries. Inc., through its educational science division, offers several models of "automated" tutoring machines. With the AutoTutor Mark II the student is given the material to be learned in small, logical units. His comprehension or ability to use the material is tested immediately. If the student passes the test question he is automatically given the next unit of information and the next question. If he fails the test queston, the preceding unit of information is reviewed, the nature of his error is explained to him, and he is retested.

The Auto Tutor machine is basically a semi-random access film projector with a rear-projection screen. To the right of the viewing screen is a row of nine selector buttons and one return button. When the student presses the button corresponding to his response to a multiple-choice question, the AutoTutor machine immediately presents the student with the page corresponding to the button he pressed. A code on each film frame (or page) determines which response button will be activated. When the student makes an error and reaches a corrective page, the code on that page will permit only the return button to operate. As a result, the student is required to go back and reread the original material and answer the question again.

The AutoTutor machine is simple to operate and maintain. It is of sturdy construction. Reels of film can be changed quickly. All pages on the reel are numbered, and the rapid search speed (using the rapid traverse switch) of 13 pages per second, makes it possible to move quickly to any point on the reel. Errors are recorded on a counter beneath the lid of the machine.

CONCLUSION

Programmed materials and equipment have been subjected to many experimental studies in the classroom. The results and findings in most cases have been specific to the circumstances and the situations in which they were useful. In general, the findings indicate that a well-constructed program—logically sequenced in short steps—can produce good results in total teaching situations and also in situations in which the program supplements other instruction.

It has been demonstrated in many studies that students learn at least as much through programmed instruction as they do through other methods of instruction—and this usually occurs with a saving in time.[6] Students generally enjoy working with programmed material.[7]

The key role of teacher attitude toward this medium cannot be over-emphasized. When teachers understand the programs and integrate them with other channels of teaching—such as textbooks, workbooks, television, films, and other audiovisual aids, while constantly checking on the effectiveness of presentation—programmed materials can serve a useful function in the classroom.[8]

SELECTED REFERENCES

Burns, Richard W., and Craik, Mary B. "Using Programs in the Classroom," *Audiovisual Instruction*, **10**, 697–699 (November, 1965).

Bushnell, Donald D. "The Role of the Computer in Future Instructional Systems," *AV Communication Review*, **11**, 1–70 (March–April, 1963).

Center for Programmed Instruction. *The Use of Programmed Instruction in U.S. Schools*. U.S. Office of Education, 1963.

Corrigan, Robert F. "Student Response Systems: A Defense of the Concept," *Audio-visual Instruction*, **8**, 599–601 (October, 1963).

Cram, David. *Explaining "Teaching Machines" and Programming*. San Francisco: Fearon 1961.

Cronbach, Lee J. "What Research Says about Programmed Instruction" *NEA Journal*, **51**, 45–47 (December, 1962).

Finn, James D., and Donald G. Perrin. *Teaching Machines and Programmed Learning. A Survey of the Industry*. U.S. Office of Education, 1962.

Fry Edward. *Teaching Machines and Programmed Instructions: An Introduction*. New York: McGraw-Hill, 1963.

Galanter, Eugene (ed.). *Automatic Teaching: The State of the Art*. New York: Wiley, 1959.

Hanson, Lincoln F. (ed.). *Programs '63: A Guide to Programmed Instructional Materials Available to Education by September 1963*. U.S. Office of Education, Bulletin 1964, no. 3, OE-34015-63.

Jacobs. Paul I. "Some Relationships between Testing and Auto-instructional Programming." *AV Communication Review*, **10**, 317–327 (November–December, 1962).

[6]Center for Programmed Instruction, Inc., *The Use of Programmed Instruction in U.S. Schools*. U.S. Office of Education, 1963, pp. 55–57.

[7]Lee J. Cronbach, "What Research Says About Programmed Instruction," *Nea Journal*, **51**, (December, 1962). 45–47.

[8]Wilbur Schramm, *op. cit.*, pp. 38–40.

Lambert, Philip (ed.). *The Teacher and the Machine*. Madison, Wisconsin: Dember Educational Research Services, Inc., 1962.

Lumsdaine, A. A. "The Development of Teaching Machines and Programmed Self-Instruction," in Wilbur Schramm (ed.), *New Teaching Aids for the American Classroom*, Stanford, California: Institute for Communication Research, 1960,

Lumsdaine, A. A. and Robert Glaser, *Teaching Machines and Programmed Learning: A Source Book*. NEA Department of Audiovisual Instruction, 1960.

Lysaught, Jerome P., and Clarence M. Williams. *A Guide to Programmed Instruction*. New York: Wiley, 1963.

Mager, Robert F. *Preparing Objectives for Programmed Instruction*. San Francisco: Fearson, 1961.

Markle, S. M., L. D. Eigen, and P. K. Komoski. *A Programmed Primer on Programming*. vol. I and vol. II. New York: The Center for Programmed Instruction, 1961.

Schramm, Wilbur. *Programmed Instruction Today and Tomorrow*. New York: The Fund for the Advancement of Education, 1962.

Silberman, Harry F. "Self-Teaching Devices and Programmed Materials," *Review of Educational Research*, **32**, 179–193 (April, 1962).

Stolurow, Lawrence, *Teaching by Machine*. U.S. Office of Education, Cooperative Research Monograph No. OE-34010, 1961.

INSTRUCTIONAL MATERIALS

Auto-Instructional Programming, 16-mm Kinescope, 40 min., sound, b & w, Lawrence M. Stolurow, University of Illinois.

An Example of a Teaching Machine Program. 35-mm filmstrip, 62 frames, color, Basic Skill Films, 1961.

Learning and Behavior (The Teaching Machines). 16-mm, 26 min., sound, b & w, New York: Carousel Films, 1960.

Our Step at a Time, 16-mm film, 28 min., sound, color, Pittsburgh, Pa.: American Institute for Research, 1961.

A Probing Mind, 16-mm film, 29 min., sound, b & w, Washington D.C.: Norwood Films.

Teaching Machines, 35-mm filmstrip, 62 frames, silent, color, Basic Skill Films, 1960.

Teaching Machines and Programmed Learning, 16-mm film, 30 min., sound, b & w, NEA Department of Audiovisual Instruction, 1961.

11

SUPPORTING EQUIPMENT FOR AUDIOVISUAL USE

There was a tendency at one time to provide in a single room of a school building the facilities for the projection of pictures and playback of audio material. Such a room was called the "Audiovisual Room." Students were marched into the room according to carefully drawn-up schedules in order to watch a "movie" or a filmstrip or to listen to a recording.

The heavy emphasis on the use of audiovisual materials in the classroom now renders obsolete the idea of the "Audiovisual Room." Moreover, extensive educational research has proven the constantly increasing value of projected materials in regular classrooms rather than in a room specifically set aside for that purpose. Using audiovisual materials in the regular classroom has meant that certain physical arrangements in the classroom needed to be altered. Matters that required some attention included the following: room darkening, acoustic characteristics, ventilation, power, storage, and access to audiovisual equipment.

ROOM DARKENING

With the emphasis being placed on projected materials in the classroom, greater attention should be given to the control of light in the classroom. The brilliance of projected images depends upon the level of room light as well as on the light output of projectors.

Manufacturers of projection equipment have long stressed the relative merits of their units on the basis of light output. The measurements are in terms of footcandles or lumens. Although what follows may seem obvious, such equipment projects light—and light only. The black images that appear on the screen represent the absence of light from the projector. The less *room light* there is illuminating the screen, the darker the images will appear. It follows, therefore, that the most acceptable images depend upon the greatest contrast between the room light on the screen and the projected light.

The contrast can be effected by working on either factor or on both. The nonprojected light (room light) on the screen can be reduced in several ways. Turning off the room lights will help in many instances to reduce the level. The light switches should be so located that dimming can be effected smoothly and without confusion. Moreover, the light switches should independently control the lights from front to back, allowing for partial dimming at the front screen location and a level of light at the seat locations that will facilitate note-taking.

Window shades are used to reduce the amount of light coming through the windows. Their effectiveness is dependent on the opacity (or "blocking" quality) of the shade material and on the shade's size. Most shades reduce the glare from the sun but allow too much light into the room. Some teachers have remedied this by coating the shade with a latex-base paint. Even opaque shades, however, fail to reduce the light level significantly if they do not fit the window aperture. Light coming through these openings proves annoying, especially if any movement of air induces a flutter in the shades.

Venetian blinds of several varieties have been developed recently to solve these problems of "light in the classroom." With some units, tracks provide for holding the blinds in a fixed vertical position. The tracks also act as a shade to prevent light from entering through the sides of the blinds. Ventilation through open windows is possible with this method.

The blackout drape (Figure 11.1) offers the most complete approach to room darkening. Care should be exercised in hanging the drapes to guarantee full coverage of the window opening. The draw cords should be readily accessible to prevent any confusion or commotion in adapting a room for projection purposes. Such drapes are relatively expensive and must be handled with care or else they may be torn.

Much of the expense of light reduction could be avoided by reducing the number of windows in the classroom. Some cognizance is being taken of this fact in the design of new windowless school buildings. Economies are effected not only in light control but also in heating and maintenance. (There seems to be little justification for use of the skylight; yet, they seem to be in evidence in much of the recent school construction.)

Many users of projection equipment have little understanding of the characteristics of the projector they might be using. Their knowledge does not extend beyond knowing how to turn the lamp on and off, and how to focus the image. Yet classroom projectors have specific light values. Awareness of their use will make for better projections than are now

Figure 11.1 The use of projected materials in the classroom requires effective room darkening facilities. Light-proof drapery can help transform any classroom into an "audiovisual room."

common. The list below compares the wattage and light output for lamps used in typical classroom projectors:

Projector	Watts	Code	Lumens
8-mm	150	DCH	100
16-mm	750	DDB	290
Opaque	1000	DRS	145
35-mm	500	CZX	270
Overhead	420	FAL	1150
Overhead	750	DDB	2500

A glance at the figures reveals at once that an overhead projector with a 750-watt, DDB lamp produces about 20 times more illumination on the screen than does the opaque projector. Since the readability of projected images depends on the contrast between projected light and room light, it is obvious that the opaque projector requires a much darker room than does the overhead projector.

Few standards exist today for proper ratios between projected light and room light. The usual approach is to snap off the room lights, turn on the projector, and be satisfied with anything that appears on the screen. The result is usually a dull, drab, uninteresting presentation of material that is robbed of its brilliant, contrasting tones.

Eastman Kodak has set forth certain recommendations for ratios between light from motion pictures and room light. These guides are helpful and should serve as a basis for continuing development.

A useful approach to be followed by the teacher without any reference to ratios or guides would be the following:

1. Set up the projector so that it is focused on its smallest picture on a screen in a dimmed corner.
2. Preview the material.
3. Set up the equipment for normal classroom use.
4. View the projected material objectively. Has it lost its impact? Are the colors too dim? Is it difficult to read the type? Are you pleased with the effect?

A negative reaction to a projection setup should lead to some actions being taken: securing additional room-darkening facilities (blinds or drapes), or using projectors with additional light output. The latter is especially to be recommended in the case of overhead projection.

ACOUSTICS

The use of audio equipment in the classroom can prove disruptive to activities in other rooms unless special care is taken. The volume of sound should never exceed the level required for audibility in the classroom. Connecting doors and corridor doors should be closed to minimize interference with other school activities.

The use of drapes on the walls and soft, sound-absorbing ceiling panels will help to contain the sound in the classroom. These materials will also tend to make the sound more pleasing and easier to understand. Reverberations caused by sounds bouncing off hard walls and ceilings create distortions (especially in larger rooms) that make listening for information particularly difficult.

POWER

Duplex, grounded electrical outlets with standard 117-V ac power should be located on the four walls of each classroom. Since safety codes in many of the states now require grounded circuits, most portable equipment is factory-equipped with a three-conductor, universal type connector. Suitable outlets should be wired through circuit breakers with at least 15 amps available at each outlet when this load is needed *simultaneously* in a number of adjacent rooms.

Switches for control of overhead lighting should be located at the rear of the room as well as at the entrance. Provision should be made for turning off the lights individually from the front to the rear of the room. Light dimmers have been used with a great deal of success to lower the illumination to the optimum level for projection.

The trend in education is toward increased use of electronic and electro-mechanical devices for individual student use. Terminal strips along at least one side wall will facilitate use of several pieces of audiovisual equipment for such independent study.

STORAGE AND ACCESS OF EQUIPMENT

Ideally, each classroom should be equipped with its own projection and audio equipment, together with sufficient materials to minimize any delays in making use of the equipment. Past and ongoing experiments demonstrate that classroom teachers make frequent and effective use of equipment when it is readily available to them.

More frequently, however, teachers are called upon to share the usage of whatever audiovisual equipment may be assigned to a particular school. A recognized practice in school audiovisual service is to mount equipment on mobile projection stands (carts) and to store the material centrally for use in several classrooms, as needed. Paved walkways, ramps rather than steps, and very low opening thresholds on all entrances greatly facilitate the mobility of such carts.[1]

Projection Tables. There are many styles and types of table available (Figure 11.2). Commercial Picture Equipment, Inc., produces the Roll-A-Lock, Model 75-B. It has four 4-in. wheels with swivelling and braking action on each. It stands 39 in. high and has a shelf measurement of 18 × 30 in. It is of aluminum construction, and it has a plastic finish on the shelves.

The H. Wilson Corporation offers several models and sizes of projection tables. One of them is especially designed for motion-picture, filmstrip, and slide projectors. It has three 18 × 24 shelves. A 20-ft electric assembly with two outlets permits the projector to be operated anywhere in the classroom, thus eliminating the need for extension cords.

[1] *A Treasure Chest of Audiovisual Ideas*, Plainville, Connecticut: The Kalart Company, Inc., 1965, pp. 25–27.

Figure 11.2   A projection table gives easier accessibility of audiovisual equipment to the classroom. *Courtesy of H. Wilson Corp.*

The Advance Products Company, in addition to manufacturing a complete line of tables of all sizes, produces accessories that take the obstacles out of stairs and curbings. The Pixmobile Model "Loadmaster" Set utilizes 10-in. treaded rubber tires to effect better steering control. It also allows the projection table to be moved up and down stairs quite readily. A rubber-covered kick plate welded to the axle provides a convenient foot position for a tilt assist of the table. Additional storage is offered in the handle basket (Figure 11.3*a*) for film cans, transparencies, power cords, etc. Handle grips on the basket give comfortable positive control of the load, especially when the table is being moved in the tilt position. Steel equipment guards are an important part of the Loadmaster because they safeguard equipment from being dropped while ascending or descending a flight of stairs.

The Pixmobile Lock-Tite Cabinet (Figure 11.3*b*) is a projection table

Figure 11.3 (*a*) **Projection table with handle basket accessory and stair-step accessory;** (*b*) **Pixmobile lock-tite Cabinet.**

that can solve the "security storage problem." It is designed to do the same job as the 42-in. projection—table with added advantages. The lower section of the unit is fully enclosed with welded steel panels and a hinged locking and latching door. It is a safe area for storing projectors, tape recorders, record players, or audiovisual materials.

Mention was made in an earlier chapter of portable rear-projection units. The H. Wilson Corporation is one of several suppliers of such a unit, which is an adaptation of the projection table. The Movie-Mover RP II (Figure 11.4) has a table 40 in. high, 22 in. wide, and 42 in. long, plus a 12-in. drop shelf. The table is completely enclosed; it has metal sliding doors which can be locked if equipment of value is being stored in it. Permanently mounted to the top of the table is a screen measuring 18 × 24 in., and made of unbreakable translucent vinyl optically engineered to provide brilliant sharp pictures in undarkened rooms.

The Movie-Mover RP II is designed to work with any standard classroom projector. Special wide-angle lenses must be used in order to increase the rate of magnification.

The advantages of this unit are several:

1. Films can be viewed in any daylit (undarkened) learning area. An

Figure 11.4   Movie-Mover RP II. Film can be revised in any daylit (undarkened) learning area when projected on the unit. *Courtesy of H. Wilson Corp.*

RP has easy mobility and this fact, coupled with using the schools' existing projector, spells practical economy.

2. No valuable learning time is wasted moving individuals to a special viewing room.
3. The student remains in his normal learning environment.
4. The student can take notes while viewing films in an undarkened room.
5. A teacher can maintain visual contact with students and utilize supplementary teaching materials. The film program can be controlled via a remote control switch, and the teacher can remain at the best position for control.

The storage of audiovisual materials can pose some problems for the classroom teacher unless facilities are provided for safeguarding these materials (Figure 11.5). Manufacturers and suppliers, such as Jack C. Coffey Co., Inc., offer several different units for the filing of filmstrips,

Figure 11.5 Storage of materials and equipment should be given careful attention. Cabinets offer greater security and compactness than do open shelves. *Courtesy of Jack C. Coffey, Inc.*

sound filmstrips, disk recordings, tape recordings, 16 and 8-mm. films, film cartridges, and overhead transparencies (Figure 11.6). The units adapt themselves to a compact filing system without occupying a great deal of space.

STUDY CARRELS

Study carrels fall into the classification of equipment that supplements and supports the audiovisual program in the classroom. Individual study cubicles can be set up in any convenient location either in the classroom or in corridors, foyers, libraries, and cafeterias. The carrels are designed for individual study. They may be single units or modules; they can also be in clusters of two or four modules.

Creative design and application of the latest developments in instructional techniques have resulted in startling innovations for the study carrels (Figure 11.7). Various models are now being equipped with slide projectors and with 8-mm. projectors. Other units are designed to pick up tape programs supplied from a remote location. Multichannel closed-circuit television is being offered in other study carrels. Study carrels are, of

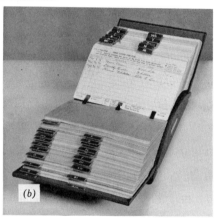

Figure 11.6 Various types and sizes of cabinets are available for the storage of records, tapes, films, and filmstrips. *Courtesy of Jack C. Coffey, Inc.*

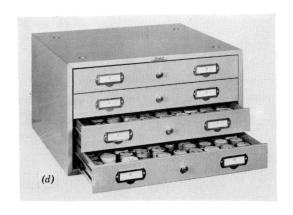

(d)

(e)

Figure 11.6 (*continued*)

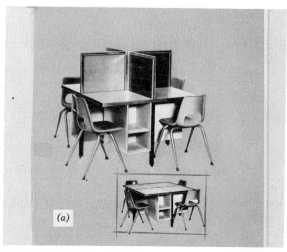

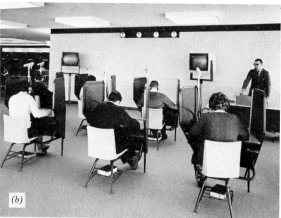

Figure 11.7   Latest innovations in study carrels include use of magnetic tape, motion picture film, and television.

course, ideal for individualized study activities involving typing, use of teaching machines, or work with textbooks.

Dage-Bell, Inc., has done much work in developing individual study areas. The Advance Products Company and other suppliers of furniture for learning laboratories now offer carrels that can be adapted for existing layouts or for newly designed learning centers.

SELECTED REFERENCES

"AV Commission Sets *Minimum   Standards* and Expenditures for School Programs," *Film World*, **XII**, 440 (August, 1956).

Audio-Visual Education Association of California: *Setting Up Your Audiovisual Education Program*. Stanford, California: Stanford University Press, 1949.

Beust, Nora E. *School Library Standards*. Washington, D.C.: The Department of Health, Education, and Welfare, Bulletin No. 15, 1954.

Brown, James W., W. R. B. Lewis, and Fred F. Harcleroad, *Av Instruction: Materials And Methods*. New York: McGraw-Hill., 1959.

Brubaker, Charles William. *Architecture and Equipment for the Language Laboratory*. New York: Educational Facilities Laboratories, 1961.

Bush, Robert N. *A New Design for High School Education*. New York: McGraw-Hill, 1964.

Chapman, Dave. *Planning for Schools With Television: Design for Educational TV*. New York: Educational Facilities Laboratories, 1960.

Cross, A. J. Foy, and Irene Cypher. *Planning Schools for the Use of Audiovisual Materials*, No. 1: *Classrooms* (3rd ed.). NEA: Department of Audiovisual Instruction, 1958.

Curl, David J. "Automated Equipment Operation Training," *Audiovisual Instruction*, **10**, 564–565 (September, 1965).

De Bernadis, Amos, and others. *Planning Schools For New Media*. Portland, Oregon: Portland State College, Division of Education, 1961.

Department of Audiovisual Instruction, NEA, *Audio Programs*. Entire issue of *Audiovisual Instruction*, February, 1958; *Teacher Education*. Entire issue of *Audiovisual Instruction*, January, 1959. Washington, D.C.

Department of Audio-visual Instruction, NEA, *Planning Schools For Use of Audiovisual Materials*, No. 2: *Auditoriums*, 1953; No. 3: *The Audiovisual Instructional Materials Center*, 1954; No. 4: *Audiovisual Centers in Colleges and Universities*, 1955. Washington, D.C.

Department of Audiovisual Instruction, NEA. *The School Administrator and His Audiovisual Program*, Charles Schuller, ed. Washington, D.C., 1954.

Durr, William J. "What Is Your School's Instructional-Materials Quotient?" *National Education Association Journal*, **42**, 439–440 (October, 1953).

Faris, Gene, John Moldstad, and Harvey Frye, *Improving the Learning Environment*. Washington, D.C.: United States Printing Office, 1963.

Hauf, Jarold D., and others. *New Spaces for Learning*, Troy N. Y.: Rensselaer Polytechnic Institute, School of Architecture, 1961.

Hurd, Paul DeH. *Science Facilities for the Modern High School*, Stanford, California: Stanford University, 1954.

Johnston, Roy, "University of Miami Learning and Instructional Resources Center," *AVI*, **11**, 91–93 (February, 1966).

Mannino, Philip. *ABC'S of Visual Aids and Projectionist's Manual.* New York: Educational Film Library Association, 1948.

Matthew, Archie, and Potts, Jim. "Individualize Media?" *A VI,* **11,** 42–43. (January, 1966).

McClusky, Dean, and James S. Kinder. *The Audiovisual Reader.* Dubuque, Iowa: William C. Brown, 1954.

"The New School," *Audiovisual Instruction,* **7** (October, 1962).

Nimnicht, Glendon, and Arthur R. Partridge. *Designs for Small High Schools,* Colorado State College: Greeley, 1962.

Patterson, Pierce E., and others. *Audiovisual Equipment Standards.* Los Angeles: Audiovisual Association of California, 1961.

Rice, Arthur J. (ed.). *Modern Education: Its Impact on Schoolhouse Design,* (Administration Study 14). *Nation's Schools,* **71,** 49–96 (January, 1963).

School Library Association of California, Recommended Standards. *Bulletin: The School Library Association of California* (March, 1955), pp. 10–20.

Schools For Team Teaching. New York: Educational Facilities Laboratories, 1961.

Seaton, Jelen Jardt. *A Measure for Audio-Visual Programs in Schools.* Washington, D.C.: American Council on Education, 1944.

Swartout, Sherwin G. "Developing Audio-Visual Competencies in Teachers in the Audio-visual Laboratory," *Audiovisual Instruction,* (January, 1959).

Wittich, Walter A., and Charles F. Schuller. *Audiovisual Materials: Their Nature and Use.* (3rd ed.). New York: Harper, 1962. Chapter 15.

INSTRUCTIONAL MATERIALS

Accent on Learning, 16-mm film, 29 min., b & w, Ohio State University, 1949.

Audiovisual Aids To Learning. U.S. Dept of Army, 1951, 16-mm film, 11 min., b & w.

Building for Learning, 16-mm film, 19 min., sound, color, Texas A & M College, 1948.

Classroom Lighting, 16-mm film, 20 min., sound, color, Wakefiled Brass Co., 1952.

Large-City Audiovisual Aids Organization. 44 frames, b & w filmstrip. Young American, 1949.

More Take-Home Learning Through Controlled Ventilation, 35-mm filmstrip, 59 frames, sound or silent, color, NEA, 1955.

New Tools for Learning. 19 min. b & w, *Encyclopedia Britannica* Film, 1952.

Schools for Tomorrow, 16-mm 16 min., sound, b & w or color, Wayne State University, 1956.

Small-City Audiovisual Aids Department. 40 frames, b & w. Young America, 1949.

12

NONPROJECTED AUDIOVISUAL
MATERIALS AND TECHNIQUES FOR
THE CLASSROOM

The major emphasis in this book is on the use and operation of audiovisual equipment in the classroom. Projectors, tape recorders, record players, and related materials have been described in such a way that students should have little difficulty in utilizing this equipment when assuming their role as classroom teachers.

There are other techniques and devices requiring little in the way of mechanical equipment but which are also helpful in communicating information in the classroom. These techniques and methods include the use of flat pictures; working with graphic material such as charts, graphs, cartoons, posters, maps, and globes; the effective utilization of chalkboards, bulletin boards, flannel boards, magnetic boards, electric boards; setting up three-dimensional materials and displays; realizing the role of dramatizations and demonstrations; and using community resources.

The treatment of these areas will be brief. It is suggested that anyone desiring more information on any of these topics should refer to the reading list at the end of the chapter.

FLAT PICTURES

Still or flat pictures and illustrations are all about us. They are used to illustrate the news or to illustrate stories; they are used to attract our attention in various advertisements; and they are used because they help us learn. Children are exposed to pictures at a very early age, and even before they start to school they are able to recognize various objects and identify them by name. A higher level of picture study sees the student able to delineate the details in the pictures and to describe them. The highest skill in picture study involves drawing inferences based on the details and the actions in the picture and producing various interpretations based on the background of the individual analyzing the picture.

All three skills are needed by students in order to gain the full value from the study of pictures. Research has demonstrated that pictures do aid in the communication of ideas and clarification of difficult concepts. Their use, however, must be preceded by careful selection from the many illustrations that abound in books, newspapers, magazines, and from other sources catering to the educational needs of the students. The following are some of the criteria used in selecting pictures for the classroom:

1. Accuracy of detail. The picture should be technically correct in every aspect; distortions or misconceptions could easily result from viewing inaccurate or incomplete pictures.

2. Color or contrast. The picture should be so printed as to allow the student to distinguish between the various elements and details. When color would do this best, it is recommended. But color should be realistic and should not be used merely because it might "brighten up" the series.

3. Suitability. Pictures should be related as closely as possible to the content of the lesson and the topic being studied.

4. Size. The over-all dimension should be such that the picture can be conveniently used in the classroom. Extremely large pictures would necessarily be confined to tack boards or other display areas; small pictures could be enlarged through use of the opaque projector.

5. Size relationship. The size of new or unfamiliar objects should be compared with the relative size of familiar objects in the same picture.

6. Artistic value. The picture should have some appeal as far as technical qualities are concerned. It should be well-balanced; its composition should be pleasing; it should have a center of interest that would attract the eye and from which the eye would be led naturally to the other details of the picture.[1]

The teacher is always encouraged to use the four-step plan when working with audiovisual materials: preparation of teacher, preparation of students, presentation, and follow-up. A variation of this plan could be adopted when working with flat pictures. After selecting the pictures, the teacher should determine exactly the material that will be highlighted through the use of the pictures; the number of pictures should be limited in order to avoid confusion and to permit the viewer

[1]Seth Spaulding, "*Research on Pictorial Illustration,*" Audiovisual Communication Review, 3, 43–44 (Winter, 1955).

ample time to study the illustrations that are used. Picture-learning can be directed through the asking of specific and direct questions relative to the content of the pictures as well as by the inference that might be made from viewing the various objects and action. Use of the "3 C's"—comparison, contrast, and continuity—will facilitate learning from pictures: contrast the differences in the parts of one picture or between two pictures; compare the similarities between one or more pictures, establish logical relationships between a series of pictures; and develop a unity in the whole visual program.

The teacher can stimulate creative expression in the classroom through the use of flat pictures. In addition to answering questions students can display their feelings and reactions through the writing of compositions or poetry and through art activities such as modeling, painting, or drawing.

As mentioned earlier in this chapter, pictures are available from many sources. For a particular lesson the most difficult task may be one of selection of the best one from many pictures that could possibly be used. The abundance of pictures is a worthless benefit unless the pictures are properly trimmed, classified, mounted, and filed (Figure 12.1). The teacher should have pictures so organized that without too much difficulty illustrations covering much of the topical material discussed in class can be located.

Much of the impact of a picture may be lost if it is carelessly trimmed and has ragged edges or dog-eared corners. If a picture has sufficient value to merit its protection, it should be mounted on cardboard. Mounting has many advantages: it keeps the picture flat; it protects and lengthens the life of the picture; it makes the picture easier to handle and file; it facilitates the use of pictures in the opaque projector.[2]

When one is mounting pictures, it is well to keep several points in mind. The sizes should be standardized as much as possible to facilitate filing as well as to reduce the amount of material that needs to be stocked. The mounting board should be of good quality—one that will not fray or curl in use and should be of a neutral tone so as not to contrast with or detract from the picture. The proper adherents should be used: rubber cement is very popular for this purpose. When rubber cement is applied only to the back of the picture, the picture will stick to the mounting board; but it can be removed later without any damage to the picture. A permanent mounting can be achieved by applying rubber cement to both the back of the picture and the mounting board. After the surfaces dry, they are carefully placed in contact wih each other and smoothed out. Other methods that can be used include the dry-mounting-tissue method and the liquid-adhesive method. In the latter a glue or liquid paste is applied to the back

[2]Brown Lewis, and Harcleroad, op. cit., pp. 459–462.

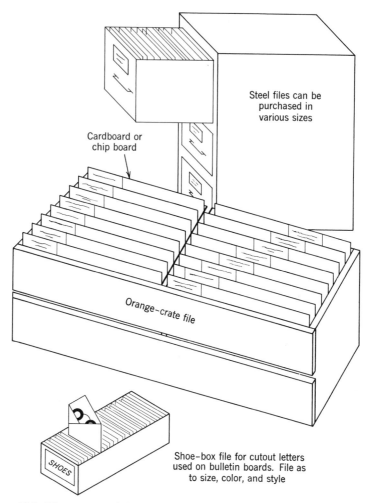

Steel files can be purchased in various sizes

Cardboard or chip board

Orange-crate file

Shoe-box file for cutout letters used on bulletin boards. File as to size, color, and style

SHOES

Figure 12.1 Pictures are of little value to the teacher unless they are properly trimmed, mounted, classified, and filed. Files could be inexpensive cardboard cartons or steel cabinets.

of the picture, the picture is positioned on the mounting board, and then covered with flat, weighted material to remove bubbles, avoid curling, and insure a good bond. When pictures might be exposed to dirt or damage through handling, the picture surface can be further protected by the application of a plastic spray coating, which is available in a pressurized can with a nozzle. It is possible also to brush or spray a thin lacquer coating over the picture.

The dry-mounting technique (Figures 12.2 and 12.3) makes use of a tissue as a bonding agent rather than rubber cement or glue. The tissue is a

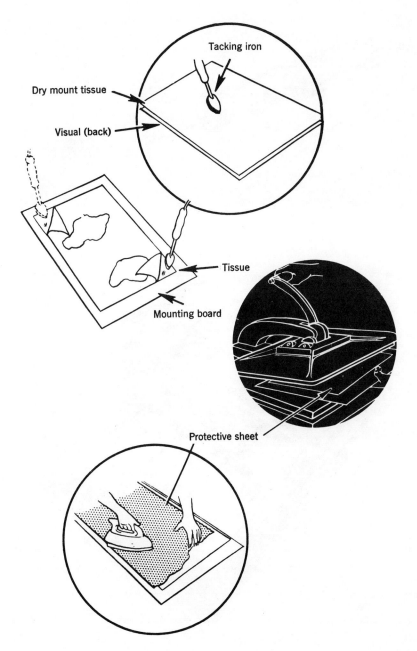

Figure 12.2   The dry-mounting technique. Ed Minor, Preparing Visual Instructional Materials, New York: *McGraw-Hill Co. Inc.*

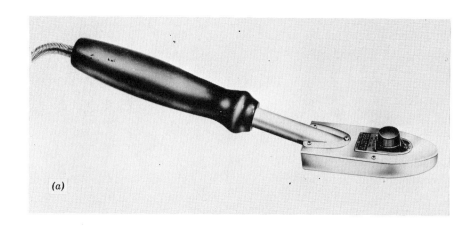

(a)

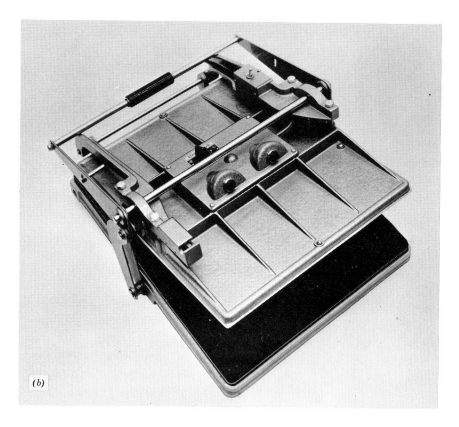

(b)

Figure 12.3 **Dry-mounting equipment.** *Courtesy of Seal, Inc.*

plastic material that will melt at a temperature of 300°. It is placed between the picture and the mounting board. The entire "sandwich" is then pressed together while heat is applied to melt the tissue. This can be accomplished with a regular flatiron, or with specially constructed dry-mounting presses.

Pictures can be filed under many different systems. Some teachers use unit designations, and *Early Explorations*, while another teacher might file the same illustration under *Transportation*. The method of storage would be largely dependent upon the extent of the picture file. A limited collection could be stored in an expandible manila folder. Wooden orange crates or sturdy cardboard cartons can be used to hold a sizable collection if standard metal filing cabinets are not available for this purpose.

Flat pictures should be given careful consideration when planning a visual presentation in the classroom. In the absence of any equipment, these pictures can be used to clarify concepts, organize and provide information, and create interest. Flat pictures are the most abundant and least expensive of the visual materials at the disposal of the teacher. For that reason, care should be exercised in the selection in order to reduce the verbal load of the lesson and to stimulate creative expression.

GRAPHIC MATERIAL FOR CLASSROOM USE

Visual material in the classroom can be divided into three categories: lettered, graphic, and pictorial. The lettered type of visual is employed to emphasize key words and phrases, to place the topics under discussion before the class, and to summarize. While not a visual in the sense that a flat picture is, the lettered type of presentation is generally considered as a valuable, although a somewhat minor, member of the visual group.

The popularity of the flat picture was considered in the previous section. It presents an easily recognizable slice of reality, one that requires little or no special knowledge or mental effort to understand and appreciate. Pictures enable us to see people, scenes, and events that because of time, distance, or cost, we could not otherwise see.

Graphics or graphic presentation (Figures 12.4, 12.5) has its own special place. It is a visual art based upon symbolic and abstract forms. It is somewhat less abstract than are words, numbers, and formulas, but more abstract than pictorial displays are. It occupies, therefore, a somewhat enviable position; one that enables it to "reach up" and give form and structure to ideas and numbers or to "bend" a bit in order to extend the visual beyond the horizons of the photograph or the artist's sketch. There are several kinds of graphic presentation: charts, maps, diagrams, graphs, and cartoons.

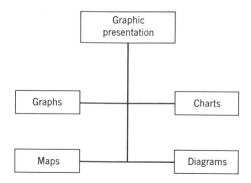

Figure 12.4 Graphic presentations are less abstract than words, numbers and formulas, but more abstract than pictorial displays. *Courtesy of Tecnifax Corp.*

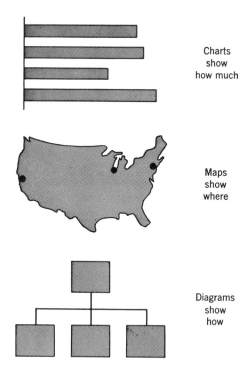

Figure 12.5 Charts, maps, and diagrams are used for specific purposes. *Courtesy Tecnifax Corp.*

Graphs depict numerical or qualitative relationships (Figure 12.6). There are two kinds: statistical amd mathematical. Statistical graphs portray data by lengths of bars, lengths and slopes of lines, by areas, by volumes, and countable units. For completeness, they require some method of estimating values, a title, and a source reference. Statistical graphs are not only effective tools for condensing, relating, and communicating data, but they are also designed and prepared for efficient and realistic recording and analysis.

A mathematical graph pictures a function in order to reveal the relationship between variables, to assist in the solution of an equation, or to speed a computation.

Charts are visualizations of nonnumerical relationships and processes. Various means can be used to clarify charts. Figure 12.7 indicates some of the techniques—by types, design, media, and materials. In the early grades a familiar use of the chart is the *experience chart*, which contains stories and accounts of the children which are written by the teacher or the children themselves on large pieces of newsprint or paper. Classroom charts at every grade level supply directions for routine activities, criteria for the evaluation of reports, and steps in the performance of tasks.

Charts showing the organization and development of a process can take various forms. The tree chart presents material symbolized by roots, trunk, branches, and leaves. Flow charts are systematic arrangements showing trends, movements, and organization. The steps involved in the enactment of a law can be depicted graphically through the flow or process chart.

The stream chart indicates how several different factors can be brought together to form a larger event. Time charts are used to indicate the chronology of a series of events or to arrange chronologically those happenings important to the development of a process, a company, or a nation. Issue charts are especially helpful in highlighting the contrasting views of individuals or organizations on pertinent topics. Pictorial charts make use of conventional or symbolic illustrations of topics that are being treated: e.g., automobiles, wheat, factories, and population growth.

Many beautifully colored charts are commercially available. Others, on various topics, are supplied free of charge to classroom teachers. Charts can be constructed by the classroom teacher as well as by the students in order to create a more meaningful learning experience.

Maps are graphic representations of the earth's surface, or portions of it. The basic problem—that of depicting the varied, boundless, and irregular surface of the earth on a limited plane surface—is a difficult one and has resulted in the development of many kinds of map projections and many types of maps. It has also resulted in many visual misrepresentations—some intentional but most of them caused by a lack of knowledge or skill on the part of the producer.

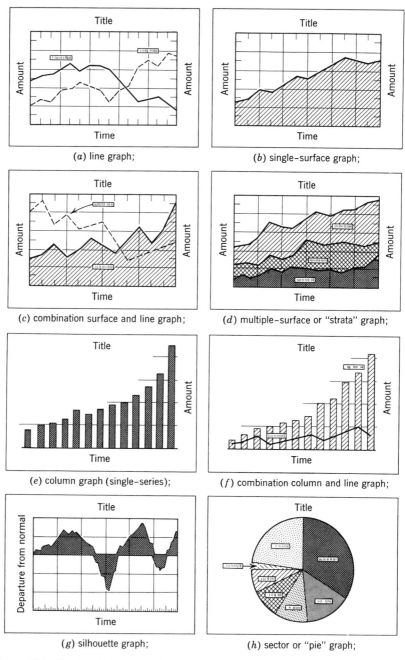

Figure 12.6 Graphs depict numerical or quantitative relationships. They portray data length of bars, length and slope of lines by area, volume, and countable units. (*a*) Line graph; (*b*) single-surface graph; (*c*) combination surface and line graph; (*d*) multiple-surface or "strata" graph; (*e*) column graph (single-series); (*f*) combination column and line graph; (*g*) silhouette graph; (*h*) sector or "pie" graph. W. A. Wittich and C. F. Schüller, *Audiovisual Materials: Their Nature and Use*, Harper, New York, 1962.

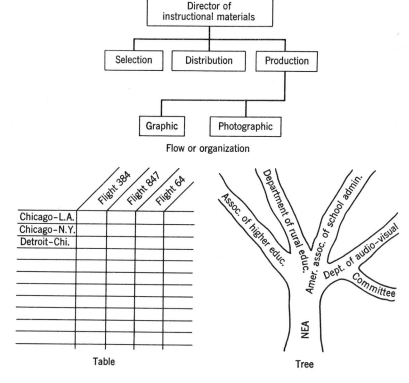

Figure 12.7 Types of charts.

Diagrams are visual descriptions that explain rather than represent (Figure 12.8). The symbolism in many cases is quite abstract and requires understanding and study on the part of the student for proper interpretation of the material. Diagrams of electrical circuits, data processing systems, how to draw a logarithmic scale or determine the radii of circles, etc., impart a form or unity to an object or process that exists only in the abstract. Diagrams should be used with care only in those instances wherein students have demonstrated a capability for comprehending such abstractions.[3]

Cartoons are another form of graphic representation that makes use of symbolism and bold exaggeration to represent quickly and at a glance a message or a point of view. Cartoons can have reference to people, news events, or situations. Their acceptance and effectiveness in the classroom have been demonstrated in various studies. Much has been contributed

[3]Francis J. McHugh, *Graphic Presentation*. An address published by Tecnifax Corporation, Holyoke, Massachusetts, 1956, pp. 6–9.

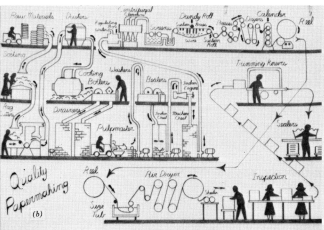

Figure 12.8 Two types of diagram: (*a*) **makes use of cartoon illustration;** (*b*) **uses a more conventional visualization.**

to learning in the classroom by cartoons' grotesque and ludicrous characterizations of individuals and distortions of certain aspects in order to emphasize comparison with the whole. The teacher must observe the subtle difference between cartoons and comics; in the latter there is little educative value. The teaching-learning relationship is best served in this situation when there is a background of understanding concerning the individuals or the scenes being depicted in a cartoon. Otherwise the illustration is accepted as a humorous one with no other impact having been made on the students.[4]

The poster is a device making use of the various graphic representations that have been described above. It is a placard utilizing an emotional appeal to convey a message aimed at reinforcing an attitude or urging a course of action (Figure 12.9). Posters may encourage safety practices or good behavior or they may promote special projects or drives. Posters in the lunchroom might emphasize good nutrition; those in the corridors might stress the need for quiet. Whatever the message, the effectiveness of a poster lies in its simplicity, directness, and use of the appropriate graphic techniques to convey its message.

Because of its abstract and therefore generalized nature, graphic presentation requires some degree of experience and intellectual maturity not only on the part of the producer, but also on the part of the reader or user. It is the responsibility of the teacher to prepare the students for the reception of this type of information. The older the student the greater should be his capability of understanding this method of communication—and also the greater should be his need.

Since graphic presentations are visual presentations, they attract and hold attention. They can describe and clarify ideas and relationships that are difficult to express in words, numbers, or formulas. Because they are abstract presentations, their scope is wide and their applications are many. Graphic presentations are savers of time and architects and builders of concepts. Perhaps the greatest advantage of graphic presentation is in its ability to communicate more-faster. Another advantage lies in the fact that a well-designed and executed graphic display can often depict the relationship between variables so clearly and vividly that the writer or speaker does not have to "spell it out." He simply pauses a moment, and the viewer—instead of being told what the relationship is—has the pleasure and satisfaction of discovering it for himself. Immediately the viewer switches from a passive listener or reader to an active, eager, and interested participant.

The purpose of graphic presentation is to communicate quickly, clearly, and memorably. Graphics should be prepared for that purpose and that purpose alone. A graphic presentation should not be produced simply to be admired, or to be funny, or to be dramatic. It should be prepared and used when it will do the job better and quicker than any other method of communication.

[4]Walter Brackman, "Cartoons in the English Class", *Clearing House*, *30*, 268. (January, 1956).

Figure 12.9 Posters should utilize an emotional appeal to convey a message aimed at reinforcing an attitude or urging a course of action. *Courtesy of Instructo Products Co.*

To accomplish its purpose, good graphic presentation must have unity, simplicity, organization, and visibility. It must have unity because it delineates one basic idea, one central theme. There is simplicity because the trivial, the unnecessary, the fancy trimmings are ruthlessly weeded out. Symbols and abbreviations unfamiliar to the viewers are not used. The lettering is simple and easy to read. Terms are not ambiguous. The amount of detail is carefully controlled.

There is organization—with an eye toward communication. The parts are arranged for rapid perception and comprehension, and the over-all picture is made as attractive and as dynamic as possible. There is visibility because every bit of information is easily seen by the most distant viewer. Briefly, the principles of effective graphic presentation can be stated in this way: be direct, be simple, be clear, and be accurate.

CHALKBOARDS

One of the first tools used in the classroom for instructional purposes was the chalkboard, and it is still with us today. The nature of its use and its physical appearance may have undergone some changes, but its importance in the instructional scheme of things remains high.

Chalkboards are so valuable because they are quick and easy to use; in many cases they may be the only tools available to the teacher for visualizing subject matter. Chalkboards can add variety and spontaneity to the teaching situation. Illustrations can be quickly changed or erased to make way for new material.

The effectiveness of the chalkboard as a teaching tool is, of course, dependent on the skill of the teacher using it (Figure 12.10). The teacher should try to put material on the chalkboard before class begins if the operation is lengthy or requires care in execution; all writing should be at the students' eye level; distracting materials should be erased or covered; variety and contrast should be worked into the chalkboard material in order to improve its appearance as well as to facilitate its study; the board surface should be kept in good condition and the chalk tray free from dust. The teacher should avoid pasting material on the chalkboard or using it strictly for the posting of notices and directives; the teacher should avoid scrawling, writing too small, or presenting too much material.

The classroom teacher and the artist are a happy and fortunate combination as far as chalkboard utilization is concerned. Few classroom teachers are artists. Yet, when reasonably accurate or close renderings of materials are required on the chalkboard, there are several techniques

Figure 12.10   The effectiveness of the chalkboard as a teaching tool is dependent on the skill of the teacher using it. de Kieffer and Cochran, *Manual of Audiovisual Techniques,* Prentice-Hall. Inc.

that the classroom teacher can use. The opaque projector or transparency projectors can direct images from books or transparencies onto the chalkboard where the lines are easily and quickly traced with chalk. Cut-out templates of simple shapes facilitate drawing on the chalkboard. Other devices that can be used in preparing chalkboard presentations are prepared patterns, grid techniques, and chalkboard drawing instruments. The prepared-pattern method utilizes holes punched at intervals in cardboard or windowshade cloth covered with chalk dust to establish outlines of often-used objects. In the grid method the material to be transferred to the board is marked off into squares, and then the chalkboard area is marked off into similar but larger squares. By following the original drawing, the chalkboard enlargement is made square by square.

Semipermanent chalk marks can be drawn by using a chalk soaked in a sugar solution. Such markings, which can be removed with a damp cloth, are useful in music work, map work, and with graphs in mathematics.

Many of the uses of the chalkboard are now being accomplished through other means and with other media: tack boards, flannel boards, and overhead projectors. The suggestion has been made that there should be less emphasis on chalkboard area in future classrooms and more on permanently mounted screens and display areas.

BULLETIN BOARDS

The bulletin board and the chalkboard in many cases are the minimal tools that the teacher has to work with for visual presentations in the classroom. It is unfortunate, therefore, that board space so often is taken up with announcements, notices, and directives that have little to do with the ongoing instructional activity in the classroom.

Bulletin boards can play a most important part in the daily instructional program. Bulletin board displays can supplement text material and give both the teacher and the students a chance to express themselves through the medium of these displays (Figure 12.11). The planned bulletin board can be used "to motivate students, develop interesting phases of the unit of study, announce new units of study, serve as a point of reference for introducing other types of audiovisual materials, and to serve as a place for student displays of individual and group projects".[5]

Figure 12.11 Bulletin boards allow the students the opportunity to express themselves through the medium of displays.

[5]Robert E. de Kieffer and Lee W. Cochran, *op. cit.,* pp. 45–49.

In order to have more effective bulletin board displays[6] the teacher should try to:

1. Have the bulletin-board display grow out of teacher-pupil planning. Greater interest in the display will be shown by the students, and learning will result from participation in the activity itself.
2. Change bulletin-board displays frequently. A display accomplishes nothing if it is not studied and looked at.
3. Have pupils care for the display as much as they are able to. Rearrange elements of the display in order to continue interest as well as to maintain student involvement.
4. Display work done by pupils. This increases the involvement of students in the display.
5. Emphasize composition through carefully selected and placed materials. This will aid in quick comprehension of the intent and purpose of the display.
6. Keep bulletin boards neat and attractive. Nothing is gained by creating a display with little appeal to it.
7. Cooperate with other teachers in setting up a file of graphic and pictorial material. The greater the resources from which to draw, the more effective will be the completed display.

As much as possible, the teacher should avoid including unrelated materials, placing many subject-matter displays into one area, leaving displays for too-long periods of time, and crowding the area with too much material.

FLANNEL BOARDS

A flannel board (or felt board) (Figure 12.12) is a place where plants grow, where phonics flourish, where number concepts become clear, where zoo animals proudly parade. A flannel board is a place to learn and a place to teach. It is a display area where the teacher places meaningful symbols in a step-by-step progression of facts. A flannel board is for introducion and motivation or for drill. It is for kindergarteners to add apples and for intermediates to study nutrition.

The construction of the flannel board is simple. It can be made of a flat piece of heavy cardboard, thin plywood, or composition board covered with a napped material. It is known under such other names as visual boards, flannelgraph, felt board, and slap board.

[6]*Audiovisual Handbook for Teachers*, State of New Jersey, Trenton, 1954, p. 7.

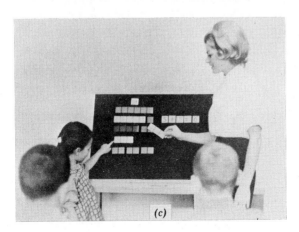

Figure 12.12 A flannel board is for introduction and motivation or for drill. *Courtesy of Instructo Products Co.*

When objects are treated with a fuzzy or napped backing or are adhesive, they may be attached to a flannel board. The principle of friction is called into play as the relatively long fibers of the flannel-like material covering the board cause the attached objects to cling to the surface.

Interest is aroused immediatly by simply pressing meaningful materials of different colors, shapes, and sizes against the flannel-board surface and having them remain in the position in which they have been placed. Children often have referred the procedure as "flannel magic."

Students and teachers should be encouraged to construct their own flannel boards and illustrations if the means are not available to purchase such materials commercially. The fabric can be either flannel, felt, or suede. It is important that the fibers be long in order to guarantee good adhesion with the templates. The size should be at least 18 × 24 in. for smaller groups. It is better to have too large a board for a particular presentation that to have one that cannot be seen by everyone in the class. The flannel must be stretched tightly and smoothly over the backing board in order to provide the proper surface for attaching the templates. Almost any color felt or flannel may be used for covering the flannel board. Many teachers prefer a light green or dark green covering because of the excellent contrast it offers for other colors that may be used in a presentation.[7]

Any light-weight and flat material can be prepared to adhere to a flannel-board surface. Ordinarily the nap of the flannel on the board will hold the nap of another piece of flannel or felt placed against it, as the fibers interlock.

Teachers can use numbers, circles, various geometric forms, letters, diecut animals, words, musical notes, and various shapes in their presentations. Resourceful teachers and students will invent many other unique materials to meet their special requirements. Paper cutouts, pictures, paper letters, title cards, drawings, and cardboard symbols may be used on a flannel board. However, a backing must be applied to each of these objects. This backing can be made of any material that will provide friction. Strips of rayon flock or strips of rough sandpaper glued to the materials are generally adequate. Flocked paper with adhesive backing is particularly effective. This material will hold objects firmly to the flannel board. It is necessary only to tear off the protective sheet from the back of the flocked paper and to press the adhesive coating to any material that is to be used.

Some materials require no preparation for attachment to the flannel board. Among these are colored yarn, steel wool, small pieces of balsa wood, velvet, suede, rough blotting paper, wool, sponge, and rough-textured string.

[7]Paul E. Long, *Teaching with the Flannel Board*, Philadelphia: Jacronda Mfg. Company, 1957, pp. 5–8.

The flannel board is a fascinating medium that can be used with students of all ages. It can be overused, however; teachers should guard against utilizing it when the chalkboard or the bulletin board might be employed with greater effect. Moreover, since the size of flannel board is limited, special care should be taken not to crowd the area with too much material and information.

HOOK 'N LOOP

The Charles Mayer Studios has devised a board that resembles a flannel board in appearance but which has a holding power many times greater. The Hook 'N Loop is a new concept in display and presentation boards. Its holding power owes to the pairing of quick-applying nylon hooked tape with countless tiny nylon loops. The hooks interlock with the loops to support virtually any size or shape material or product with almost unbelievable tenacity.

An increasing number of letters, symbols, and templates are being made available for use with this material. The "fabric" material, made up of woven nylon loops, is available in bulk or mounted in finished boards. The hook material comes in several forms and sizes. It can be glued or laminated to any item that is to be supported by the board. The holding power of the hook material per square inch is 5 to 10 lb, depending on the shape and dimension of the object being supported.

MAGNETIC BOARDS

Many of the instructional values that can be attributed to the felt board apply to the magnetic board as well. The only difference between the two lies in the method of adhesion—magnetism rather than friction is the adhesive force.

Magnets will adhere to any iron-base surface (Figure 12.13). Those produced for this particular application are extremely small and can be glued to any template or material that is to be displayed on the magnetic board. Some of the new chalkboards that are currently being installed are made from metal instead of slate or other composition material. The chalkboard, as a result, can then serve a dual purpose. Magnetic boards are relatively new, however; most of those in use are comparatively small and portable.

The uses of the magnetic board are many: physical education teachers are able to plot positions of players and show their movements with

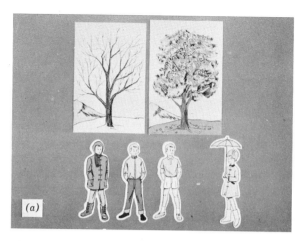

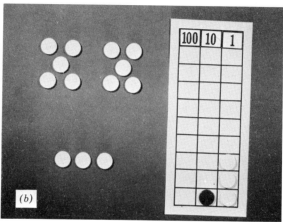

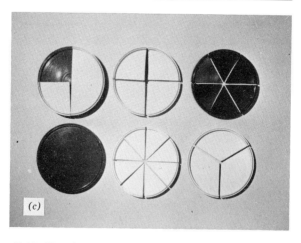

Figure 12.13 **Use of the magnetic board.** *Courtesy of Instructo Products Co.*

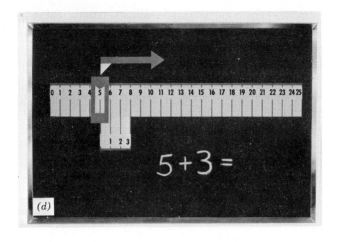

Figure 12.13 (*continued*)

greater ease than is possible with any other medium; in the teaching of anatomy, skeletal structures can be quickly assembled or disassembled; home economics teachers can demonstrate advantages of certain furniture placement by quickly shifting pieces about; journalism teachers can show the effect of type size and placement of headlines on the over-all appearance of a newspaper page.[8]

ELECTRIC BOARDS

The electric board is an instructional device, usually teacher-made, that matches cues or questions with answers in such a way that when a correct pairing is made an electrical signaling device is actuated (Ficure 12.14). As such, it has some of the characteristics of a programmed-learning device. It provides immediate information as to whether the student is making the correct response to a particular question or situation. The construction of the device is intriguing and it attracts a good deal of interest in

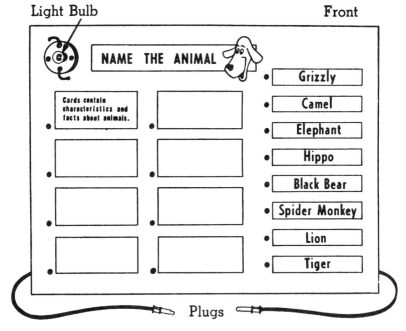

Figure 12.14   An electric board. *James S. Kinder, Using Audiovisual Materials In Education, New York: American Book Company, 1965.*

[8]James S. Kinder, *Using Audiovisual Materials in Education*, New York: American Book Company, 1965, pp. 124–125.

the learning activity. The teacher, of course, must build into the program the information, principles, or understandings that are to be imparted to the students.

To operate the electric board the student uses two pointers. One pointer is inserted into the outlet just to the left of the question or problem being considered; the other pointer is inserted into the outlet next to what he considers to be the correct answer. If the choice is wrong, nothing happens. The student is free to select another response. If correct, a light flashes or a bell rings. The clues or data on the board should be changed frequently as should the wiring—otherwise, memorization of the relationships between clues and responses on the board would defeat the purpose of this learning device.

THREE-DIMENSIONAL MATERIALS AND OBJECTS

The value of studying the real thing rather than pictures or verbal descriptions is generally accepted by most teachers. This acceptance is based upon the concrete experience-learning theory which emphasizes sense impressions. There are limitations to the extent to which real things can be brought into the classroom: the real thing may be too large to move or store in the classroom; it may be too small to be seen by a group of people; it may be too complicated in real form to be understood; it may move too rapidly for its operations to be understood; it may move too slowly for its actions to be studied completely; it may be too dangerous for the well-being of the students; and it may be too expensive for ordinary class use.[9]

In many of these examples educational substitutes for real things (Figure 12.15) have been devised by changing size, complexity, timing, and safety and cost factors.

Model refers to a copy of the real object. It can be the same size or an enlargement or reduction. For example, a model of the heart might be greatly enlarged, a model of an automobile would be greatly reduced, and a model of a battery could be the same size as the original. Models can be solid or may show just the outlines; some can be constructed in sections and disassembled to show interior structures; other can be manipulated and operated.

Mock-up refers to a specialized model or working replica of the item being depicted. A mock-up of a telephone, for example, may be set up on a board and its operation demonstrated. In driver training automobile

[9] Raymond, Wyman, *Audiovisual Devices and Techniques*, Amherst: University of Massachusetts, 1962, pp. 150–151.

Figure 12.15 Models, mock-ups, fragments, and specimens add to the learning environment of this classroom.

mock-ups are geared to special motion picture devices that simulate real driving experiences. *Fragments* and *specimens* are parts of the real thing. Fragments of coal, iron ore, rocks, wood, or historical materials prove valuable as instructional tools in many lessons. Their instructional value is enhanced when students are encouraged to search them out, bring them to class, and identify them.

In using models, mock-ups, and fragments it is important that the teacher emphasize that the items are merely representations or parts of the real thing. Students have been known to draw some weird conclusions from observing these items in the classroom. Therefore, care should be exercised in matching the complexity of the models and mock-ups with the level of maturity of the students.

Models, mock-ups, and fragments can be constructed or collected by students and, as such, provide meaningful learning activities. In addition, many items are available on loan from museums, corporations, libraries, and private individuals. The sources of these items should be noted by the teacher so that he can draw upon them at the opportune time.

Exhibits

Exhibits are usually three-dimensional displays of materials arranged by students or teachers as part of a unit of study in the classroom. Design of exhibits is important if they are to achieve their purpose of attracting and holding the attention of viewers long enough to communicate the desired information. Lighting, bright colors, movement, and sound are some of the devices that need to be incorporated into an effective exhibit.

Preparing a good exhibit requires much effort. The purpose must be clearly spelled out and the theme established; preliminary plans must be made as to the format, materials to be used, color, lighting, and dimensions; the plans must be translated into decisive action with the talents of as many students as possible being utilized; finally, the exhibit should be evaluated as to its effectiveness.

An exhibit can result in a great deal of "busy-work" for the students and teacher—with few other benefits accruing—or it can be of great value by visualizing and summarizing the learning experiences from a process or an idea. A teacher can determine which it is through consideration of the following criteria:[10]

1. Is the exhibit
   Planned for a particular audience?
   Pleasing in appearance?
   Neat and well-organized?

2. Does the exhibit
   Accomplish its purpose?
   Draw attention?
   Arouse and hold interest?
   Make effective use of color, line, and design?
   Include materials that are appropriate and carefully chosen?
   Include well-chosen and legible letters and captions?
   Provide for audience participation?
   Promote decision and action?

DRAMATIC EXPRESSION

The theater has played an important part in entertaining people throughout history. It also has been a powerful influence in social, political, and religious areas. Dramatic expression exerts its force through the involvement of participants and audiences and through its

[10]Robert E. de Kieffer, *Audiovisual Instruction*, New York: Center for Applied Research in Education, Inc., 1965, pp. 31–32.

ability to inform or to change attitudes. As such, it is a powerful means for communicating information in the classroom.

Dramatizations do more than just communicate the important points of a unit of study. They also stimulate the imagination of students and "bring out" reticent children. Increased pupil participation in classroom activities usually leads to a wide range of dramatic-type presentations. These include extemporaneous or free dramatizations where in youngsters uninhibitedly use their imagination in telephoning, in taking a trip, or in going to a wedding. Role-playing is also free and relatively unstructured. Students should be thoroughly informed of the situation that is being depicted; the selection of participants and assignment of roles is important because the student should have the ability to project himself and to pretend; students should have an opportunity to think about the roles and to interpret the roles according to their own understanding of the situation; the members of the class should be aware of the situation and background information in order to evaluate the presentation objectively.[11]

Other methods of dramatic expression include the pantomime, which is acting on a nonverbal level. This method is usually effective in depicting such actions as how to cross the street, how to eat dinner, or how to find a seat in the theater. This method will attract even the shy student who might otherwise be reluctant to participate in any dramatic activity.

Pageants and tableaux are more formal and stylized, requiring costuming and set decorations that involve considerable student activity and usually the expenditure of some money. Pageants, if carefully directed, can be colorful affairs that will leave lasting impressions on the students involved.

Puppetry is being used as a worthwhile instructional tool with younger children. Participation of most youngsters is obtained in creating the puppets, in staging the presentation, writing the script, clothing the puppets, reading the parts, and manipulating the puppets (Figure 12.16). Such productions create outlets for creative talent of the youngsters, promote cooperation among the members of the class, offer some entertainment, and provide for the meaningful communication of factual information pertaining to a lesson or unit of study. The figures used could be cleverly jointed marionettes operated with strings from a level above the stage, stick puppets (cutout figures glued or stapled to pieces of wood that are manipulated from below the stage), or hand puppets formed and fashioned out of materials such as paper bags, papier mâché, and gloves (fitted over and manipulated by the hands).

[11]James S. Kinder, *Using Audiovisual Materials in Education*, New York: American Book Company, 1965, pp. 133–135.

Figure 12.16 Meaningful learning experiences are provided youngster in having them create puppets, and stage presentations. *Courtesy of Instructo Products Co.*

There are actually no set rules for dramatic expression in the classroom. The teacher should be alert to the capabilities of the students and involve as many as possible in the various presentations. Such presentations can be primarily for entertainment or for learning; or they can be an exercise in group therapy or a method of interpreting real-life situations. It should be kept in mind that drama and dramatic expression as used in the classroom should be the means to an end rather than an end in itself. The purpose should not be to develop products for the theater but to increase the sum total of learning experiences of the students.

USING COMMUNITY RESOURCES

The effective classroom teacher looks to the community and its people for resources to supplement the material that is being presented in the school. The learning resources in any community vary widely and each community possesses unique possibilities: historical landmarks; famous and distinguished residents; extensive museums, zoos, and galleries; and varied occupational and production facilities.

Many resources are common to almost all communities—resource persons, field trips, free and inexpensive handout materials, student or teacher exchanges, telephone interviews, and camping programs, Where the circumstances allow, these resources should be utilized by the classroom teacher and the students. Their use is also dependent upon the type of experience most appropriate at the time in terms of desirable learning.[12]

Stephen Corey has developed certain criteria that he believes are important to observe in connection with the use of the community:

". . . First, we believe that the community should be used only when there are good *a priori* reasons to believe that it provides a better sort of learning experience than could be moulded within the four walls of a school. . . . A second criterion might be stated thuswise: the community should be used as a learning laboratory only when the time is adequate to permit pre-planning and post-evaluation. There are many pupils who go on field trips which are as nonfunctional and perfunctory as any school learning experience could be. In the judgment of pupils the only valuable thing about some of these field trips is the fun they have from being away from school. . . . The third principle is keep the group small, I do not know where the critical point lies but it certainly is true that for most field trips the educational advantages begin to diminish very rapidly

[12]Edward G. Olsen, *The School and Community Reader*, New York: Macmillan, 1963, pp. 160–161.

when the group gets larger than ten or twelve children per teacher. . . the last principle . . . take the youngsters out to the community only when it would be less effective to bring the community to the school. While the experiences that children have are not exactly the same, it is much more efficient to bring one fireman to a class of thirty youngsters in order to have them quiz him about firefighting in a particular city than it is to bring the thirty youngsters to the firemen. . . ."[13]

Organized district-wide surveys that catalog the resources for learning in a community—both people and places—can bring many dividends in the education and training of youngsters in the classroom; the school is brought closer to the community and its activities, and the learning potential of the school is increased. The use of community resources as an instructional tool is no different from any other medium of instruction. It requires careful preparation on the part of the teacher—determination of objectives and the means available for achieving them; it demands thorough preparation of the students so that they are not distracted or sidetracked by other sights or details; it demands precise attention to items of interest or careful adherence to a prepared outline on the part of a visiting dignitary; it requires effective follow-up in the form of discussions, ramatizations, displays, compositions, or other forms of student activity.

Much of education is designed to make better citizens for the local community, so it is important that community people and materials be used in schools and that students visit places of educational value.

SELECTED REFERENCES

Alcorn, Marvin, James S. Kinder, and Jim R. Schunert. *Better Teaching in Secondary Schools* (rev. ed.). New York: Holt, Rinehart & Winston, 1964. Chap. 9.
Anderzhon, Manie L. "The World in Your Classroom," *NEA Journal*, 39, 584–585 (November, 1950).
Bathurst, Leonard. "Developing Map Reading Skills," *Educational Screen and Audio-Visual Guide*, 39, 486–488 (September, 1960).
Brown, James W., Richard B. Lewis and Fred F. Harcleroad. *A-V Instruction: Materials and Methods*. (2nd ed.). New York: McGraw-Hill, 1964. Chapters 6 and 17.
Curran, N. E. "Yours for the Ordering," *Wilson Library Bulletin*, 37, 342–344 (December, 1962).
De Bernardis, Amo. *The Use of Instructional Materials*. New York: Appleton-Century-Crofts. 1960. Chapter 4.
Dent, Charles, and Ernest Tiemann. *Bulletin Boards for Teaching*. Austin, Texas: University of Texas, Division of Extension, 1955.

[13]Stephen M. Corey, "Tested Criteria for Using the Community," in *The School and the Urban Community*, Chicago: University of Chicago, 1942, pp. 76–78.

East, Marjorie, and Edgar Dale. *Display for Learning*. New York: Holt, 1952.

Faris, Gene, John Moldstad, and Harvey Frye. *Improving the Learning Environment*. Washington D.C.: United States Government Printing Office, 1963.

Fox, Marion W. "Try Putting a Flannelgraph to Work," *Instructor*, **62**, 35 (January, 1963).

Grassell, D. Milton. "Flannel Boards in Action," *Educational Screen and Audio-Visual Guide*, **34**, pp. 250–251 (June, 1955).

A Guide for Use With the Indiana University Film Series in the Area of Preparation and Use of Audiovisual Materials. Bloomington, Indiana: Indiana University Audiovisual center, 1958.

Improving the Use of the Chalkboard. Columbus, Ohio: Ohio State University, Bureau of Educational Research, 1957.

Kemp, Jerrold E. *Planning and Producing Audiovisual Materials*. San Francisco: Chandler Publishing Company, 1963.

Kinder, James S. *Audio-Visual Materials and Techniques*. (2nd ed.) New York: American Book Co., 1959. Chapters 2 and 8.

Kinney, Lucien, and Katharine Dresden. *Better Learning Through Current Materials*. Palo Alto California: Stanford University, 1952.

Kleinschmidt, J. W. *How to Turn Ideas into Pictures*. New York: National Publicity Council, 1950.

Kohn, Clyde. "Maps as Instructional Aids in the Social Studies," in *Audio-Visual Methods and Materials in the Social Studies*. Washington: 18th Yearbook of the National Council for the Social Studies, 1957. Chapter 14.

Landin, Leslie. *Living Blackboards*. San Francisco: Fearon, 1956.

Minor, Ed. *Simplified Techniques for Preparing Visual Instructional Materials*. New York: McGraw-Hill, 1962.

Morlan, John E. *Preparation of Inexpensive Teaching Materials*. San Francisco: Chandler, 1963. Chapters 3 and 8.

Nelson, L. Warren. *Education and Industry Cooperate*. New York: Hill and Knowlton, 1951.

Nelson, Leslie W. *Instructional Aids*. Dubuque, Iowa: Brown, 1958. Chapters 6, 7 and 8.

Olsen, Edward G. (ed.). *School and Community*. Englewood Cliffs, N. J.: Prentice-Hall, 1963.

Stolper, B. J. R.: *The Bulletin Board as a Teaching Device*. New York: Bureau of Publications, Teachers College, Columbia University, 1946.

Teaching Some Basic Concepts of Mathematical Geography. Chicago: Denoyer-Geppert Company, 1961.

Williams, Catherine M. "Sources of Teaching Materials," *Educational Research Bulletin*, **34**, 113–140 (May, 1955.)

Williams, Catherine M. "Picture File in Every School," *NEA Journal*, **50**, 40–41 (February, 1961).

Wittich, Walter A. and Schuller, Charles F. *Audiovisual Materials: Their Nature and Use*. New York: Harper, 1962. Chapters 5 and 7.

INSTRUCTIONAL MATERIALS

Accent on Learning, 16-mm film, 30 min., second, b & w, Ohio State University, 1949.

Better Bulletin Boards, 16-mm film, 13 min., b & w, Indiana University, 1956.

Calk and Chalkboards. 16-mm film, 15 min., sounds, color, Bailey, 1959.

Creating Instructional Materials, 16-mm film, 15 min., sound, b & w and color, McGraw-Hill, 1963.

Design, 16-mm film, 10 min., sound, b & w, Bailey, 1955.

Elements of Design: Composition, Light and Shade, Line, Shape. 16-mm films, each 11 min., sound, b & w., Young America, 1950.

Federal Government, 16-mm film, 13 min., sound, color and b & w, Coronet.

Make Your Chalk Teach, 35-mm filmstrip, 47 frames, silent, b & w, Wayne University, 1951.

Pictures Teach at Penfield, 16-mm film, 19 min., sound, color, Eastman Kodak Company, 1958.

School and the Community, 16-mm film, 14 min., sound, b & w, McGraw-Hill, 1952.

Selecting and Using Ready-Made Materials. 16-mm film, 15 min., sound, b & w and color, McGraw-Hill, 1963.

Teaching With Visual Materials Series: Exciting Bulletin Boards, Pt. I; *Exciting Bulletin Boards*, Pt. II; *The Flannel Board; Posters for Teaching; The Chalkboard*, Pt. I; *The Chalkboark*, Pt. II, 35-mm filmstrips, average 38 frames, silent, color, McGraw-Hill, 1963.

Understanding a Map., 16-mm film, 10 min., sound, b & w McGraw-Hill, 1952.

Using Maps and Globes, 35-mm filmstrips, 48 frames, silent, color, Rand McNally, 1954.

13

PRODUCTION OF AUDIOVISUAL MATERIALS

The major portion of the book has been given over to a discussion of the use and operation of audiovisual equipment in the classroom. This information is basic to the teacher's training and development for the role that he or she is to assume in the classroom. Effective use of the equipment will speed the communication of information and insure that the subject matter will be remembered longer.

Equipment ("hardware") functions as an effective communication medium, however, only when appropriate materials are employed. These materials can be purchased, or they can be produced locally in the school systems by the teachers or other school personnel. A study of this section will indicate the tremendous variety of materials available and the large number of companies that are engaged in supplying materials to schools.

With this tremendous supply to choose from, one might not expect that there would be much need for producing materials locally. Such is not the case, however; increased utilization of the overhead projector, slide projector, the opaque projector, the tape recorder, and other equipment has brought about an increased awareness of the values and the need for local production (Figure 13.1). Some of these values are listed below:

1. Locally produced materials are up-to-date. There is not that time lag usually so evident between a new discovery or noteworthy event and the availability of the visual or audio materials.
2. Local production allows for the visualization of experimental programs and theories for which no commercial programs may be available, such as teaching set theories in mathematics or using visuals in teaching languages.
3. Local production provides for functional flexibility in the form and type of visual. A single photographic negative could be used for print-

MOUNTING
DRY MOUNTING PRESS
DRY MOUNTING TISSUE

LETTERING
FELT-POINT PENS
STENCILS
MECHANICAL LETTERING

COLORING
SLIDE CRAYONS
INKS OF VARIOUS KIND

PHOTOGRAPHY
35 mm. CAMERA
ENLARGER
DARKROOM
COPY EQUIPMENT
4 x 5 CAMERA
POLAROID CAMERA

REPRODUCTION
COPY PROCESSES
MIMEOGRAPH DUPLICATION
SPIRIT DUPLICATION

Figure 13.1   Recommended production equipment and materials for a minimal program.

ing a slide for overhead projection, or making a 2 × 2 slide, or printing a picture for use on television, or creating a spirit duplicator master for producing student prints.

4. Locally produced materials are particularly adapted for the physical and environmental areas in which they are to be used.
5. Locally produced materials draw on the local community for illustrations and examples to clarify basic concepts—pictures of erosion, local construction, community services, and the like.

The teacher also gains from participating in the creation of instructional materials as follows:

1. More thought is given to objectives and organization of a particular concept or subject area.
2. The teacher is more alter to the effectiveness of the materials that are employed and adapts them to the needs and characteristics of the student body.
3. Teachers take pride in using their own materials effectively.
4. Teachers are more amenable to evaluation of their techniques by the students than they would be if oral presentations alone were used.

A survey conducted by the United States Office of Health, Education and Welfare in 1963 indicated that the establishment of local production facilities was gaining favor throughout the country. School systems were sampled, representing a high percentage of the population. It was found that most of these systems had facilities for servicing individual buildings as well as the entire system. The most frequently produced visual instructional materials for classroom or television use noted (Figure 13.2) were 2 × 2 slides, photographs, graphic materials (including charts and graphs), mounted pictures, and overhead transparencies.[1]

HAND-DRAWN TRANSPARENCIES (Figure 13.3)

Simple slides can be prepared easily for use with the $3\frac{1}{4}$ × 4 lantern slide projector or for use in the $7\frac{1}{2}$ × 10 in overhead projector. Although the size

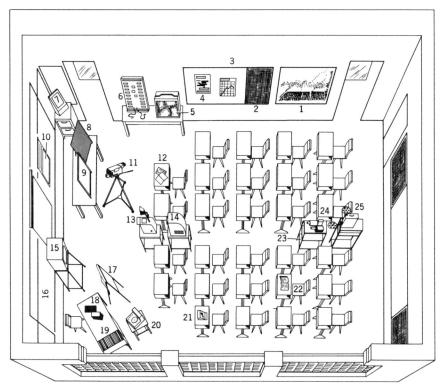

Figure 13.2 Major types of instructional material and equipment useful in classrooms. 1. Display case; 2. peg board; 3. bulletin board; 4. posters; 5. diorama; 6. electric board; 7. light box; 8. magnetic board; 9. flannel board; 10. wall charts and maps; 11. TV camera; 12. books and manuals; 13. overhead projector; 14. opaque projector; 15. TV receiver; 16. chalk board; 17. flip chart; 18. passouts; 19. still picture file; 20. sound recorder and playback; 21. teaching machine; 22. programmed learning materials; 23. 2 × 2 slide-filmstrip projector; 24. $3\frac{1}{4}$ × 4 projector; 25. motion picture projector.

[1]Gene Faris, John Molstad, and Harvey Frye, "Improving the Learning Environment," Washington, D.C.: United States Department of Health, Education, and Welfare, Office of Education, Government Printing Office, 1963.

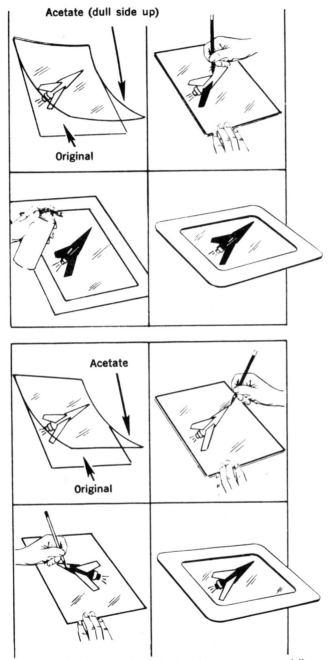

Acetate (dull side up)

Original

Acetate

Original

Figure 13.3 *Steps involved in producing a hand-made transparency on dull acetate and on clear acetate.* Ed. Minor, *Simplified Techniques for Preparing Visual Instructional Materials,* McGraw-Hill.

of the finished transparencies may vary, the materials and the techniques are similar for both.

The base material is a clear transparent cellulose acetate film, though matte or frosted acetate can also be used. This latter material is more receptive to a wider variety of marking devices and inks, but its light transmission is considerably less than that of clear transparent film.

Creative teachers are able to utilize a wide variety of materials and marking devices for the making of transparencies. Some of these include the following:

Translucent paper (tracing paper)
Clear acetate film
Acetate drawing inks, black as well as colored
Felt pens
Bamboo-tip pens
Drawing pens
Pressure-sensitive tape: colored, transparent, and opaque
Marking pencils: black, opaque, and colored transparent
Pressure-sensitive pattern materials
Pressure-sensitive colored sheets
Cardboard frames (for mounting individual sheets of acetate or hinging additional layers of acetate)

The procedure for producing these transparencies will vary with the individual teacher; but a general approach would include the following steps:

1. Mark off on the tracing paper the outline of the projection area. (Available are punched materials with registration bars and printed layout guids that facilitate the design of the transparency.)
2. Trace or sketch the basic illustration and other symbols or lettering positioned according to plan. This sheet serves as a rough layout or representation of the visual that is to be made. The teacher at this point also determines the type of ink to be used as well as colors, tapes, or other graphic materials.
3. Work on the actual transparency begins by placing a sheet of clear acetate over the original sketch or layout. Use a drawing pen or marking pencil to trace the artwork or lettering directly onto the acetate.
4. One can add color symbols, and patterns by use of any pencils, inks, tapes, and colored adhesive sheets.
5. If the design calls for all the information to be placed on one sheet, that sheet of acetate when completed is attached to the back of a cardboard mount with pressure-sensitive tape. Mounting the sheet

makes it easier to handle and position the acetate on the overhead projector ($3\frac{1}{4} \times 4$ film is sandwiched between two pieces of glass and sealed by tapping around all four sides).

6. When the transparency is to be used frequently or is to be stored for future use, a clear plastic spray can be applied to the surface of the film which will seal in and protect the artwork. The spray should not be used if it is the intent to re-use the film.

7. Overlay films with information to be added to the basic frame are hinged with pressure-sensitive tape on the face of the mount. Available commercially are Mylar tape hinges which can be attached to the edge of the film and then stapled to the mount.

8. After the taping and hinging is completed, the transparency is ready for use on the projector.

Although not necessarily a transparency, any silhouette or opaque cut-out when placed on the stage of the overhead pojector can be projected on the screen. Sometimes when one is working with a large group it could be desirable to perform this operation on the stage of the projector so that all could see the operation. In fact, for extemporaneous visualization, it is possible to use clear acetate and the grease pencil directly on the stage of the overhead projector.

Typewritten transparencies can be prepared by facing one sheet of carbon paper to one side of the clear acetate and a second sheet of carbon paper to the backside of the clear acetate. The acetate, sandwiched between the carbon paper, is set in the type writer. Typing with a stencil setting, each stroke of the typewriter key causes a transfer of carbon onto the face and back of the acetate film. A red or orange carbon is recommended because of the greater transfer of carbon that can be effected. The lettering should be protected with a clear plastic spray, face and back, to prevent smudging.

Carbon film and carbon-coated plastic are available commercially and can prove effective for some applications. The carbon film can be placed directly on the stage of the overhead projector. Drawing a stylus (even a pencil) across the carbon removes the carbon and allows the light to pass through. The result on the screen is a white image on a black background as one writes or draws. Information can be typewritten on carbon film by placing the carbon film carbon-side down, between a sheet of tracing paper and a heavier sheet of paper. One then inserts the sandwiched carbon film into the typewriter and types, using the stencil setting. Each stroke of the typewriter causes the carbon to be transferred to the backing sheet, leaving clear lettering on the carbon film.

The pressure-sensitive color sheets and pattern sheets are becoming increasingly popular because of their value in highlighting and defining areas and information on transparencies. The sheets are easy to handle; a section matching roughly the area to be covered on the transparency is cut from the pressure-sensitive sheet; the protective backing sheet is peeled away; the cut section is placed carefully on the acetate film so as not to form any air bubbles or wrinkles; the pressure-sensitive material is carefully trimmed to conform to the designated area; the surplus is removed. In trimming with a stencil knife, care must be used to cut only through the pressure-sensitive film and not into the clear acetate film as well.

It should be pointed out here that in order to be effective transparencies need to be readable and understandable. The type should be large enough and bold enough so that it can be read by everyone in a viewing area. The projection area should not be crowded by too many elements and pictorial details. Color and shading should be used to differentiate elements or highlight details. Complicated constructions should be presented in simple stages through the use of overlay films or through the use of masking devices that allow only certain portions of the projection area to be shown at any one time.

DIAZOTYPE PROCESS

The diazotype process allows the teacher to print brightly colored images on clear transparent film (Figures 13.4, 13.5). The film is coated by the manufacturer with a diazo salt solution and a colorless compound called a coupler. In the presence of ammonia vapors, the coupler combines with the diazo salts to form dyes, the color of which is determined by the choice of coupler.

To make a print, the diazo-sensitized material is exposed to ultraviolet light through a translucent original or "master" carrying an opaque image (pencil, ink, paper cut-out, etc.). Sunlight, photo flood lamps, fluorescent lamps, and mercury-vapor tubes are but a few of the ordinary sources of ultraviolet light. Where the diazo-sensitized material is not protected by the opaque sections of the "master," light passes through and "burns out" the diazo. The opaque lines and areas, on the other hand, hold back the light and prevent the corresponding area on the diazo film from being burned out.

After exposure, the diazo film is placed in an enclosure containing ammonia vapors. The ammonia vapors cause the chemical reaction that produces an image only in the areas that were *not* affected by ultraviolet light. The diazotype image is a direct reproduction of the image on the original or master. A positive original produces a positive print; a negative original produces a negative print.[2]

"Dark-rooms" are not required for the handling of diazotype materials as the diazo is affected only by ultraviolet light. Diazo-sensitized materials can be printed and developed in any normally lighted room just so long as the materials are not subjected to direct sunlight or to prolonged exposure under fluorescent lamps. Diffused sunlight and incandescent lamps do not yield enough ultraviolet to affect seriously the diazotype sensitization during the normal time of processing.

Diazo films which produce many colors and tones are commercially available but because of the nature of the process, there is only one color possible on each sheet of film. The color is identified by the manufacturer on the label of the package. If a teacher is interested in producing a three-color transparency, preparation would require the use of three sheets of diazo film, one for each color. Since the diazo image is transparent, it is possible to achieve secondary colors by superimposing one color over another; for example: blue over yellow produces green; red over blue produces purple, etc. The wide range of available colors makes it possible to produce dramatic multicolor transparencies at a fraction of the cost and the labor involved in making colored photographic transparencies.

Producing a Diazo Transparency

The steps involved in the production of a diazo transparency are simple and easy to follow if the previous information on the diazotype process has been understood. There are three principal procedures involved in these operations: preparation of the master or original, exposure and development, and mounting.

Preparation of the Master

1. When the master is being drawn or constructed, prepare a sketch or layout of all the elements—visual and verbal—that are to be contained in the transparency. For legibility, the size of type should be a minimum of $\frac{1}{4}$ in. For ease of comprehension, the design should be simple and not crowded. Decisions should be made at this point as to the nature of the opaquing or drawing techniques that are to be used: ink, pencil, cut-outs; or pressure-sensitive patterns. The producer should indicate the colors that are to be used, as well as the method of mounting the various sheets of film. The sketch should be drawn to the exact size of the projection area, 10×10 or $7\frac{1}{2} \times 10$ in.

[2]*Diazochrome Projectuals for Visual Communication*, Holyoke, Massachusetts: Tecnifax Corporation, 1964, p. 11.

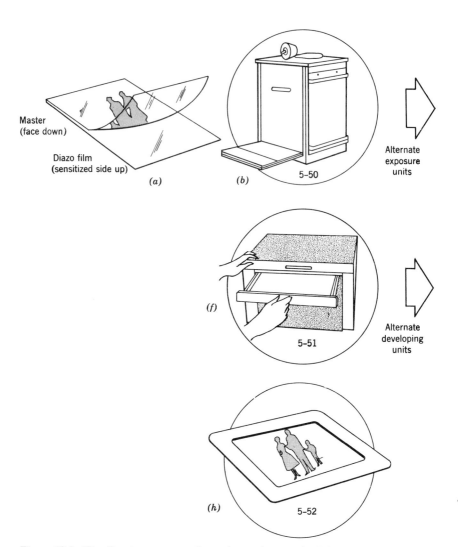

Figure 13.4 The diazotype process allows the teacher to print brightly colored images on clear, transparent film. (*a*) Assemble materials for exposure as illustrated. Insert in Tecnifax Proto-printer and expose for the recommended time. Exposure will vary according to the type of master and equipment. Alternative exposure units with film and master in contact-print frames, may be (*c*) sunlight exposure, (*d*) Sun lamp exposure; and (*e*) 1000-W number PH4 Photo-Flood bulb. (*f*) Develop exposed film in Tecnifax Proto-Coupler. This unit is designed to develop materials exposed in the Tecnifax Proto-Printer. Usually exposure and developing times are approximately equal. Another developing unit might be (*g*) a large-mouth jar developer. Place sponge in bottom of jar and pour over it a few ounces of commercial aqua-ammonia (26 Baume). Insert exposed film, replace top quickly and tightly. Development takes about 3 to 5 minutes. (*h*) Mount transparency for projection. Transparencies may be projected unmounted. Ed. Minor *Simplified Techniques for Preparing Visual Instructional Materials,* McGraw-Hill Co.

332

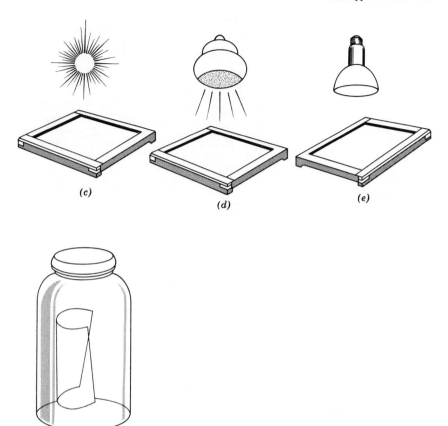

(c)

(d)

(e)

(g)

Figure 13.4   *(continued)*

2. A separate master is prepared for each color or each film that is to be printed for the transparency. A sheet of tracing papers placed over the sketched layout and the various pictorial or verbal elements are constructed on the tracing paper according to the sketch. The markings *must be opaque to ultraviolet light* in order for color to be printed in those areas.

3. The opaquing techniques that can be utilized include drawing pens with black ink, soft-lead pencils, heavy paper cut-outs, pressure sensitive patterns, and opaque tapes.

4. A master should include just those items and elements that are to be printed in a particular color or on a particular overlay film.

5. Master for diazo printing, containing opaque images on a translucent or transparent base, can be produced through other copying and

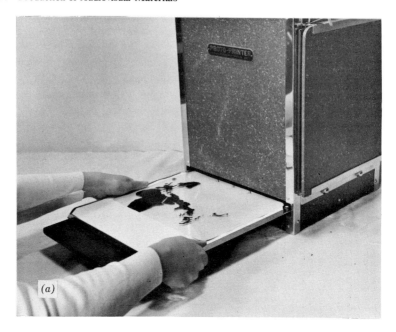

Figure 13.5 Producing diazo projectuals for use on the overhead projector. From the printer (*a*) to the "pickle" jar (*b*) and finally to the projector (*c*).

printing techniques: photocopy reproductions from books and magazines on translucent or transparent film; thermocopy prints on transparent film; photographic film positives and negatives; electrostatic print reproductions on tracing paper and film.

These prints can be used in their original form for making copies on colored diazo film. The illustration can also be trimmed, edited, and separated; taped down on tracing paper, these elements can be printed in different colors or on overlay films. In this manner, it is possible to create a multicolor transparency without necessarily drawing or sketching the illustration. This is a boon to those who feel that they do not have the artist's capability.

Printing and Devoloping. After the masters have been prepared, the next procedure involves the printing of the images of the master onto the diazo film. The steps involved are as follows:

1. Take a sheet of diazo film from the appropriately labelled package. The interleaf sheet of paper can be thrown away or used as a backing sheet during exposure.

(b)

(c)

Figure 13.5   (*continued*)

2. Most diazo film is notched to indicate the surface which is coated. Orient the film so that the notch is on the upper right edge of the film. The coated side of the film is on top, facing the holder of the film.
3. Place the master over the diazo film with the image side of the master in contact with the coated side of the film. (This results in a reverse print on the diazo film; but as the film is transparent, the readability of the print is not affected.)
4. Be certain that the master is pressed tightly against the diazo film. Use a contact frame or heavy plate glass when exposure is being made to sunlight or photo flood lamps.
5. Regardless of the equipment being used, be certain that the master is positioned between the source of ultraviolet light and the diazo film. The length of exposure can be determined through experimentation or by checking the directions that accompany the printing devices.
6. After the exposure is completed, the diazo film is placed in a jar, or tube, or box, or any enclosure containing ammonia vapors. The film is left in the container until the full intensity of color has been developed. This may take from $\frac{1}{2}$ to 10 minutes, depending on the concentration of ammonia vapors and the temperature—the higher the temperature the faster the development.

   Diazo films cannot be overdeveloped. The ammonia vapors act as a catalyst in producing a chemical formation of color only in those areas that have not been exposed to ultraviolet light. Once the diazo salts and coupler have joined, no further action takes place.
7. It is possible to place more than one film at a time into developing container.

Mounting. The completed diazo prints can be used immediately on the overhead projector when single films are involved. But when overlay films are to be used—and for convenience in handling and positioning even single films—it is recommended that the films be mounted (Figure 13.6).

1. For "static" transparencies, the outline and the color film are bound together on the mounting frame as a unit, forming a permanent multicolor transparency. The outline, or black print, is first placed on the reverse side of the mounting frame and each corner fastened to the frame with pressure-sensitive tape. Each additional print is superimposed, registered, and fastened on the corners to the frame. All four sides of the composite are then taped to the mount with pressure-sensitive tape.
2. Dynamic transparencies are those with overlays which are hinged so that they can be raised or lowered individually to build up or take

apart the composite image. The basic films are also attached to the reverse side of the mount with pressure-sensitive tape. The overlays, however, are superimposed and registered on the front of the mount. On edge of the film can be taped to the frame to provide a hinging action. Another method is to attach metalized Mylar tabs to the film and then staple the tabs to the slide mount.

If the color overlays always follow the same sequence, the prints can be hinged on the same edge, preferably on the ledt side of the film. If the sequence is to be varied, the prints should be hinged on different edges.

The Slidemaster System

Tecnifax Corporation is one of several producers of diazo materials and equipment. Its Slidemaster System is a completely integrated procedure designed to accomplish the production of diazo multicolor transparencies for use with the overhead projector. The system includes all the essential elements of the operations required—from the original drawing to the projection of the completed slide on the screen for audience viewing.

An important part of the Slidemaster System is the pin registration system. It involves the use of three pins carefully and precisely positioned in a work board; it also involves the three-hole punching of all tracing paper, diazo materials, and mounts. The materials can be purchased already punched or can be punched locally by securing the equipment.

Masking Techniques. It is often desirable to focus the attention of the class on a particular item in a transparency that is mounted as a "static." This can be done by using various masking techniques (see Figure 13.6). Opaque plastic or card stock can be attached to the face of the mount and so manipulated that only portions of the transparency can be revealed, or portions can be successively revealed until the whole is projected.

The masking materials, in combination with opaque tapes and plastic tracks, can be used to produce some interesting devices: a vertical sliding mask, a horizontal sliding mask, individual aperture masks, a circular rotating mask, or hinged segmented masks.

With these masking devices, it is possible to create more interest and attention to otherwise static presentation.

Comments

The diazo process for making transparencies is proving to be extremely popular. It allows for a great deal of flexibility and variety in the types of presentations possible. It is easy to use; exposure settings offer the only problem—a minor one. If a background color appears on the developed

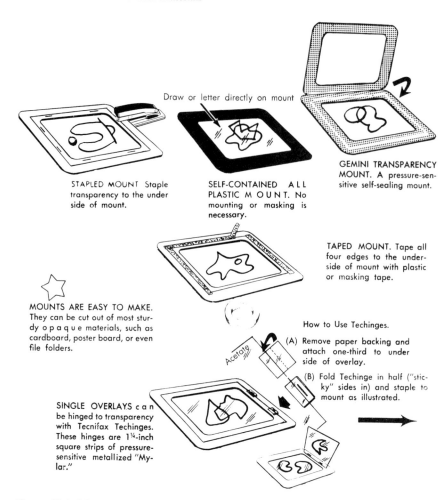

Draw or letter directly on mount

STAPLED MOUNT Staple transparency to the under side of mount.

SELF-CONTAINED ALL PLASTIC MOUNT. No mounting or masking is necessary.

GEMINI TRANSPARENCY MOUNT. A pressure-sensitive self-sealing mount.

TAPED MOUNT. Tape all four edges to the under-side of mount with plastic or masking tape.

MOUNTS ARE EASY TO MAKE. They can be cut out of most sturdy o p a q u e materials, such as cardboard, poster board, or even file folders.

How to Use Techinges.

(A) Remove paper backing and attach one-third to under side of overlay.

(B) Fold Techinge in half ("sticky" sides in) and staple to mount as illustrated.

Acetate

SINGLE OVERLAYS c a n be hinged to transparency with Tecnifax Techinges. These hinges are 1¼-inch square strips of pressure-sensitive metallized "Mylar."

Figure 13.6 Masking and mounting transparencies for overhead projector. Ed. Minor *Simplified Techniques for Preparing Visual Instructional Materials,* McGraw-Hill Co.

diazo film, the film was not exposed to ultraviolet light long enough for all the coating to be destroyed in the clear areas. To correct this, lengthen the exposure time. When the background is clear but the type and lines appear to be eroded and thin, the film was exposed to ultraviolet light for too long a period of time. To correct for this condition, shorten such exposure times. Films left in the developing jar for the optimum time will develop colors to maximum intensity.

The diazo method offers a wonderful means for producing duplicate copies of transparencies for distribution throughout the school system. It also provides the means for producing copies that can be used in

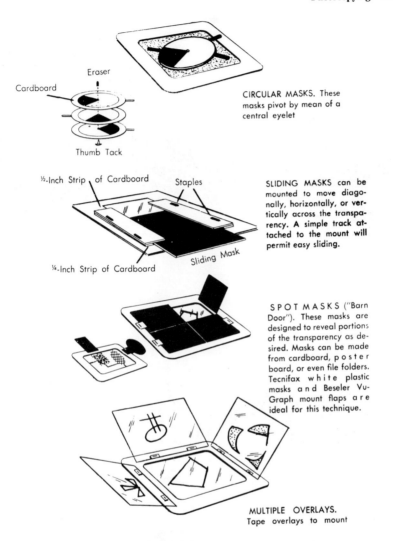

CIRCULAR MASKS. These masks pivot by mean of a central eyelet

Eraser

Cardboard

Thumb Tack

SLIDING MASKS can be mounted to move diagonally, horizontally, or vertically across the transparency. A simple track attached to the mount will permit easy sliding.

½-Inch Strip of Cardboard

Staples

¼-Inch Strip of Cardboard

Sliding Mask

SPOT MASKS ("Barn Door"). These masks are designed to reveal portions of the transparency as desired. Masks can be made from cardboard, poster board, or even file folders. Tecnifax white plastic masks and Beseler Vu-Graph mount flaps are ideal for this technique.

MULTIPLE OVERLAYS. Tape overlays to mount

Figure 13.6   (continued)

exchange programs with other school systems. Once the original artwork is completed, it takes little effort to produce prints.

PHOTOCOPYING

Photocopying, or the diffusion transfer reflex process, is a method which permits the converting of print from the pages of books, newspapers, and

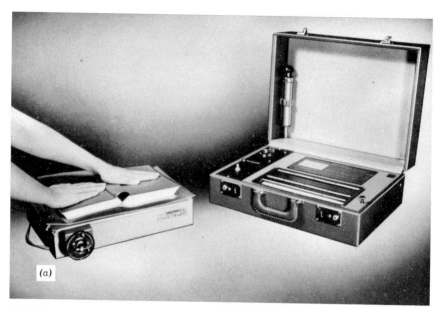

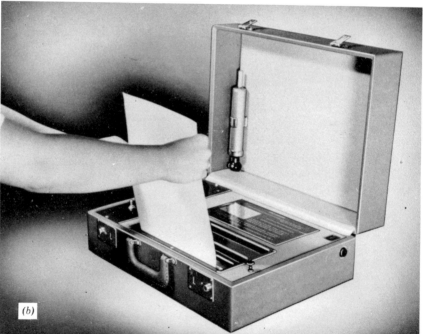

Figure 13.7 Photocopy allows the flexibility of copying from bound books or individual pages. *Courtesy of Tecinfo Corp.*

magazines into projection transparencies. (Figure. 13.7) It also can be used as an office copier for duplication of correspondence and reports. It is a contact photographic process that can be carried on under subdued room-light conditions. The process is basic and easy to understand. A negative sheet is taken from its light-tight container and placed in contact with the image surface to be copied. A light is transmitted through the negative paper to reach the original image area. The light areas on the original reflect light back to the negative sheet while the image areas absorb the light. This is known as a *reflex exposure* because of the reflected characteristic of the light on the original. The exposure time will vary from 4 to 18 seconds, depending on the type and speed of negative paper being used.

Immediately after exposure, the negative is put in contact with a specially treated sheet of transparent film, and both are run through a single developing chemical solution. The two sheets pass through rubber rollers which press them together. The developing solution produces on the exposed negative a negative image which is immediately transferred in positive form onto the transparent film. The two sheets are pressed together, and remain in contact for 15 to 30 seconds. They are then peeled apart; the negative is no longer usable and is discarded. Immediately after drying, the positive film print thus produced can be used on the overhead projector.

Contoura Attaché.   F. G. Ludwig, Inc., is one of several producers of photocopy materials and equipment. One of its models, called the Contoura Attaché, is a compact portable unit that contains a sheet exposing unit, a book copier, and a developing tank.

Individual items for copying, such as letters, reports, or cutouts from newspapers and magazines, can be covered by the photocopy negative paper and the two sheets inserted into the exposing section. A revolving cylinder and moving belts carry the two sheets past a light source, which reflects the desired information onto the negative sheet, and then quickly out of the exposing section.

The exposed negative is then placed in contact with the treated surface of the transfer film. The treated surface is located by positioning the clipped corner of the transfer film at the upper right-hand corner. The transfer film is advanced about $\frac{1}{4}$ in.

The two sheets are inserted into the developing tank. A divider bar across the opening serves to separate the two sheets as they pass into the developing tank. This ensures that the inside surfaces of the sheets will come into contact with the developing solution. A steady downward movement of the sheets will cause them to feed into the rubber rollers, which will propel the sheets the rest of the way. The sheets are kept together for 15 to 30 seconds, separated, and the negative thrown away.

The book copier is a portable light source covered with a translucent plastic air pillow. When partially inflated, the pillow serves as an effective compression device for keeping the negative paper tightly pressed against whatever surface is being copied. The book copier is popular because of its built-in versatility. The negative paper can be placed over any book page, magazine, or wall illustration and can then be covered by the book-copier exposure unit. A timing device on the light-box allows adjustment of expsure from 0 to 30 seconds. The actual exposure will range from 4 to 18 seconds, depending on the type and speed of the negative paper. After exposure, the negative paper is placed in contact with the transfer positive film and developed in the manner described above.

If the transparency image is too light or is faint, it means that the negative material was overexposed. Another exposure, for a shorter period of time, should be made. On the other hand, if the image is muddy, letters are filled, or there is a background discoloration to the film, it means that the exposure was too short. If another copy is made the exposure time should be extended.

Photocopying can be used for purposes other than direct transparencies for use on the overhead projector. A translucent paper print is more economical than the film print; it can be edited, taped down on tracing paper, added to, and then used as a master for diazo printing.

Opaque paper prints can be made of letters and documents by means of the same procedure as that used for producing transparencies and translucent masters. This process can be used for copying paste-ups and moving on to other reproductions without any signs of paste-up marks. Inexpensive aluminum offset plates can be made from the negative where large numbers of copies are needed for distribution.

Photocopying is used primarily for reproducing type and line work. It is a high-contrast copying process, which means that it will reproduce the extremes—black and white—faithfully, but will tend to draw the intermediate tones of gray toward the white or the black extreme. Regular halftone pictures—landscapes, portraits, candid snapshots, etc.—will therefore not reproduce well with this process.

Any low-intensity light source can be used for exposing the photocopy negative paper. A 60-W lamp placed in a Proto-Printer, for example, would allow that unit to be used for exposing individual copies at an exposure time of 20 to 25 seconds. With other light sources that might be too powerful, a light-absorbing filter can be used to reduce the intensity of the light striking the negative paper. A photocopy developing unit only can be pruchased when identical light sources may be used for both diazo printing and photocopying.

SPIRIT DUPLICATOR TRANSPARENCIES

The spirit duplicator is a copying device that most teachers make use of quite frequently for the preparation of desk work and the distribution of information supplementary to that in a textbook. A transparency (Figure 13.8) can be made on frosted acetate from the same duplicator master used for producing the paper prints.

Steps in the preparation of the duplicator master are as follows:

1. Remove the interleaf sheet separating the master sheet from the carbon sheet.
2. Insert the material into the typewriter if it is the lettering technique to be used. Primary type would be best for transparencies. Any other lettering instruments can be used as well.
3. For drawing or sketching, use a ballpoint pen or hard-lead pencil while working on a hard surface in order to get maximum transfer of carbon onto the back of the master sheet.
4. For multicolor effects, insert color carbon sheets (carbon side up) beneath the master before preparing the area that is to appear in color.
5. Position the master on the drum of the spirit duplicator. Set the controls for printing.
6. Feed several sheets of paper through the developer until optimum print is effected. Hand feed the frosted acetate through the duplicator, dull side up.
7. Place the frosted acetate, dull side up, on a piece of paper; use a plastic spray to apply an even protective coating over the printed surface.
8. Allow the film to dry, then mount the transparency in a cardboard frame. Place a protective sheet of clear transparent film over the face of the transparency if any additional marking are to be made.

With the thermocopy process, it is possible to produce a spirit master and retain the carbon sheet as a negative-type transparency. The carbon is applied to film and is removed during the preparation of the master, leaving transparent areas where the carbon was transferred. By applying a plastic spray to the carbon surface, the film can be mounted and used for projection purposes.

Our references to spirit duplication should include a more complete description of the equipment (Figure 13.9). One one side of the unit is the feed tray, where the paper to be printed is stacked. Guides are set on the sides and front of the tray to position the paper for proper feeding into the machine. Rubber feed wheels can be dropped into position during

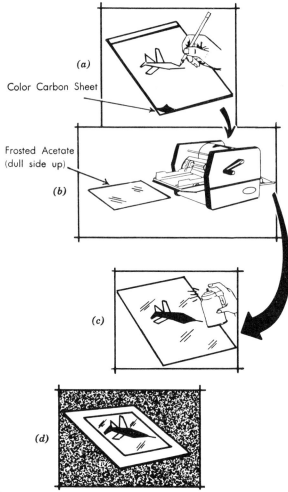

(a)

Color Carbon Sheet

Frosted Acetate
(dull side up)

(b)

(c)

(d)

Figure 13.8 Fluid duplicator transparencies. A fluid duplicating machine can be used to make excellent color slides and transparencies for projection or display. The simple steps for preparing transparencies are similar to those required for preparing regular fluid paper copies, except that frosted acetate is used in place of paper. Several colors can be applied to a single transparency in one operation. Directions: (*a*) prepare master for processing. Follow the same steps used in making a master for paper duplications. Several colors can be placed on a single master by inserting the desired color carbon sheet under the master during the preparation. A stylus, ball-point pen, or hard lead pencil can be used to draw or letter on the master. Several lettering devices can be used to make attractive letters on the master. (*b*) Insert finished master in fluid duplicator and feed frosted acetate into the machine. Several sheets of fluid duplicating paper should be fed into the machine before running the frosted acetate. Hand feeding the acetate is recommended. (*c*) Spray frosted (dull) side of acetate with clear plastic spray. Lay acetate on a flat surface, with a protective sheet of paper under acetate to prevent spray from adhering to working surface. Hold spray can about 10 in. above the acetate and spray back and forth to place an even coat of spray on the printed surface. (*d*) Mount for projection or viewing. Ed. Minor, *Simplified Techniques for Preparing Visual Instructional Materials*, **McGraw-Hill Co.**

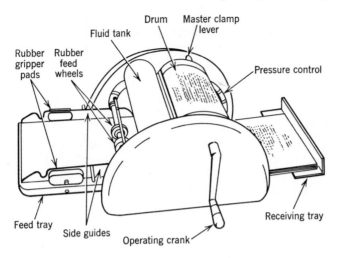

Figure 13.9   Schematic drawing of a spirit duplicator.

operation. This device moves a sheet of paper into the machine with each revolution of the drum; a stack of fifty sheets of paper on the feed tray will facilitate the feed action, even though the intent is to run through only several sheets.

The level of duplicator fluid in the tank should be checked frequently because this fluid is necessary to the proper functioning of the process. The flow of the fluid is controlled on some machines by a lever; with others, the tank itself must be rotated in order for the duplicator fluid to flow into the tray, which contains the wick. The wick must be moist in order for good duplication to occur. Prewetting the wick with fluid may help to speed operation.

The master is positioned around the drum, carbon side up, by turning the handle clockwise until the handle is at the lowest point. A clamp lever at the side of the drum, or recessed in the top of the drum, is depressed to open the clamp that holds the master on the drum. The top edge of the master is fitted into the groove of the clamp (about $\frac{1}{4}$ in.), the clamp lever is released, and the master is locked into place—carbon side up.

It is important to check the quality of the prints as they run through. Faint images may indicate a necessary adjustment of duplicator flow or an increase in the action of the pressure roller against the drum. This control takes the form of either a lever or a pressure-control knob on the front of the machine. Pressure control should be set at OFF when the machine is not in use.

The paper prints feed into the receiving tray after they come out of the copier. The tray has guides that can be adjusted for various lengths and quantities of paper.

At the completion of a run, the master is removed by turning the handle to the DOWN position, pressing down on the clamp lever, and lifting off the master. The master can be stapled to a print in order to protect the carbon side, and filed for future use and reference. The flow of duplicator fluid is turned off, and the pressure control is set at zero.

In preparing the master one first removes the interleaf sheet separating the master sheet from the carbon paper. It is possible to type, write, or draw on the master material. For drawing or lettering, it is best to use a ballpoint pen or hard-lead pencil against a hard smooth surface in order to assure maximum pickup of carbon on the back of the master sheet. Corrections can be made by scraping away the unwanted image from the back of the master sheet; the dye image can also be covered with pressure-sensitive tape or grease-pencil markings. Unwanted sections can be cut out with scissors or a sharp knife; new sections can be taped into place. If retyping or redrawing is necessary after the original dye image is removed, one places a fresh piece of dyepaper under the area to be redone.

The spirit duplicator has proved to be popular with teachers because of its ease of operation and its tie-in with other methods of instruction. New developments in the copying field, especially thermocopying (to be considered next) have increased the value and worth of the spirit duplicator to the classroom teacher.

THERMOCOPYING

The heat-transfer process, or thermocopying, uses infrared energy to activate the image area on the transfer sheets. It is growing in popularity as the medium to use for reproducing newspaper reports, magazine articles, charts, graphs, pictorial illustrations, and most typed, written, or drawn materials. The image transfer (Figure 13.10) can be made on transparent film—negative or positive, black or colored—or on white opaque paper. The image transfer can be made onto a spirit duplicator master, which can then be set immediately in the spirit duplicator for running multiple copies. The thermocopy unit can also be used for laminating clear plastic sheets to the surface of any item to be safeguarded and protected. It also can be used in the "heat-lift" process of making transparencies.

3M Visual Products, with its "Thermofax" brand infrared Model 45 Copying Machine, has been active in developing the many applications that are currently being enjoyed. The user of the equipment requires little instruction to obtain good results. The copying machine can be plugged into any regular room outlet; the ON switch is depressed and the machine is ready for use.

The material to be copied should be in the dimension of $8\frac{1}{2} \times 11$ in. (Variations from this size are possible but special care must be taken.) The transfer material and the original are inserted into the copying machine; in approximately four seconds the completed transfer sheet and the original material come out of the machine.

The transfer material is ready for immediate use when it comes out of the copying machine. Transparent films can be mounted and additional colors and information applied to the surface of the film. (All the devices discussed in the section on hand-drawn transparencies can be used with this film.)

Material to be copied may be edited by covering the unwanted areas with white paper before the material is inserted into the copying machine. Additions to a thermocopy transparency can be made by carefully registering the transparency over the new material to be copied and inserting the material into the copying machine. The new information will be printed with no effect on the image of the transparency previously printed.

PICTURE TRANSFER (LIFT PROCESS)

Development of the heat process for copying led to experiments in other areas of transparency-making. One technique is that of lifting ink pigments off of the printed sheet and causing the ink to adhere to a transparent film (Figures 13.11, 13.12). Previously developed techniques made use of rubber cement and frosted acetate; another technique made use of rubber cement and frosted acetate; another technique made use of a pressure-sensitive transparent film that was applied against the surface to be lifted.

With the thermocopy machine it is possible to laminate a special heat-sensitive film (Figure 13.13) to the surface of the material to be copied (the print on clay-coated paper can be colored or black and white). The seal heat press and seal transparent film can be used for the same purpose. The laminated material is then set in a pan of water to which is added a few drops of detergent. Within a few minutes the paper will soak away from the film, leaving the ink adhering to the film. Carefully, with use of a cotton swab, the paper fibers are removed and the clay coating is washed away. The film is allowed to dry and then a plastic spray coating can be applied to the image surface.

PHOTOGRAPHY

The local production of visual and audio materials aids teachers in more carefully planning and organizing their instructional programs. One

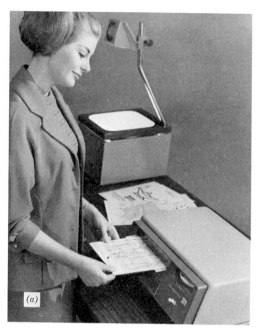

Figure 13.10 The transfer material and original are inserted in the machine and in 4 seconds a transparency is produced ready for use on the projector. *Courtesy 3M Visual Products Co.*

Figure 13.10   *(continued)*

technique which is especially effective involves the use of the camera and photographic materials.

When the students are called upon to assist in the planning of a picture series—"shooting" the series, editing, and presentation—there are many specific advantages that can be pointed out: students practice how to communicate visually; they learn to think through problems and discover novel ways of solving them; they learn new basic skills and practice them; they learn the value of working as a team toward the accomplishment of a goal; and they many times are able to produce visual materials having public relations value as well as having lasting educational value.

Whether the teacher and the students are planning a record or a field trip or are preparing illustrations for lessons still to be presented—pictures of flowers, insects, fabrics, etc.—attention must be given to the choice of films and cameras. The range and types of films are considerable:

1. Color films for transparencies are packed in roll form and are used for the production of 35-mm. slides as well as $2 \times 2, 2\frac{1}{4} \times 2\frac{1}{4},$ or $3\frac{1}{4} \times 4$ slides; if the equipment and technical skill are available, such film can be used also for producing filmstrips.
2. Color paper films are available, but they are expensive and their educative value is questionable.

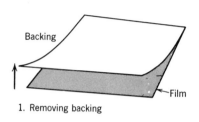

1. Removing backing

2. Bonding print and film

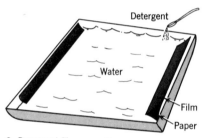

3. Paper and film separation

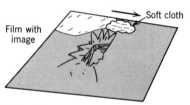

4. Cleaning

5. Finishing

Figure 13.11 Chemical-bond-lift transparencies. John E. Morlan, *Preparation of Inexpensive Teaching Materials,* Chandler Publishing Co.

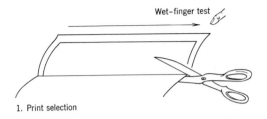

Wet–finger test

1. Print selection

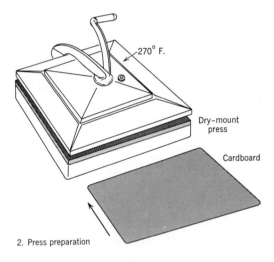

270° F.

Dry–mount press

Cardboard

2. Press preparation

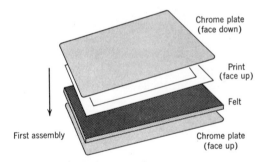

Chrome plate (face down)

Print (face up)

Felt

First assembly

Chrome plate (face up)

3. Drying the print

Figure 13.12 Heat-lift transparencies (dry-mount press). Several methods are available for lifting (transferring) pictorial or illustrative material directly from the printed page onto a transparent plastic sheet. One of the most successful of these processes is offered by Seal, Inc. This process is not complex, but does take special equipment if good results are to be obtained. Materials and equipment: picture or print to be transferred; dry-mount press with temperature control that allows a temperature of 270° Fahreheit; two chrome plates (photographic print-drying plates may be used); Transpara-film cut to size of print to be lifted; pan of water; wetting agent, such as household detergent; piece of felt, cut to the size of the chrome plates; clear plastic spray; scissors. John E. Morlan, *Preparation of Inexpensive Teaching Materials***, Chandler Publishing Co.**

3. Panchromatic negative films for black-and-white photography are designed to fit all cameras and to answer the specific needs of any photographic situation.

The film is produced or coated in various speeds ranging from "slow" to "extremely fast." The slower the film, the finer is the print enlargement that can be made. The faster films tend toward graininess and are less desirable for enlargements and transparencies. (d) Copy films are used primarily for photographing line work or type. It is a high-contrast material; the negatives can be used for immediate projection. (e) Positive-reversal films are used for making transparencies directly without first going through the negative step. Processing is complicated, but the results can be quite good.

The numbers and types of cameras seem to be infinite and the teacher is often perplexed in picking out the camera that would be of greatest benefit. The following are a few suggestions for features that a good camera should possess:

1. Produces color and black-and-white pictures. This means the camera should have a color-corrected lens.
2. Produces negatives that will allow enlargements up to 8×10 in.
3. Produces transparencies directly without having to copy from negatives.
4. Allows a close focus without the use of supplementary lenses.
5. Is able to stop fast action—which means a shutter speed of at least $\frac{1}{300}$ second.
6. Uses standard film that is readily available anywhere that film is sold.
7. Produces pictures in focus without complicated procedures for determining distances. Camera should be equipped with a range-finder or through-the-lens viewing device (single-lens reflex).
8. Takes flash shots without complicated or make-shift attachments. A camera with an internally synchronized flash mechanism will prove of great great value in taking both indoor and outdoor pictures.[3]

Use of the camera and films allows the teacher and students to produce paper prints that can be handed around or mounted for display purposes; it allows for the reproduction of projection slides of all sizes, ranging from 35-mm. to 8×10 transparencies; it also can be used for the production of filmstrips. Planning for photographs, whatever the final form may take, is as important as it is in the production of any other visual material. Much can be said for building interest in the illustration and emphasizing

[3]Lewis Brown, and Fred Harcleroad, *op. cit.*, p. 481.

various esthetic factors of design, balance, and composition. But it is possible to be so completely engrossed in the technical aspects that the education value may be overlooked.

It is important that the camera be close enough to the subject to show details clearly. If a particular operation is being photographed, the sequence of shots should be logical and comprehensive and should demonstrate the continuity of action. Distracting or irrelevant items should be removed from the picture area. Relative size should be indicated by including something in the picture of a recognizable size. Pictures of people should show them engaged in some activity rather than posing for the camera. If possible, the picture should be framed by looking under, over, or through something familiar.[4]

Much time and film can be wasted unless careful thought is given to the nature and the organization of the picture series. The purposes and objectives should be carefully defined; story outlines and expanded "shooting" scripts will aid in confining picture-taking to specific subject areas. After all the pictures are processed, the important task of editing, discarding, and arranging pictures in the proper sequence must be performed. Finally, the worth or value of the picture series should be judged on the basis of how well the educational objectives were achieved rather than the degree of technical excellence embodied in the series.

SELECTED REFERENCES

Audiovisual Instruction, 7, entire issue (April, 1962).

Coltharp, Joe, *Production of 2 × 2 inch Slides For School Use*. Austin, Texas: Visual Instruction Bureau, University of Texas, 1958.

De Kieffer, Robert, and Lee W. Cochran. *Manual of Audiovisual Techniques* (2nd ed.). Englewood Cliffs, N.J.: Prentice-Hall, 1961.

Delaney, Arthur A. "Movie-Making in Teachers College," *Educational Screen and Audiovisual Guide*, 42, 80–81 (February, 1963).

Diazochrome Slides For Visual Communication. Holoyoke, Massachusetts: Tecnifax Corporation, 1956.

Planning and Producing Visual Aids; Film: The Versatile Medium; Photographic Production of Slides and Filmstrips; Kodak School and Club Services; How to Make Good Movies; Industrial Motion Pictures, Rochester, New York: Eastman Kodak Company.

Faris, Gene, John Molstad, and Harvey Frye. *Improving the Learning Environment: A Study on The Local Preparation of Visual Instructional Materials*. Bloominton, Indiana: Indiana University, 1961.

Feinstein, Sol, "Photography Course for Junior High Students," *AVI*. 10, 695–696 (November, 1965).

Frye, Roy A. *Graphic Tools for Teachers, Practical Techniques* (2nd ed.). Austin, Texas: E and I Printing Company, 1963.

[4]Raymond Wyman, *op. cit.*, p. 164.

Hartsell, Horace C., and W. L. Veenendaal. *Overhead Projection*. Buffalo, N.Y.: Henry Stewart, Inc. (for American Optical Co.); 1960.

"How Your Teachers Can Use Overhead Projectors," *School Management*, 7, 52–55 (February, 1963).

Indiana University Audiovisual Center Staff. *AV Materials Handbook* (2nd ed.) Bloomington, Indiana: Indiana University, 1960.

Kemp, Jerrold E. *Planning and Producing Audiovisual Materials*, San Francisco, California: Chandler Publishing Co., 1963.

Kemp, Jerrold E. "Producing Transparencies for College Instruction," *Educational Screen and Audiovisual Guide*, 37, 280–281 (June, 1958).

King, William J. "What's New in Cameras?" AVI, **11**, 216 (March, 1966).

Lewis, Philip. "Slides in Three Minutes," *Educational Screen and Audiovisual Guide*, 36, 22–23 (January, 1957).

Minor, Ed. *Simplified Techniques For Preparing Visual Instructional Materials*. New York: McGraw-Hill, 1962.

Morlan, John E. *Preparation of Inexpensive Teaching Materials*. San Francisco: Chandler, 1963.

Murray, William. "Using the Camera: Expanded Use of Photography in Englewood Public Schools," *Educational Screen and Audiovisual Guide*, 42, 199 (March 1963).

Noble, Joseph V. "The Pictures Viewed as Photographs," *Saturday Review*, May 16, 1959, pp. 51–52.

Ozalid Corporation. *They See What You Mean*. Johnson City, New York: Ozalid Division of the General Aniline and Film Corporation, Audiovisual Department, 1959.

Rothschild, Norma. *Making Slide Duplicates, Titles, and Filmstrips*. New York: Universal Photo Books, 1962.

Rudsill, Mable. "Children's Preferences for Color vs. Other Qualities in Illustration," *Elementary School Journal*, 444 (April, 1952).

Spaulding, Seth. "Research on Pictorial Illustration," *Audiovisual Communication Review*, 3, 43–44 (Winter, 1955).

Schultz, Morton J. *The Teacher and Overhead Projection*. Englewood Cliffs, New Jersey: Prentice-Hall, Inc., 1965.

Tecnifax Corporation, *Visucom* (vol. 1. no. 1–6), Holyoke, Massachusetts: Tecnifax Corporation, 1961–1966.

Ter Louw, Adrian. "Look beyond the Pictures," *Audiovisual Instruction*, **1**, 45 (March, 1956).

Williams, Catherine. *Learning from Pictures*. Washington, D.C.: NEA, 1963.

INSTRUCTIONAL MATERIALS

Basic Camera, 16-mm film, 15 min., sound, b & w. United States Navy, 1948.

Handmade Materials For Projection, 16-mm film, 20 min., sound, b & w, Indiana University, 1956.

How To Make Handmade Lantern Slides, 16-mm film, 21 min., sound, color, Indiana University, 1947.

Let's Make Movies, 16-mm film, 17 min., sound, color, Eastman Kodak, 1963.

Magazines To Transparencies, 16-mm film, 12 min., sound, color, Florida State University, 1959.

Overhead Projection, 16-mm film 17 min., sound, b & w, Iowa State University, 1953.

Pictures Clear and Sharp, 16-mm film, 12 min., sound, color, Eastman Kodak, 1956.

Photographic Slides for Instruction, 16-mm film, 11 min., sound, b & w or color, Indiana University, 1956.

Teaching with Still Pictures, 35-mm filmstrip, 53 frames, color, Basic Skills, 1958.

INDEX